$$-\nabla V = \bar{E}$$

$$\bar{E}\,\epsilon = \bar{D}$$

$$\varrho_v = \nabla \cdot \bar{D}$$

$$|\varrho_s| = |D|$$

$$W_E = \frac{1}{2} \int_{vol} \bar{D}\cdot\bar{E}\, dv$$

$$W_H = \frac{1}{2} \int_{vol} \bar{B}\cdot\bar{H}\, dv$$

$\left. \rule{0pt}{40pt} \right\}$ Pg 230

MAXWELL'S EQUATIONS

$$\nabla \times \bar{E} = -\frac{\partial \bar{B}}{\partial t}$$

D1006753

$$\nabla \cdot \bar{B} = 0$$

$$I = \int_s i \cdot ds$$

$$\nabla \cdot i = -\frac{\partial \varrho}{\partial t} \quad \text{continuity equation}$$

$$\int_s \bar{B}\cdot ds = \Phi$$

ENGINEERING ELECTROMAGNETICS

McGRAW-HILL ELECTRICAL AND ELECTRONIC ENGINEERING SERIES

FREDERICK EMMONS TERMAN, *Consulting Editor*
W. W. HARMAN and J. G. TRUXAL, *Associate Consulting Editors*

AHRENDT AND SAVANT · Servomechanism Practice
ANGELO · Electronic Circuits
ASELTINE · Transform Method in Linear System Analysis
BAILEY AND GAULT · Alternating-current Machinery
BERANEK · Acoustics
BRENNER AND JAVID · Analysis of Electric Circuits
BRUNS AND SAUNDERS · Analysis of Feedback Control Systems
CAGE · Theory and Application of Industrial Electronics
CAUER · Synthesis of Linear Communication Networks
CHIRLIAN AND ZEMANIAN · Electronics
CLEMENT AND JOHNSON · Electrical Engineering Science
COTE AND OAKES · Linear Vacuum-tube and Transistor Circuits
CUCCIA · Harmonics, Sidebands, and Transients in Communication
    Engineering
CUNNINGHAM · Introduction to Nonlinear Analysis
EASTMAN · Fundamentals of Vacuum Tubes
EVANS · Control-system Dynamics
FEINSTEIN · Foundations of Information Theory
FITZGERALD AND HIGGINBOTHAM · Basic Electrical Engineering
FITZGERALD AND KINGSLEY · Electric Machinery
FRANK · Electrical Measurement Analysis
FRIEDLAND, WING, AND ASH · Principles of Linear Networks
GEPPERT · Basic Electron Tubes
GLASFORD · Fundamentals of Television Engineering
GREINER · Semiconductor Devices and Applications
HAMMOND · Electrical Engineering
HANCOCK · An Introduction to the Principles of Communication Theory
HAPPELL AND HESSELBERTH · Engineering Electronics
HARMAN · Fundamentals of Electronic Motion
HARRINGTON · Introduction to Electromagnetic Engineering
HARRINGTON · Time-harmonic Electromagnetic Fields
HAYT · Engineering Electromagnetics
HILL · Electronics in Engineering
JOHNSON · Transmission Lines and Networks
KOENIG AND BLACKWELL · Electromechanical System Theory
KRAUS · Antennas
KRAUS · Electromagnetics
KUH AND PEDERSON · Principles of Circuit Synthesis
LEDLEY · Digital Computer and Control Engineering
LePAGE · Analysis of Alternating-current Circuits
LePAGE · Complex Variables and the Laplace Transform for Engineers

LePage and Seely · General Network Analysis
Ley, Lutz, and Rehberg · Linear Circuit Analysis
Linvill and Gibbons · Transistors and Active Circuits
Lynch and Truxal · Introductory System Analysis
Millman · Vacuum-tube and Semiconductor Electronics
Millman and Seely · Electronics
Millman and Taub · Pulse and Digital Circuits
Mishkin and Braun · Adaptive Control Systems
Moore · Traveling-wave Engineering
Pettit · Electronic Switching, Timing, and Pulse Circuits
Pettit and McWhorter · Electronic Amplifier Circuits
Pfeiffer · Linear Systems Analysis
Reza · An Introduction to Information Theory
Reza and Seely · Modern Network Analysis
Rogers · Introduction to Electric Fields
Rudenberg · Transient Performance of Electric Power Systems
Ryder · Engineering Electronics
Schwartz · Information Transmission, Modulation, and Noise
Seely · Electrical Engineering
Seely · Electron-tube Circuits
Seely · Introduction to Electromagnetic Fields
Seely · Radio Electronics
Seifert and Steeg · Control Systems Engineering
Siskind · Direct-current Machinery
Skilling · Electronic Transmission Lines
Skilling · Transient Electric Currents
Spangenberg · Fundamentals of Electron Devices
Spangenberg · Vacuum Tubes
Stevenson · Elements of Power System Analysis
Stewart · Fundamentals of Signal Theory
Storer · Passive Network Synthesis
Strauss · Wave Generation and Shaping
Terman · Electronic and Radio Engineering
Terman and Pettit · Electronic Measurements
Thaler · Elements of Servomechanism Theory
Thaler and Brown · Analysis and Design of Feedback Control Systems
Thompson · Alternating-current and Transient Circuit Analysis
Tou · Digital and Sampled-data Control Systems
Truxal · Automatic Feedback Control System Synthesis
Valdes · The Physical Theory of Transistors
Williams and Young · Electrical Engineering Problems

Engineering Electromagnetics

WILLIAM H. HAYT, JR.

Associate Professor of Electrical Engineering
Purdue University

McGRAW-HILL BOOK COMPANY, INC.

New York   Toronto   London

1958

ENGINEERING ELECTROMAGNETICS

VII

27380

THE MAPLE PRESS COMPANY, YORK, PA.

PREFACE

Although most electrical-engineering curricula begin with a study of electric and magnetic circuits, it is now recognized that the more basic theory of the electric and magnetic fields deserves subsequent attention in the curriculum. Some familiarity with circuit concepts and a knowledge of calculus both allow a treatment of field theory in the junior year which proceeds through Maxwell's equations and justifies the approximations which lead to circuit theory.

This text uses Maxwell's equations as the central theme. These equations are developed from the historical approach in which the several experimental laws are gradually introduced and manipulated with the help of a gradually increasing knowledge of vector calculus. Maxwell's equations are identified as they occur, even as they apply to static fields, and a certain sense of accomplishment should be felt when the theory is finally completed. Several applications of these equations are described in the subsequent sections, including circuit theory, skin effect, wave motion, and radiation.

The material is more than adequate for a one-semester course. Depending on the instructional level, it may be desirable to omit portions of the chapters on experimental mapping methods, the solution of Laplace's equation, the application of Maxwell's equations, and particle motion.

This book has been written with the goal of making it as easy as possible for the student to teach himself. This has been done by applying a carefully graduated scale of difficulty within each chapter and among the chapters themselves, by providing numerous examples interpreting and applying every basic result and also numerical examples where possible, by providing a large number of drill problems to which numerical answers are given, and by avoiding an excessive involvement with analytic geometry and its detailed use in interpreting fields.

The more difficult material has been placed near the ends of the chapters or at the end of the study of some definite phase of the subject. The poorer student, who admittedly cannot assimilate the same amount of material as the better one, will thus be attracted to the more basic material at the beginning of each chapter. Since the subject matter of the following chapter is not usually built on the most advanced material of the previous chapter, he can then make a fresh start from his poorer but adequate background. The more advanced material does, however, offer a needed challenge to the better students.

Drill problems are placed at the ends of most sections in which a formula or law is introduced which is capable of expression in problem form. Each drill problem has three parts of a generally similar nature, and the answer is given as the sum of the answers to the three parts. In reality, then, each of these problems is three problems and all must be worked before the answer can be checked. The problems appearing at the ends of the chapters are more difficult, more interesting, and are given without answers. Their order corresponds to the order of the corresponding text material. In all, there are 86 drill problems and 231 other problems.

The mks system of units is used throughout, and the general philosophy behind dimensions, dimensional analysis, and the several systems of units is discussed in an Appendix. Also relegated to an Appendix is the general curvilinear coordinate system. It is felt that these two topics do little to help the average student become familiar with field relationships but that they should certainly be pointed out and available to those who can profitably use them. Relativistic effects are discussed in the final section of the text, although earlier reference is made to this material.

This text is the outgrowth of courses presented at Purdue University during the past ten years at both an introductory graduate and undergraduate level.

William H. Hayt, Jr.

CONTENTS

ix

CHAPTER 1

VECTOR ANALYSIS

Vector analysis is a mathematical subject which is much better taught by the mathematicians than by the engineers. Most junior and senior engineering students, however, have not had the time (or perhaps the inclination) to take a course in vector analysis, and for that reason the fundamentals are introduced in this chapter. The viewpoint here is also that of the engineer or physicist and not that of the mathematician in that proofs are indicated rather than rigorously expounded and that the physical interpretation is stressed. It is easier for an engineer to take a more rigorous and complete course in the mathematics department after he has a few physical pictures and applications to which to cling.

It is possible to study electricity and magnetism without the use of vector analysis, and most engineering students have probably done so in a basic physics course. Carrying this elementary work on a little bit farther, however, soon leads to line-filling equations often composed of terms which all look about the same. A quick glance at one of these long equations discloses little of the physical nature of the equation and may even lead to slighting an old friend.

Vector analysis is a mathematical shorthand. It has some new symbols, some new rules, a pitfall here and there like most new fields, and it demands concentration, attention, and practice. The drill problems, first met at the end of Sec. 1.4, should be considered an integral part of the text and should all be worked. It takes a little longer to "read" the chapter this way, but the investment in time will produce a surprising interest.

1.1. Scalars and Vectors. The term *scalar* refers to a quantity which has only a magnitude. The x, y, and z we used in basic algebra are scalars, and the quantities they represent are scalars. If we speak of a body falling a distance L in a time t, or the temperature T at any point in a bowl of soup whose coordinates are x, y, and z, then L, t, T, x, y, and z are all scalars. Other scalar quantities are mass, density, pressure (but not force), volume, and volume resistivity. Voltage is also a scalar quantity, although the complex representation of a sinusoidal voltage, an artificial procedure, produces a *complex scalar*.

A *vector* quantity has both a magnitude and a direction in space. We shall be concerned with two- and three-dimensional spaces only, but vectors may be defined in *n*-dimensional space in more advanced applications. Force, velocity, acceleration, and a line from the positive to the negative terminal of a storage battery are examples of vectors. Each quantity is characterized by both a magnitude and a direction.

We shall be mostly concerned with scalar and vector *fields*. A field may be strictly defined as an area of influence. The earth's magnetic field would then be the region in which compass needles are affected. However, "field" has gradually taken on a broader meaning and often implies the physical basis of the effects produced in the field. We may thus speak of compass needles being affected either "in" or "by" the earth's magnetic field. Note that the field concept invariably is related to a region. Some quantity is defined at every point in a region. Both *scalar fields* and *vector fields* exist. The temperature throughout the bowl of soup and the density at any point in the earth are examples of scalar fields, for a scalar quantity has some specific value at every point in the given region, a value in general varying from point to point. The gravitational and magnetic fields of the earth, the voltage gradient in a cable, and the temperature gradient in a soldering-iron tip are examples of vector fields.

In this book, as in most others using vector notation, vectors will be indicated by boldface type, that is, **A**. Scalars are printed in italic type and have no special symbol. When writing longhand or using a typewriter, it is customary to draw a line or an arrow over a vector quantity to show its vector character. (CAUTION: This is the first pitfall. Sloppy notation, such as the omission of the line or arrow which is the symbol for a vector, is the major cause of errors in vector analysis.)

1.2. Vector Arithmetic. With the definitions of vectors and vector fields now accomplished, we may proceed to define the rules of vector arithmetic, vector algebra, and (later) of vector calculus. Some of the rules will be similar to the rules of scalar algebra, some will differ slightly, and some will be entirely new and strange. This is to be expected, for a vector represents more information than does a scalar, and there will consequently be, for example, more to the multiplication of vectors than to that of scalars.

The rules are those of a branch of mathematics which is firmly established. Everyone "plays by the same rules," and we, of course, are merely going to look at and interpret these rules. However, it is enlightening to consider ourselves pioneers in the field. We are making our own rules, and we can make any rules we wish. The only requirement is that the rules be self-consistent. Of course, it would be nice if the rules agreed with those of scalar algebra where possible, and it would be even nicer if the rules enabled us to solve a few practical problems.

One should not fall into the trap of "algebra worship" and believe that the rules of college algebra were delivered unto man at the Creation. These rules are merely self-consistent and extremely useful. There are other less familiar algebras, however, with very different rules. In Boolean algebra the product AB can only be either unity or zero. Vector algebra has its own set of rules, and we must be constantly on guard against the mental forces exerted by the more familiar rules of scalar algebra.

Vectors are added vectorially, not algebraically. Vectorial addition follows the parallelogram law, and this is easily, if inaccurately, accomplished graphically. Figure 1.1 shows the sum of two vectors, **A** and

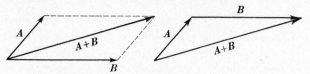

Fig. 1.1. The vector addition of vectors **A** and **B**.

B. It is easily seen that $\mathbf{A} + \mathbf{B} = \mathbf{B} + \mathbf{A}$, or that vector addition obeys the commutative law. Vector addition also obeys the associative law:

$$\mathbf{A} + (\mathbf{B} + \mathbf{C}) = (\mathbf{A} + \mathbf{B}) + \mathbf{C}$$

Coplanar vectors, or vectors lying in a common plane, such as those of Fig. 1.1 which both lie in the plane of the paper, may also be added by expressing each vector in terms of "horizontal" and "vertical" components and adding the corresponding components.

Vectors in three dimensions may likewise be added by expressing the vectors in terms of three components and adding the corresponding components. Examples of this process of addition will be given after vector components are discussed in Sec. 1.4.

The rule for the subtraction of vectors follows easily from that for addition, for we may always express $\mathbf{A} - \mathbf{B}$ as $\mathbf{A} + (-\mathbf{B})$. Hence, the sign and direction of the second vector are reversed, and this vector is then added to the first by the rule for vector addition.

Vectors may be multiplied by scalars. The magnitude of the vector changes, but not its direction. Multiplication of a vector by a scalar also obeys the associative and distributive laws of algebra, leading to

$$(r + s)(\mathbf{A} + \mathbf{B}) = r(\mathbf{A} + \mathbf{B}) + s(\mathbf{A} + \mathbf{B}) = r\mathbf{A} + r\mathbf{B} + s\mathbf{A} + s\mathbf{B}$$

Division of a vector by a scalar is merely multiplication by the reciprocal of that scalar.

The multiplication of a vector by a vector is discussed in Secs. 1.6 and 1.7 below.

Two vectors are said to be equal if their difference is zero, or $\mathbf{A} = \mathbf{B}$ if $\mathbf{A} - \mathbf{B} = 0$.

Vectors may be added and subtracted even though they are *not* defined at the same point. For example, the sum of the gravitational force acting on a 150-lb man at the North Pole and that acting on a 175-lb man at the South Pole may be obtained by shifting each force vector to the South Pole before addition. The resultant is a 25-lb force directed toward the center of the earth at the South Pole, or, if we wanted to be difficult, we could just as well describe the force as 25 lb directed *away* from the center of the earth (or "upward") at the North Pole.[1]

Vectors having the same magnitude and direction are equal, regardless of their location in space or positions relative to each other. Certainly it is true that the *result* of the application of equal force vectors at different points may be entirely different, such as the application of 10 lb of force to the brake pedal or to the accelerator pedal, but our definition is not concerned with equality of results, or equivalence.

1.3. The Cartesian Coordinate System. In order to describe a vector accurately, some specific lengths, directions, angles, projections, or components must be given. There are three simple methods of doing this and about eight or ten others which are useful in very special cases. We are going to use only the three simple methods, and the simplest of these is through the use of the *cartesian*, or *rectangular, coordinate system*.

In the cartesian coordinate system we set up three coordinate axes, mutually at right angles to each other, and call them the x, y, and z axes. It is customary to choose a *right-handed* coordinate system in which a rotation (through the smaller angle) of the x axis into the y axis would cause a right-handed screw to progress in the direction of the z axis. Using the three fingers of the right hand, the thumb, forefinger, and middle finger, they may then be identified, respectively, as the x, y, and z axes. Figure 1.2a shows a right-handed cartesian coordinate system.

---

[1] Someone has also pointed out that the force might be described at the equator as being in a "northerly" direction. He is right, but enough is enough.

A point is located by giving its x, y, and z coordinates. These are, respectively, the distances from the origin to the intersection of a perpendicular dropped from the point to the x, y, and z axes. An alternative method of interpreting coordinate values, and a method corresponding to that which *must* be used in all other coordinate systems, is to consider the point as being at the common intersection of

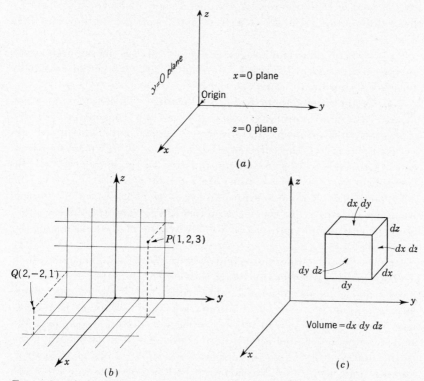

Fig. 1.2. (a) A right-handed cartesian coordinate system. (b) The location of points $P(1,2,3)$ and $Q(2,-2,1)$. (c) The differential volume in cartesian coordinates.

three planes, given by $x = $ constant, $y = $ constant, and $z = $ constant, the constants being the coordinate values of the point.

Figure 1.2b shows the points P and Q whose coordinates are $(1,2,3)$ and $(2,-2,1)$, respectively. Point P is therefore located at the common point of intersection of the planes $x = 1$, $y = 2$, and $z = 3$, while point Q is located at the intersection of the planes $x = 2$, $y = -2$, $z = 1$.

As we meet other coordinate systems in Secs. 1.8 and 1.9, we should expect points to be located by the common intersection of three surfaces, not necessarily planes, but still mutually perpendicular at the point of intersection.

A differential length of line in the cartesian coordinate system dL is given by $\sqrt{(dx)^2 + (dy)^2 + (dz)^2}$, where dx, dy, and dz represent vanishingly small increments to each of the three coordinate variables. If a differential-volume element is constructed having sides of length dx, dy, and dz, the differential volume dv is $dx\,dy\,dz$ and the surfaces have differential areas dS of $dx\,dy$, $dy\,dz$, or $dx\,dz$, as shown in Fig. 1.2c.

All this is familiar from trigonometry or solid geometry and as yet involves only scalar quantities. We shall begin to describe vectors in terms of a coordinate system in the next section.

1.4. Vector Components and Unit Vectors. To describe a vector in the cartesian coordinate system, let us first consider a vector **r** extending outward from the origin. A logical way to identify this vector is by giving the three *component vectors*, lying along the three coordinate axes, whose vector sum must be the given vector. If the component vectors of the vector **r** are **x**, **y**, and **z**, then $\mathbf{r} = \mathbf{x} + \mathbf{y} + \mathbf{z}$. The component vectors are shown in Fig. 1.3a. Instead of one vector, we now have three, but this is a step forward because the three vectors are of a very simple nature; each is always directed along one of the coordinate axes.

In other words, the component vectors have a magnitude which depends on the given vector (such as **r** above), but they each have a known and constant direction. This suggests the use of *unit vectors* having unit magnitude, by definition, and directed along the coordinate axes in the direction of the increasing coordinate values. We shall reserve the symbol **a** for a unit vector and identify the direction of the unit vector by an appropriate subscript. Thus $\mathbf{a}_x$, $\mathbf{a}_y$, and $\mathbf{a}_z$ are the unit vectors in the cartesian coordinate system. They are directed along the x, y, and z axes, respectively, as shown in Fig. 1.3b.

If the component vector **y** happens to be 2 units in magnitude, we should then write $\mathbf{y} = 2\mathbf{a}_y$. A vector $\mathbf{r}_P$ pointing from the origin to point $P(1,2,3)$ is written $\mathbf{r}_P = \mathbf{a}_x + 2\mathbf{a}_y + 3\mathbf{a}_z$. The vector from P to Q may be obtained by applying the rule of vector addition. This rule shows that the vector from the origin to P plus the vector from P to Q is equal to the vector from the origin to Q. The desired vector from P (1,2,3) to Q (2,-2,1) is therefore

$$\mathbf{r}_Q - \mathbf{r}_P = (2 - 1)\mathbf{a}_x + (-2 - 2)\mathbf{a}_y + (1 - 3)\mathbf{a}_z = \mathbf{a}_x - 4\mathbf{a}_y - 2\mathbf{a}_z$$

This last vector does not extend outward from the origin as did the vector **r** we initially considered. However, we have already learned that vectors having the same magnitude and pointing in the same direction are equal, so we see that, if it helps our visualization processes, we are at liberty to slide any vector over to the origin before determining its component vectors. Parallelism must of course be maintained during the sliding process.

If we are discussing a force vector **F**, or indeed any vector other than a displacement-type vector such as **r**, the problem arises of providing suitable letters for the three component vectors. It would not do to call them **x**, **y**, and **z**, for these are displacements, or directed distances, and are measured in meters, or some other unit of length. The problem is most often avoided by using *component scalars*, simply called

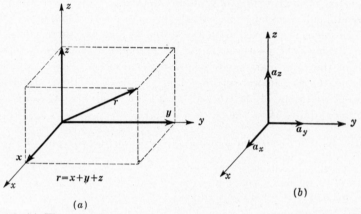

(a)

FIG. 1.3. (a) The component vectors **x**, **y**, and **z** of vector **r**. (b) The unit vectors of the cartesian coordinate system.

components, F_x, F_y, and F_z. The components are the magnitudes of the component vectors. We may then write $\mathbf{F} = F_x\mathbf{a}_x + F_y\mathbf{a}_y + F_z\mathbf{a}_z$. The component vectors are $F_x\mathbf{a}_x$, $F_y\mathbf{a}_y$, and $F_z\mathbf{a}_z$. These expressions are sufficiently simple so that no other nomenclature is commonly used.

Any vector **B** then may be described by $\mathbf{B} = B_x\mathbf{a}_x + B_y\mathbf{a}_y + B_z\mathbf{a}_z$. The magnitude of **B**, written $|\mathbf{B}|$ or simply B, is given by

$$|\mathbf{B}| = \sqrt{B_x{}^2 + B_y{}^2 + B_z{}^2}$$

Each of the three coordinate systems we discuss will have its three fundamental and mutually perpendicular unit vectors which are used to resolve any vector into its component vectors. However, unit vectors are not limited to this application. It is often very helpful to be able to write a unit vector having a specified direction. This is simply done, for a unit vector in a given direction is merely a vector in that direction divided by its magnitude. A unit vector in the **r** direction is $\mathbf{r}/\sqrt{x^2 + y^2 + z^2}$, and a unit vector in the direction of the vector $\mathbf{B}$ is $\mathbf{B}/\sqrt{B_x{}^2 + B_y{}^2 + B_z{}^2} = \mathbf{B}/|\mathbf{B}|$. A special identifying symbol is desirable for a unit vector so that its character is immediately apparent. Symbols which have been used are $\mathbf{u}_B$, $\mathbf{a}_B$, $\mathbf{1}_B$, or even $\mathbf{b}$. We shall consistently use the lower case $\mathbf{a}$ with an appropriate subscript.

[NOTE: Throughout the text drill problems appear following sections in which a new principle is introduced in order to allow the student to test his understanding of the basic fact itself. The problems are only occasionally stimulating and require little imagination. They are useful in gaining familiarization with new terms and ideas. It is suggested strongly that they all be worked. More interesting and more difficult problems appear at the ends of the chapters. Each drill problem is prefixed with the letter D and has three parts. In order to check the answer given for the problem, it is necessary to work each of the three parts and then add the results. The total should agree with the answer given. For example, in Prob. D1.1, the answers are (a) $4\mathbf{a}_y + 3\mathbf{a}_z$, (b) $6\mathbf{a}_x + 2\mathbf{a}_y - \mathbf{a}_z$, and (c) $-\mathbf{a}_x - \mathbf{a}_y + 3\mathbf{a}_z$ and their sum is $5\mathbf{a}_x + 5\mathbf{a}_y + 5\mathbf{a}_z$.]

D1.1. Write in component form the expression for the vector which extends from:
    (a) The origin to $M(0,4,3)$.
    (b) $N(-5,3,1)$ to $S(1,5,0)$.
    (c) $S(1,5,0)$ to $M(0,4,3)$.

Ans. $5\mathbf{a}_x + 5\mathbf{a}_y + 5\mathbf{a}_z$.

D1.2. Find the magnitude of the vector:
    (a) $2\mathbf{a}_x + 2\mathbf{a}_y + \mathbf{a}_z$.
    (b) $\mathbf{a}_x/\sqrt{2} + \mathbf{a}_z/\sqrt{2}$.
    (c) $\cos \alpha \, \mathbf{a}_x + \sin \alpha \, \mathbf{a}_y$.

Ans. 5.

D1.3. Write the unit vector in component form which lies in the direction defined by:
    (a) The vector $\mathbf{a}_x - 2\mathbf{a}_y - 2\mathbf{a}_z$.
    (b) The line from $A(0,1,0)$ to $B(2,3,-1)$.
    (c) The z axis.

Ans. $\mathbf{a}_x$.

1.5. The Vector Field. We have already defined a vector field as a region of space in which a vector quantity is defined at every point. In general, the magnitude and direction of the vector quantity will change as we move throughout the region, and its value must be determined from the coordinate values of the point in question. Since we have considered only the cartesian coordinate system, we therefore should expect the vector to be a function of the variables x, y, and z.

If we consider the velocity of the water in the ocean in some region near the surface where tides and currents are important, we may obtain a velocity vector which is in any direction, even up or down. If the z axis is taken as upward, the x axis in a northerly direction, the y axis to the west, we have a right-handed coordinate system and may write the velocity vector as $\mathbf{U} = U_x\mathbf{a}_x + U_y\mathbf{a}_y + U_z\mathbf{a}_z$, where each of the components U_x, U_y, and U_z may be a function of the three variables x, y, and z. If the problem is simplified by assuming that we are in some portion of the Gulf Stream where the water is moving only to the north, then U_y and U_z are zero. Further simplifying assumptions may be made, for the velocity usually falls off with depth and changes very slowly as we move north, south, east, or west. A suitable expression might be $\mathbf{U} = 2e^{z/100}\mathbf{a}_x$. We have a velocity of 2 m/sec (assuming mks units) at the surface, a velocity of $(0.368)(2)$, or 0.736 m/sec, at a depth of 100 m ($z = -100$), and the velocity continues to decrease with depth.

While the example given above is fairly simple and only a rough approximation to a physical situation, a more exact expression would be correspondingly more complex and difficult to interpret. We shall meet many fields in our study of electricity and magnetism which are simpler than the velocity example, an example in which only one component and one variable were involved (the x component and the variable z). We shall also study more complicated fields, and methods of interpreting these expressions physically will be discussed then.

1.6. The Dot Product. We now consider the first of two types of vector multiplication. The second type will be discussed in the following section.

Given two vectors $\mathbf{A}$ and $\mathbf{B}$, define the *dot product*, or *scalar product*, as the product of the magnitude of $\mathbf{A}$, the magnitude of $\mathbf{B}$, and the cosine of the smaller angle between them:

$$\mathbf{A} \cdot \mathbf{B} = |\mathbf{A}|\,|\mathbf{B}|\,\cos\theta_{AB}$$

The dot appears between the two vectors and should be made heavy for emphasis. The dot, or scalar, product is a scalar, as one of the names implies, and it obeys the commutative law,

$$\mathbf{A} \cdot \mathbf{B} = \mathbf{B} \cdot \mathbf{A}$$

for the sign of the angle does not affect the cosine term. The expression $\mathbf{A} \cdot \mathbf{B}$ is read "$\mathbf{A}$ dot $\mathbf{B}$."

Perhaps the most common application of the dot product is found in mechanics, where a constant force $\mathbf{F}$ applied over a straight displacement $\mathbf{L}$ does an amount of work $FL \cos\theta$, which is more easily written

F · L. We might anticipate one of the results of the fourth chapter by pointing out that if the force varies along the path, integration is necessary to find the total work and the result becomes

$$\text{Work} = \int \mathbf{F} \cdot d\mathbf{L}$$

Another example might be taken from magnetic fields, a subject we shall have a lot more to say about later. The total flux Φ crossing a surface of area S is given by BS if the magnetic flux density B is perpendicular to the surface and uniform over it. If we define a vector surface $\mathbf{S}$ as having the usual area for its magnitude and having a direction *normal* to the surface (avoiding for the moment the problem of which of the two possible normals to take), then the flux becomes $\mathbf{B} \cdot \mathbf{S}$. This expression is valid for any direction of the uniform magnetic flux density. However, if the flux density is not constant over the surface, the total flux is $\Phi = \int \mathbf{B} \cdot d\mathbf{S}$. Integrals of this general form appear in the third chapter.

Finding the angle between two vectors in three-dimensional space is often a job we would prefer to avoid, and for that reason the definition of the dot product is usually not used in its basic form. A more helpful result is obtained by considering two vectors whose cartesian components are given, such as $\mathbf{A} = A_x\mathbf{a}_x + A_y\mathbf{a}_y + A_z\mathbf{a}_z$ and $\mathbf{B} = B_x\mathbf{a}_x + B_y\mathbf{a}_y + B_z\mathbf{a}_z$. Application of the dot-product definition then yields the sum of nine scalar terms, each involving the dot product of two unit vectors. Since the angle between two different unit vectors of the cartesian coordinate system is 90°, we have then

$$\mathbf{a}_x \cdot \mathbf{a}_y = \mathbf{a}_y \cdot \mathbf{a}_x = \mathbf{a}_x \cdot \mathbf{a}_z = \mathbf{a}_z \cdot \mathbf{a}_x = \mathbf{a}_y \cdot \mathbf{a}_z = \mathbf{a}_z \cdot \mathbf{a}_y = 0$$

The remaining three terms involve the dot product of a unit vector with itself, which is unity, giving finally

$$\mathbf{A} \cdot \mathbf{B} = A_xB_x + A_yB_y + A_zB_z$$

which is an expression involving no angles.

A vector dotted with itself yields the magnitude squared, or

$$\mathbf{A} \cdot \mathbf{A} = A^2 = |\mathbf{A}|^2$$

Probably the most important application of the dot product is that of finding the component of a vector in a given direction. If $\mathbf{a}$ represents a unit vector in any direction, then

$$\mathbf{A} \cdot \mathbf{a} = |\mathbf{A}|\,|\mathbf{a}|\,\cos\theta_{Aa} = |\mathbf{A}|\cos\theta_{Aa}$$

is the component of $\mathbf{A}$ in the direction of the unit vector $\mathbf{a}$. As a simple example, we note that $\mathbf{A} \cdot \mathbf{a}_x$ is the component of $\mathbf{A}$ in the direction of $\mathbf{a}_x$, or $\mathbf{A} \cdot \mathbf{a}_x = A_x$. Hence, the problem of finding the component of a vector in any desired direction becomes the problem of finding a unit vector in that direction, and this has been done (see Sec. 1.4 and Prob. D1.3).

D1.4. Find the dot product of the vectors **A** and **B** if:
(a) $\mathbf{A} = \mathbf{a}_x - 2\mathbf{a}_y + \mathbf{a}_z$, $\mathbf{B} = 3\mathbf{a}_x + 2\mathbf{a}_y - \mathbf{a}_z$.
(b) $\mathbf{A} = 4\mathbf{a}_x + 4\mathbf{a}_y + 4\mathbf{a}_z$, $\mathbf{B} = \mathbf{a}_x - \mathbf{a}_y + \mathbf{a}_z$.
(c) $\mathbf{A} = \mathbf{a}_z$, $\mathbf{B} = 2\mathbf{a}_y + 3\mathbf{a}_z$.

Ans. 2.

D1.5. Find the component of the vector $\mathbf{C} = -3\mathbf{a}_x - 4\mathbf{a}_y + 14\mathbf{a}_z$ in the direction defined by the vector:
(a) $3\mathbf{a}_x + 4\mathbf{a}_y$.
(b) $\mathbf{a}_x + 2\mathbf{a}_y - 2\mathbf{a}_z$.
(c) $-3\mathbf{a}_x - 4\mathbf{a}_y - 12\mathbf{a}_z$.

Ans. −29.

1.7. The Cross Product. Given two vectors **A** and **B**, we shall now define the *cross product*, or *vector product*, of **A** and **B**, written with a cross between the two vectors as **A** $\times$ **B** and read "A cross B." The cross product **A** $\times$ **B** is a vector; the magnitude of **A** $\times$ **B** is equal to the product of the magnitudes of **A**, **B**, and the sine of the smaller angle between **A** and **B**; the direction of **A** $\times$ **B** is perpendicular to the plane containing **A** and **B**, and is directed along that one of the two possible perpendiculars which is in the direction of advance of a right-handed screw as **A** is turned into **B**. This direction is illustrated in Fig. 1.4. Remember that either vector may be moved about at will, maintaining its direction constant, until the two vectors have a "common origin." This determines the plane containing both. However, in most of our applications we shall be concerned with vectors defined at the same point.

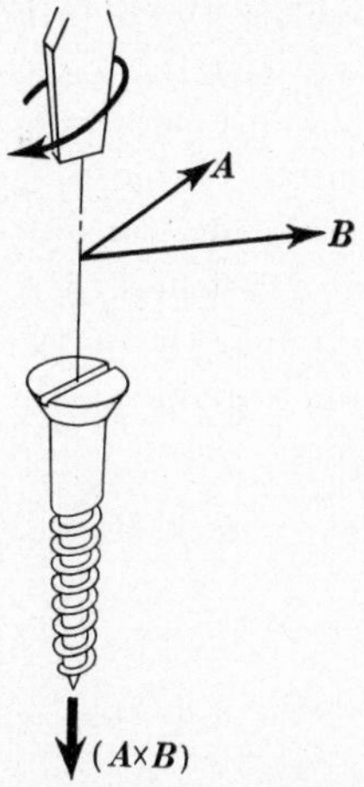

As an equation we can write

$$\mathbf{A} \times \mathbf{B} = |\mathbf{A}|\,|\mathbf{B}|\,\sin\theta_{AB}\mathbf{a}_N$$

Fig. 1.4. The direction of **A** $\times$ **B** is in the direction of advance of a right-handed screw as **A** is turned into **B**.

where an additional statement, such as that given above, is still required to explain the direction of the unit vector $\mathbf{a}_N$. The subscript stands for "normal."

Reversing the order of the vectors **A** and **B** results in a unit vector in the opposite direction, and we see that the cross product is not commutative, for $\mathbf{B} \times \mathbf{A} = -(\mathbf{A} \times \mathbf{B})$.

If the definition of the cross product is applied to the unit vectors $\mathbf{a}_x$ and $\mathbf{a}_y$, we find $\mathbf{a}_x \times \mathbf{a}_y = \mathbf{a}_z$, for each vector has unit magnitude, the two vectors are perpendicular, and the rotation of $\mathbf{a}_x$ into $\mathbf{a}_y$ indicates the positive z direction by the definition of a right-handed coordinate system. In a similar way, $\mathbf{a}_y \times \mathbf{a}_z = \mathbf{a}_x$ and $\mathbf{a}_z \times \mathbf{a}_x = \mathbf{a}_y$. Note the alphabetic symmetry. As long as the three vectors $\mathbf{a}_x$, $\mathbf{a}_y$, $\mathbf{a}_z$ are written in order (and assuming that $\mathbf{a}_x$ follows $\mathbf{a}_z$, like three elephants in a circle holding tails, so that we could also write $\mathbf{a}_y$, $\mathbf{a}_z$, $\mathbf{a}_x$ or $\mathbf{a}_z$, $\mathbf{a}_x$, $\mathbf{a}_y$), then the cross and equal sign may be placed in either of the two vacant spaces. As a matter of fact, it is now simpler to define a right-handed cartesian coordinate system by saying that $\mathbf{a}_x \times \mathbf{a}_y = \mathbf{a}_z$.

A simple example of the use of the cross product may be taken from geometry or trigonometry. To find the area of a parallelogram, the product of the lengths of two adjacent sides is multiplied by the sine of the angle between them. Using vector notation for the two sides, we then may express the (scalar) area as the *magnitude* of $\mathbf{A} \times \mathbf{B}$.

The cross product may be used to replace the right-hand rule familiar to all electrical engineers. Consider the force on a straight conductor of length $\mathbf{L}$ carrying a steady current of I amp in a uniform magnetic field of flux density $\mathbf{B}$. Using vector notation we may write the result neatly as $\mathbf{F} = I\mathbf{L} \times \mathbf{B}$.

The evaluation of a cross product by means of its definition turns out to be more work than the evaluation of the dot product from its definition, for not only must we find the angle between the vectors but we must find an expression for the unit vector $\mathbf{a}_N$. This work may be avoided by using cartesian components for the two vectors $\mathbf{A}$ and $\mathbf{B}$ and expanding the cross product as a sum of nine simpler cross products, each involving two unit vectors:

$$\mathbf{A} \times \mathbf{B} = A_x B_x \mathbf{a}_x \times \mathbf{a}_x + A_x B_y \mathbf{a}_x \times \mathbf{a}_y + A_x B_z \mathbf{a}_x \times \mathbf{a}_z$$
$$+ A_y B_x \mathbf{a}_y \times \mathbf{a}_x + A_y B_y \mathbf{a}_y \times \mathbf{a}_y + A_y B_z \mathbf{a}_y \times \mathbf{a}_z$$
$$+ A_z B_x \mathbf{a}_z \times \mathbf{a}_x + A_z B_y \mathbf{a}_z \times \mathbf{a}_y + A_z B_z \mathbf{a}_z \times \mathbf{a}_z$$

We have already found that $\mathbf{a}_x \times \mathbf{a}_y = \mathbf{a}_z$, $\mathbf{a}_y \times \mathbf{a}_z = \mathbf{a}_x$, and $\mathbf{a}_z \times \mathbf{a}_x = \mathbf{a}_y$, and it follows that $\mathbf{a}_y \times \mathbf{a}_x = -\mathbf{a}_z$, $\mathbf{a}_z \times \mathbf{a}_y = -\mathbf{a}_x$, and $\mathbf{a}_x \times \mathbf{a}_z = -\mathbf{a}_y$. The three remaining terms are zero, for the cross product of any vector with itself is zero since the included angle is zero. These results may be combined to give

$$\mathbf{A} \times \mathbf{B} = (A_y B_z - A_z B_y)\mathbf{a}_x + (A_z B_x - A_x B_z)\mathbf{a}_y + (A_x B_y - A_y B_x)\mathbf{a}_z$$

or, written as a determinant in a more easily remembered form,

$$\mathbf{A} \times \mathbf{B} = \begin{vmatrix} \mathbf{a}_x & \mathbf{a}_y & \mathbf{a}_z \\ A_x & A_y & A_z \\ B_x & B_y & B_z \end{vmatrix}$$

D1.6. Find the cross product of the vectors **A** and **B** if:

(a) $\mathbf{A} = \mathbf{a}_x - 2\mathbf{a}_y + \mathbf{a}_z$, $\mathbf{B} = 3\mathbf{a}_x + 2\mathbf{a}_y - \mathbf{a}_z$.

(b) $\mathbf{A} = 4\mathbf{a}_x + 4\mathbf{a}_y + 4\mathbf{a}_z$, $\mathbf{B} = \mathbf{a}_x - \mathbf{a}_y + \mathbf{a}_z$.

(c) $\mathbf{A} = \mathbf{a}_x$, $\mathbf{B} = 2\mathbf{a}_y + 3\mathbf{a}_z$.

Ans. $8\mathbf{a}_x + \mathbf{a}_y + 2\mathbf{a}_z$.

D1.7. Find the area of a:

(a) Parallelogram, two sides being $\mathbf{A} = 4\mathbf{a}_x + 6\mathbf{a}_y - 3\mathbf{a}_z$, $\mathbf{B} = -4\mathbf{a}_x - 3\mathbf{a}_y + 2\mathbf{a}_z$.

(b) Parallelogram, two sides being $\mathbf{A} = \mathbf{a}_x + \mathbf{a}_y + \mathbf{a}_z$, $\mathbf{B} = -2\mathbf{a}_x - 2\mathbf{a}_y - 2\mathbf{a}_z$.

(c) Triangle, two sides being $\mathbf{A} = 6\mathbf{a}_x - 3\mathbf{a}_y + 4\mathbf{a}_z$, $\mathbf{B} = 6\mathbf{a}_x - 4\mathbf{a}_y + 8\mathbf{a}_z$.

Ans. 26.

1.8. Other Coordinate Systems—Cylindrical Coordinates.

The cartesian coordinate system is, in general, the one in which students prefer to work every problem. This often means a lot more work for the student because many problems possess a type of symmetry which pleads for a more logical treatment. It is easier to do the work now, once and for all, which is required to become familiar with cylindrical and spherical coordinates, instead of applying an equal or greater effort to every problem involving cylindrical or spherical symmetry later. With this future saving of labor in mind, we shall take a careful and unhurried look at cylindrical and spherical coordinates.

The cylindrical coordinate system is the three-dimensional version of the polar coordinates of analytic geometry. In the two-dimensional polar coordinates, a point was located in a plane by giving its distance r from the origin, and the angle ϕ between the line joining the point to the origin and an arbitrary radial line taken as $\phi = 0$.* A three-dimensional coordinate system, cylindrical coordinates, is obtained by also specifying the distance z of the point from an arbitrary $z = 0$ reference plane which is perpendicular to the line $r = 0$.

We no longer set up three axes as in cartesian coordinates, but must instead consider any point as the intersection of three mutually perpendicular surfaces. These surfaces are a cylinder ($r = $ constant), a plane ($\phi = $ constant), and another plane ($z = $ constant). This corresponds to the location of a point in a cartesian coordinate system by the intersection of three planes ($x = $ constant, $y = $ constant, and $z = $ constant). The three surfaces of cylindrical coordinates are shown in Fig. 1.5a. Note that three such surfaces may be passed through any point.

Three unit vectors must also be defined, but we no longer may direct them along the "coordinate axes," for such axes exist only in cartesian

---

* In polar coordinates it is customary to call this angle θ, but we cannot use θ here, for this choice would conflict with an entirely different angle in the spherical coordinate system which has been consistently called θ.

coordinates. Instead we take a broader view of the unit vectors in cartesian coordinates and realize that they are directed toward increasing coordinate values and are perpendicular to the surface on which that coordinate value is constant; i.e., the unit vector $\mathbf{a}_x$ is normal to the plane x = constant and points toward larger values of x. In a corresponding way we may now define three unit vectors in cylindrical coordinates, $\mathbf{a}_r$, $\mathbf{a}_\phi$, and $\mathbf{a}_z$.

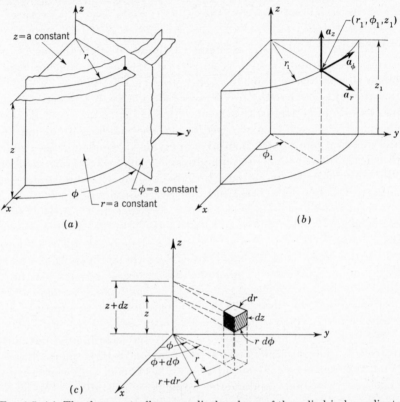

FIG. 1.5. (a) The three mutually perpendicular planes of the cylindrical coordinate system. (b) The three unit vectors of the cylindrical coordinate system. (c) The differential volume unit in the cylindrical coordinate system.

The unit vector $\mathbf{a}_r$ at any point (r_1, ϕ_1, z_1) is directed radially outward, normal to the cylindrical surface $r = r_1$. It lies in the planes $\phi = \phi_1$ and $z = z_1$. The unit vector $\mathbf{a}_\phi$ is normal to the plane $\phi = \phi_1$, points in the direction of increasing ϕ, lies in the plane $z = z_1$, and is tangent to the cylindrical surface $r = r_1$. The unit vector $\mathbf{a}_z$ is the same as the unit vector $\mathbf{a}_z$ of the cartesian coordinate system. Figure 1.5b shows the three unit vectors in cylindrical coordinates. Two of these unit vectors change in direction (but not in magnitude, of course) as we construct them at various points; this is not the case in cartesian coordinates.

The unit vectors are again mutually perpendicular, for each is normal to one of the three mutually perpendicular surfaces, and we may define a right-handed cylindrical coordinate system as one in which $\mathbf{a}_r \times \mathbf{a}_\phi = \mathbf{a}_z$, or for those who have flexible fingers, as one in which the thumb, forefinger, and middle finger point in the direction of increasing r, ϕ, and z, respectively.

A differential volume element in cylindrical coordinates may be obtained by increasing r, ϕ, and z by the differential increments dr, $d\phi$, and dz. The two cylinders of radius r and $r + dr$, the two radial planes at angles ϕ and $\phi + d\phi$, and the two "horizontal" planes at "elevations" z and $z + dz$ now enclose a small volume, shown in Fig. 1.5c and having the shape of a truncated wedge. As the volume element becomes very small, its shape approaches that of a rectangular parallelepiped having sides of length dr, $r\, d\phi$, and dz. The surfaces then have areas of $r\, dr\, d\phi$, $dr\, dz$, and $r\, d\phi\, dz$, and the volume becomes $r\, dr\, d\phi\, dz$.

1.9. The Spherical Coordinate System. We have no two-dimensional coordinate system to help us understand the three-dimensional spherical coordinate system. In certain respects we can draw on our knowledge of the latitude-and-longitude system of locating a place on the surface of the earth, but usually we consider only points on the surface and not those below or above ground.

Let us start by building a spherical coordinate system on the three cartesian axes (Fig. 1.6a). We first define the distance from the origin to any point as r, the same letter we used in cylindrical coordinates to designate the distance from a line, but definitely not the same meaning. This is a fault of the nomenclature, for which everyone apologizes but can do little. When the small letter r is seen, it must be immediately determined whether it is a coordinate in the cylindrical or spherical system. In spherical coordinates, the surface r = constant is a sphere.

The second coordinate is an angle θ between the z axis and the line drawn from the origin to the point in question. The surface θ = constant is a cone, and the two surfaces, cone and sphere, are everywhere perpendicular. The intersection of the cone and sphere is a circle of radius $r \sin \theta$. The coordinate θ corresponds to latitude, except that latitude is measured from the equator and θ is measured from the "North Pole."

The third coordinate ϕ is also an angle and in this case is exactly

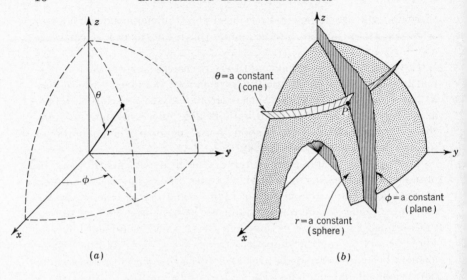

(a)   (b)

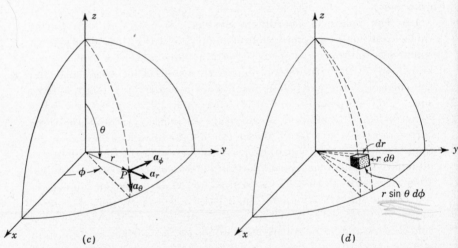

(c)   (d)

FIG. 1.6. (a) The three spherical coordinates. (b) The three mutually perpendicular surfaces of the spherical coordinate system. (c) The three unit vectors of spherical coordinates. (d) The differential volume unit in the spherical coordinate system.

the same as the angle ϕ of cylindrical coordinates. It is the angle between the x axis and the projection in the $z = 0$ plane of the line drawn from the origin to the point. It corresponds to the angle of longitude, but the angle ϕ increases to the "east." The surface ϕ = constant is a plane passing through the $\theta = 0$ line (or the z axis).

We should again consider any point as the intersection of three mutually perpendicular surfaces, a sphere, a cone, and a plane, each oriented in the manner described above. The three surfaces are sketched in Fig. 1.6b.

Three unit vectors may again be defined at any point. Each unit vector is perpendicular to one of the three mutually perpendicular surfaces and oriented in that direction in which the coordinate increases. The unit vector a_r is directed radially outward, normal to the sphere $r = $ constant, and lies in the cone $\theta = $ constant and the plane $\phi = $ constant. The unit vector a_θ is normal to the conical surface, lies in the plane, and is tangent to the sphere. It is directed along a line of "longitude" and points "south." The third unit vector a_ϕ is the same as in cylindrical coordinates, being normal to the plane and tangent to both the cone and sphere. It is directed to the "east."

The three unit vectors are shown in Fig. 1.6c. They are of course mutually perpendicular, and a right-handed coordinate system is defined by causing $a_r \times a_\theta = a_\phi$. Our system is right-handed, as an inspection of Fig. 1.6c will show, on application of the definition of the cross product. The right-hand rule serves to identify the thumb, forefinger, and middle finger with the direction of increasing r, θ, and ϕ, respectively. (Note that the identification in cylindrical coordinates was with r, ϕ, and z, and in cartesian coordinates with x, y, and z.)

A differential volume element may be constructed in spherical coordinates by increasing r, θ, and ϕ by dr, $d\theta$, and $d\phi$, as shown in Fig. 1.6d. The distance between the two spherical surfaces of radius r and $r + dr$ is dr; the distance between the two cones having generating angles of θ and $\theta + d\theta$ is $r\,d\theta$; and the distance between the two radial planes at angles ϕ and $\phi + d\phi$ is found to be $r \sin\theta\,d\phi$, after a few moments of trigonometrical thought. The surfaces have areas of $r\,dr\,d\theta$, $r\sin\theta\,dr\,d\phi$, and $r^2\sin\theta\,d\theta\,d\phi$, and the volume is

$$r^2 \sin\theta\,dr\,d\theta\,d\phi$$

1.10. Transformations between Coordinate Systems. After we have begun to use vector analysis as a tool in solving electric and magnetic field problems, we shall meet several of the more difficult problems in which it is easier to carry out a first step using cartesian coordinates but desirable to have an answer expressed in cylindrical or spherical coordinates. Sometimes the transformation between coordinate systems in the reverse direction is wanted. There are even cases here and there where it is advantageous to use a mixed coordinate system for a special problem in which the transformation between coordinate systems essentially occurs from line to line. Again it is a matter of learning a method well and then using it to simplify problems whenever necessary. The initial time is always repaid many times over.

First let us consider specifically the transformation of a vector in cartesian coordinates into one in cylindrical coordinates. This is fundamentally a two-step problem, that of changing variables and that of changing components. A vector in cartesian coordinates $\mathbf{A} = A_x\mathbf{a}_x + A_y\mathbf{a}_y + A_z\mathbf{a}_z$, where A_x, A_y, and A_z are functions of x, y, and z, must be changed to a vector in cylindrical coordinates which we may call $\mathbf{A}'$ to indicate the change in coordinate system, given by

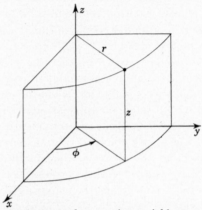

Fig. 1.7. The relationship between the cartesian variables x, y, z and the cylindrical coordinate variables r, ϕ, z. There is no change in the variable z between the two systems.

$\mathbf{A}' = A_r\mathbf{a}_r + A_\phi\mathbf{a}_\phi + A_z\mathbf{a}_z$, where A_r, A_ϕ, and A_z are functions of r, ϕ, and z.

The order of the two steps makes little difference, so we may consider the change of variables first. If we set up our two coordinate systems as shown in Fig. 1.7 so that the $z = 0$ planes coincide and the $y = 0$ plane is the $\phi = 0$ plane, then the following relationships exist between the variables:

$$x = r \cos \phi \qquad y = r \sin \phi \qquad z = z$$

$$r^2 = x^2 + y^2 \qquad \tan \phi = \frac{y}{x} \qquad z = z$$

The first line gives x, y, and z in terms of r, ϕ, and z, and the second gives r, ϕ, and z in terms of x, y, and z. It can be seen that no change is involved in the variable z and, furthermore, that the unit vector $\mathbf{a}_z$ is the same in each system.

To illustrate the change of variable, consider the vector

$$\mathbf{B} = z\mathbf{a}_x + (1 - x)\mathbf{a}_y + (y/x)\mathbf{a}_z$$

which becomes $z\mathbf{a}_x + (1 - r \cos \phi)\mathbf{a}_y + \tan \phi \, \mathbf{a}_z$. This is the first step in a transformation between coordinate systems.

Now consider the change in the components. In general terms, we have the three cartesian components A_x, A_y, and A_z of the vector $\mathbf{A}$ and desire the three cylindrical components A_r, A_ϕ, and A_z of $\mathbf{A}'$. Immediately we realize that the A_z terms are the same since the unit vectors have the same significance in each system. To find the A_r component, we recall from the discussion of the dot product that a component in a desired direction may be obtained by taking the dot product of the vector and a unit vector in the desired direction. Hence,

$$A_r = \mathbf{A} \cdot \mathbf{a}_r$$

and
$$A_\phi = \mathbf{A} \cdot \mathbf{a}_\phi$$

Expanding these dot products, then, we have

$$A_r = (A_x\mathbf{a}_x + A_y\mathbf{a}_y + A_z\mathbf{a}_z) \cdot \mathbf{a}_r = A_x\mathbf{a}_x \cdot \mathbf{a}_r + A_y\mathbf{a}_y \cdot \mathbf{a}_r$$

and $\quad A_\phi = (A_x\mathbf{a}_x + A_y\mathbf{a}_y + A_z\mathbf{a}_z) \cdot \mathbf{a}_\phi = A_x\mathbf{a}_x \cdot \mathbf{a}_\phi + A_y\mathbf{a}_y \cdot \mathbf{a}_\phi$

since $\mathbf{a}_z \cdot \mathbf{a}_r$ and $\mathbf{a}_z \cdot \mathbf{a}_\phi$ are zero.

In order to complete the transformation of the components it is necessary to know the dot products $\mathbf{a}_x \cdot \mathbf{a}_r$, $\mathbf{a}_y \cdot \mathbf{a}_r$, $\mathbf{a}_x \cdot \mathbf{a}_\phi$, and $\mathbf{a}_y \cdot \mathbf{a}_\phi$. Applying the definition of the dot product, we see that since we are concerned with unit vectors the result is merely the cosine of the angle between the two unit vectors in question. Referring to Fig. 1.7, we then have

$$\mathbf{a}_x \cdot \mathbf{a}_r = \cos \phi$$
$$\mathbf{a}_y \cdot \mathbf{a}_r = \sin \phi$$
$$\mathbf{a}_x \cdot \mathbf{a}_\phi = - \sin \phi$$
$$\mathbf{a}_y \cdot \mathbf{a}_\phi = \cos \phi$$

Collecting these results leads to the final expression for transforming the cartesian vector $\mathbf{A}$ into the cylindrical vector $\mathbf{A}'$:

$$\mathbf{A}' = (A_x \cos \phi + A_y \sin \phi)\mathbf{a}_r + (-A_x \sin \phi + A_y \cos \phi)\mathbf{a}_\phi + A_z\mathbf{a}_z$$
$$(1)$$

To complete the example of the vector

$$\mathbf{B} = z\mathbf{a}_x + (1 - x)\mathbf{a}_y + (y/x)\mathbf{a}_z = z\mathbf{a}_x + (1 - r \cos \phi)\mathbf{a}_y + \tan \phi \, \mathbf{a}_r$$

we apply (1) above and have

$$\mathbf{B} = (z \cos \phi + \sin \phi - r \sin \phi \cos \phi)\mathbf{a}_r$$
$$+ (-z \sin \phi + \cos \phi - r \cos^2 \phi)\mathbf{a}_\phi + \tan \phi \, \mathbf{a}_z$$

Basically the problem of transformation between coordinate systems is simple: first change variables and then change components. Often the details are involved although the method itself is straightforward. It is useful to prepare a table showing the equations for changing variables in either direction, and showing also the components of each system in terms of the components of the other system. Such a table (Table 1.1) is given below. Note that it includes the

TABLE 1.1. RELATION BETWEEN THE VARIABLES AND COMPONENTS OF THE CARTESIAN AND CYLINDRICAL COORDINATE SYSTEMS

Change of variable		Change of component	
Cartesian to cylindrical	Cylindrical to cartesian	Cartesian to cylindrical	Cylindrical to cartesian
$x = r \cos \phi$	$r = \sqrt{x^2 + y^2}$	$A_r = A_x \cos \phi$ $+ A_y \sin \phi$	$A_x = A_r \dfrac{x}{\sqrt{x^2 + y^2}} - A_\phi \dfrac{y}{\sqrt{x^2 + y^2}}$
$y = r \sin \phi$	$\phi = \tan^{-1}\dfrac{y}{x}$	$A_\phi = -A_x \sin \phi$ $+ A_y \cos \phi$	$A_y = A_r \dfrac{y}{\sqrt{x^2 + y^2}} + A_\phi \dfrac{x}{\sqrt{x^2 + y^2}}$
$z = z$	$z = z$	$A_z = A_z$	$A_z = A_z$

results for a transformation in the reverse direction, for expressions are given for the components in cartesian coordinates in terms of those in cylindrical coordinates. These are obtained by the same method used in arriving at (1) and again make use of the expressions for the dot products of the unit vectors which we developed then.

The transformation of a vector from cartesian coordinates to spherical coordinates, or the reverse, is accomplished by following the same general procedure. The relationships between the variables are somewhat more involved but are obtained readily with the aid of Fig. 1.6a:

$$x = r \sin \theta \cos \phi \qquad y = r \sin \theta \sin \phi \qquad z = r \cos \theta$$

$$r^2 = x^2 + y^2 + z^2 \qquad \cos \theta = \frac{z}{\sqrt{x^2 + y^2 + z^2}} \qquad \tan \phi = \frac{y}{x}$$

The dot products of the unit vectors in the two coordinate systems are determined from Fig. 1.6c and a little trigonometry. Since the dot product of any spherical unit vector with any cartesian unit vector is the component of the spherical vector in the direction of the cartesian vector, the dot products with $\mathbf{a}_z$ are found to be

$$\mathbf{a}_r \cdot \mathbf{a}_z = \mathbf{a}_z \cdot \mathbf{a}_r = \cos \theta$$
$$\mathbf{a}_\theta \cdot \mathbf{a}_z = \mathbf{a}_z \cdot \mathbf{a}_\theta = -\sin \theta$$
$$\mathbf{a}_\phi \cdot \mathbf{a}_z = \mathbf{a}_z \cdot \mathbf{a}_\phi = 0$$

The dot products involving $\mathbf{a}_x$ and $\mathbf{a}_y$ require first the projection of the spherical unit vector on the xy plane and then the projection onto the desired axis. For example, $\mathbf{a}_r \cdot \mathbf{a}_x$ is obtained by projecting $\mathbf{a}_r$ on the xy plane, giving $\sin \theta$, and then projecting $\sin \theta$ on the x axis, which yields $\sin \theta \cos \phi$. The remaining dot products are

$$\mathbf{a}_r \cdot \mathbf{a}_x = \sin \theta \cos \phi$$
$$\mathbf{a}_\theta \cdot \mathbf{a}_x = \cos \theta \cos \phi$$
$$\mathbf{a}_\phi \cdot \mathbf{a}_x = -\sin \phi$$
$$\mathbf{a}_r \cdot \mathbf{a}_y = \sin \theta \sin \phi$$
$$\mathbf{a}_\theta \cdot \mathbf{a}_y = \cos \theta \sin \phi$$
$$\mathbf{a}_\phi \cdot \mathbf{a}_y = \cos \phi$$

With this information we are now able to write the components A_r, A_θ, and A_ϕ in terms of A_x, A_y, and A_z, or vice versa. This information is tabulated in Table 1.2, which should be referred to when the need arises to make a transformation between cartesian and spherical coordinates.

D1.8. Locate on a sketch and give the cartesian coordinates of the point whose cylindrical coordinates are:
(a) $r = 2$, $\phi = 30°$, $z = 1$.
(b) $r = 0$, $\phi = 51°$, $z = 2$.
(c) $r = 1$, $\phi = 180°$, $z = 0$.

Ans. (0.732,1.0,3).

D1.9. Locate on a sketch and give the cartesian coordinates of the point whose spherical coordinates are:
(a) $r = 2$, $\theta = 30°$, $\phi = 60°$.
(b) $r = 1$, $\theta = 90°$, $\phi = 90°$.
(c) $r = 2$, $\theta = 150°$, $\phi = 300°$.

Ans. (1,1,0).

D1.10. Transform the following vectors to cylindrical coordinates:
(a) $x\mathbf{a}_x + y\mathbf{a}_y + z\mathbf{a}_z$.

(b) $\dfrac{1}{x}\mathbf{a}_x - \dfrac{1}{y}\mathbf{a}_y$.

(c) $\dfrac{x}{x^2 + y^2 + z^2}\mathbf{a}_x + \dfrac{y}{x^2 + y^2 + z^2}\mathbf{a}_y + \dfrac{z}{x^2 + y^2 + z^2}\mathbf{a}_z$.

Ans. $\left(r + \dfrac{r}{r^2 + z^2}\right)\mathbf{a}_r - \dfrac{1}{r \sin \phi \cos \phi}\mathbf{a}_\phi + \left(z + \dfrac{z}{r^2 + z^2}\right)\mathbf{a}_z$.

TABLE 1.2. RELATION BETWEEN THE CARTESIAN AND SPHERICAL COORDINATE SYSTEMS

Change of variable		Change of component	
Cartesian to spherical	Spherical to cartesian	Cartesian to spherical	Spherical to cartesian
$x = r \sin\theta \cos\phi$	$r = \sqrt{x^2 + y^2 + z^2}$	$A_r = A_x \sin\theta \cos\phi + A_y \sin\theta \sin\phi + A_z \cos\theta$	$A_x = \dfrac{A_r x}{\sqrt{x^2 + y^2 + z^2}} + \dfrac{A_\theta xz}{\sqrt{(x^2 + y^2)(x^2 + y^2 + z^2)}} - \dfrac{A_\phi y}{\sqrt{x^2 + y^2}}$
$y = r \sin\theta \sin\phi$	$\theta = \cos^{-1} \dfrac{z}{\sqrt{x^2 + y^2 + z^2}}$	$A_\theta = A_x \cos\theta \cos\phi + A_y \cos\theta \sin\phi - A_z \sin\theta$	$A_y = \dfrac{A_r y}{\sqrt{x^2 + y^2 + z^2}} + \dfrac{A_\theta yz}{\sqrt{(x^2 + y^2)(x^2 + y^2 + z^2)}} + \dfrac{A_\phi x}{\sqrt{x^2 + y^2}}$
$z = r \cos\theta$	$\phi = \tan^{-1} \dfrac{y}{x}$	$A_\phi = -A_x \sin\phi + A_y \cos\phi$	$A_z = \dfrac{A_r z}{\sqrt{x^2 + y^2 + z^2}} - \dfrac{A_\theta \sqrt{x^2 + y^2}}{\sqrt{x^2 + y^2 + z^2}}$

D1.11. Transform the following vectors from cylindrical coordinates to cartesian coordinates:

(a) $r \cos \phi \, \mathbf{a}_r - r \sin \phi \, \mathbf{a}_\phi$.

(b) $\dfrac{\tan \phi}{r} \mathbf{a}_r + \dfrac{1}{r} \mathbf{a}_\phi$.

(c) $\dfrac{1}{r} \mathbf{a}_r + \dfrac{1}{r} \mathbf{a}_z$.

$$Ans. \left(\sqrt{x^2 + y^2} + \frac{x}{x^2 + y^2} \right) \mathbf{a}_x + \left(\frac{1}{x} + \frac{y}{x^2 + y^2} \right) \mathbf{a}_y + \frac{1}{\sqrt{x^2 + y^2}} \mathbf{a}_z.$$

D1.12. Transform the following vectors to spherical coordinates:

(a) $x\mathbf{a}_x + y\mathbf{a}_y + z\mathbf{a}_z$.

(b) $\dfrac{1}{z} \mathbf{a}_z$.

(c) $\mathbf{a}_y$.

$$Ans. \left(r + \frac{1}{r} + \sin \theta \sin \phi \right) \mathbf{a}_r + \left(\cos \theta \sin \phi - \frac{1}{r} \tan \theta \right) \mathbf{a}_\theta + \cos \phi \, \mathbf{a}_\phi.$$

D1.13. Transform the following vectors from spherical coordinates to cartesian coordinates:

(a) $\dfrac{1}{r} \mathbf{a}_r$.

(b) $\dfrac{\tan \theta}{r} \mathbf{a}_\theta$.

(c) $\dfrac{\sin \theta}{r} \mathbf{a}_\phi$.

$$Ans. \frac{1}{x^2 + y^2 + z^2} \left[(2x - y)\mathbf{a}_x + (2y + x)\mathbf{a}_y + \left(z - \frac{x^2 + y^2}{z} \right) \mathbf{a}_z \right].$$

SUGGESTED REFERENCES

1. Guillemin, E. A.: "The Mathematics of Circuit Analysis," John Wiley & Sons, Inc., New York, 1951. Chapter 5 is devoted to vector analysis.
2. Lass, Harry: "Vector and Tensor Analysis," McGraw-Hill Book Company, Inc., New York, 1950. A more comprehensive and mathematical treatment of vector analysis.
3. Reed, M. B., and G. B. Reed: "Mathematical Methods in Electrical Engineering," Harper & Brothers, New York, 1951. In chap. 6 vector analysis is discussed at an introductory level.
4. Sokolnikoff, I. S., and E. S. Sokolnikoff: "Higher Mathematics for Engineers and Physicists," McGraw-Hill Book Company, Inc., New York, 1941. Vector analysis is discussed in chap. 9. The notation for products is different. Answers are given for a number of problems.

PROBLEMS

1. By making a suitable drawing, show that (a) $\mathbf{A} + (\mathbf{B} + \mathbf{C}) = (\mathbf{A} + \mathbf{B}) + \mathbf{C}$; (b) $2(\mathbf{A} + \mathbf{B}) = 2\mathbf{A} + 2\mathbf{B}$; (c) $\mathbf{A} - \mathbf{B} = -(\mathbf{B} - \mathbf{A})$.

2. It is desired to construct a right-handed cartesian coordinate system using axes which may be described as (1) in or out of the paper, (2) horizontal and in the plane of the paper, and (3) vertical and in the plane of the paper. Select one suitable grouping of x, y, and z axes which describe a right-handed cartesian coordinate system and call the result one "combination." If the origin is unchanged: (a) How many such combinations are possible? (b) How many different locations result for the physical location of the point (1,2,3)? (c) For the point (1,1,2)? (d) For the point (1,0,−1)? (e) For the point (1,1,1)?

3. Vector **A** extends from the origin to (1,2,3) and vector **B** from the origin to (2,3,−2). (a) Find the unit vector in the direction of (**A** − **B**). (b) Find the unit vector in the direction of a line extending from the origin to the mid-point of the line joining the ends of **A** and **B**.

4. If x, y, and z axes are laid out at the surface of the sea in directions described as north, west, and up, respectively, and if the velocity of the water is given as **U** $= y\mathbf{a}_x - x\mathbf{a}_y$: (a) Make a sketch of the surface of the sea and draw short directed line segments, directed in the direction of the water velocity and with a length proportional to the magnitude of the velocity, at the points (0,0), (1,0), (0,1), (−1,0), (0,−1), (2,0), (0,2), (−2,0), (0,−2). (b) Obtain the expression for the magnitude of the velocity as a function of x and y. (c) From the results of (a) and (b) above, describe carefully the physical field.

5. Let us consider a sufficiently small section of the surface of the earth as small variations above or below a reference plane. The x and y axes both lie in this reference plane. We then define a vector **s** as the slope of the surface, **s** $= 0.2\mathbf{a}_x$ signifying that the surface rises 0.2 m for each horizontal meter in the x direction. If at any point, then, **s** $= (\cos x)e^{-y^2}\mathbf{a}_x - 2y(\sin x)e^{-y^2}\mathbf{a}_y$, describe the general nature of the terrain.

6. Two unit vectors $\mathbf{a}_A$ and $\mathbf{a}_B$, lying in the xy plane and passing through the origin, make angles of θ_A and θ_B with the x axis, respectively. (a) Express each vector in cartesian components. (b) Take the dot product and then show that $\cos(\theta_A - \theta_B) = \cos\theta_A \cos\theta_B + \sin\theta_A \sin\theta_B$.

7. If **a** is a unit vector in a given direction, B is a scalar constant, and $\mathbf{r} = x\mathbf{a}_x + y\mathbf{a}_y + z\mathbf{a}_z$, describe the surface $\mathbf{r}\cdot\mathbf{a} = B$. What is the relation of the unit vector **a** and the scalar B to this surface? (HINT: Consider first a simple example with $\mathbf{a} = \mathbf{a}_x$, $B = 1$, and then consider any **a** and B.)

8. (a) Choose a suitable cylindrical coordinate system and write the vector expression for the velocity **U** m/sec of a point r m from the center of a wheel rotating at an angular velocity of ω radians/sec. (b) Express the velocity in cartesian coordinates as a function of x and y.

9. The dot product of two vectors is zero. What conditions must these vectors satisfy for this to be so?

10. If a scalar voltage is represented as a complex phasor having a real part V_r and an imaginary part V_i, $V = V_r + jV_i$, and if the phasor is then drawn as a directed line segment on a phasor diagram, this line may be considered a vector and represented by **V** $= V_r\mathbf{a}_x + V_i\mathbf{a}_y$, where $\mathbf{a}_x$ and $\mathbf{a}_y$ are now unit vectors in the directions of the real and imaginary axes, respectively. Similarly, the directed line segment representing the current may be written **I** $= I_r\mathbf{a}_x + I_i\mathbf{a}_y$. Show that the dot product **V** $\cdot$ **I** is equal to the average power if **V** and **I** represent rms values.

11. Show that (a) **A** $\cdot$ (**A** $\times$ **B**) $\equiv 0$; (b) **A** $\cdot$ (**B** $\times$ **C**) $\equiv$ (**A** $\times$ **B**) $\cdot$ **C**; (c) (**A** $\times$ **B**) $\cdot$ (**A** $\times$ **B**) $+$ (**A** $\cdot$ **B**)(**A** $\cdot$ **B**) $\equiv$ (**A** $\cdot$ **A**)(**B** $\cdot$ **B**).

12. The cross product of two vectors is zero. What conditions must these vectors satisfy for this to be so?

13. Two unit vectors a_A and a_B, lying in the xy plane and passing through the origin, make angles of θ_A and θ_B with the x axis, respectively. (a) Express each vector in cartesian components. (b) Take the cross product and then show that $\sin(\theta_B - \theta_A) = \sin\theta_B \cos\theta_A - \cos\theta_B \sin\theta_A$.

14. Show that the vector fields $\mathbf{A} = r\cos\phi\,a_r + r\sin\phi\,a_\phi + ra_z$ and $\mathbf{B} = r\cos\phi\,a_r + r\sin\phi\,a_\phi - ra_z$ are everywhere perpendicular to each other.

15. Show that the vector fields $\mathbf{A} = a_r(\sin 2\theta)/r^2 + 2a_\theta(\sin\theta)/r^2$ and $\mathbf{B} = r\cos\theta\,a_r + ra_\theta$ are everywhere parallel to each other.

16. Using the definition of the dot product, find the angle between the two vectors $\mathbf{A} = 2a_x + a_y + 3a_z$ and $\mathbf{B} = a_x - 3a_y + 2a_z$.

17. Find the angle between the vectors of Prob. 16 by using the definition of the cross product.

18. State whether or not $\mathbf{A} = \mathbf{B}$ and, if not, what conditions are imposed on $\mathbf{A}$ and $\mathbf{B}$ when (a) $\mathbf{A}\cdot a_x = \mathbf{B}\cdot a_x$; (b) $\mathbf{A}\times a_x = \mathbf{B}\times a_x$; (c) $\mathbf{A}\cdot a_x = \mathbf{B}\cdot a_x$ and $\mathbf{A}\times a_x = \mathbf{B}\times a_x$; (d) $\mathbf{A}\cdot\mathbf{C} = \mathbf{B}\cdot\mathbf{C}$ and $\mathbf{A}\times\mathbf{C} = \mathbf{B}\times\mathbf{C}$, where $\mathbf{C}$ is any vector except $\mathbf{C}\neq 0$.

19. If $\mathbf{A} = 2a_r - 3a_\phi + 2a_z$ and $\mathbf{B} = 3a_r + 5a_\phi - a_z$, find (a) $\mathbf{A}+\mathbf{B}$; (b) $\mathbf{A}\times\mathbf{B}$; (c) $\mathbf{A}\cdot\mathbf{B}$; (d) $\mathbf{A}-\mathbf{B}$; (e) $\mathbf{B}\cdot(\mathbf{B}\times\mathbf{A})$; (f) $|\mathbf{B}|\mathbf{A}$; (g) $\mathbf{A}/|\mathbf{B}|$; (h) $|\mathbf{A}| + |\mathbf{B}|$; (i) $|\mathbf{A}+\mathbf{B}|$; (j) $\mathbf{B}\times\mathbf{A}$; (k) $(\mathbf{A}\cdot\mathbf{B})\mathbf{B}$; (l) component of $\mathbf{B}$ in the z direction.

20. Prove by vector methods, independent of any coordinate system, that in any triangle the square on the side opposite to an acute angle is equal to the sum of the squares on the sides containing that acute angle minus twice the rectangle contained by one of those sides and the projection on it of the other side.

CHAPTER 2

COULOMB'S LAW AND ELECTRIC FIELD INTENSITY

Now that we have formulated a new language in the first chapter, we shall establish a few basic principles of electricity and attempt to describe them in terms of it. If we had used vector analysis for several years and already had a few correct ideas about electricity and magnetism, we might jump in now with both feet and present a handful of equations, which included Maxwell's equations and a few other auxiliary equations, and proceed to describe them physically by virtue of our knowledge of vector analysis. This is perhaps the ideal way, starting with the most general results and then showing that Ohm's, Gauss's, Coulomb's, Faraday's, Ampère's, Biot-Savart's, Kirchhoff's, and a few less familiar laws are all special cases of these equations. It is philosophically satisfying to have the most general result and to feel that we are able to obtain the results for any special case at will. However, such a jump would lead to many frantic cries of "Help" and not a few drowned students.

Instead we shall present at decent intervals the experimental laws mentioned above, expressing each in vector notation, and use these laws to solve a number of simple problems. In this way our familiarity with vector analysis and electric and magnetic fields will both gradually increase, and by the time we have finally reached our handful of general equations, little additional explanation will be required. The entire field of electromagnetic theory is then open to us, and we may use Maxwell's equations to describe wave propagation, radiation from antennas, skin effect, waveguides and transmission lines, traveling-wave tubes, and even to obtain a new insight into the 60-cps power transformer.

We shall start by discussing the experimental law of Coulomb.

2.1. The Experimental Law of Coulomb. It was at least 600 years before the birth of Christ that records show of the knowledge of static electricity. The Greeks were responsible for the term "electricity," derived from their word for amber, and they spent many a leisure hour rubbing a small piece of amber on their sleeves and observing how it

26

would then attract pieces of lint and fluff. However, their main interest lay in philosophy and logic, not in experimental science, and it was many centuries before the attracting effect was considered to be anything other than magic or a "life force."

Dr. Gilbert, physician to Her Majesty the Queen of England, was the first to do any true experimental work with this effect and in 1600 stated that glass, sulfur, amber, and other materials which he named would "not only draw to themselves straws and chaff, but all metals, wood, leaves, stone, earths, even water and oil."

Shortly thereafter a colonel in the French Army Engineers, Col. Charles Coulomb, a precise and orderly-minded officer, performed an elaborate series of experiments using a delicate torsion balance, invented by himself, to determine quantitatively the force exerted between two objects, each having a static charge of electricity. His published result is now known to many high-school students and bears a great similarity to Newton's gravitational law (discovered about a hundred years earlier). Coulomb stated that the force between two very small objects, separated in some uniform or homogeneous medium by a distance which is large compared to their size, is proportional to the charge on each and inversely proportional to the square of the distance between them:

$$F = k \frac{Q_1 Q_2}{R^2} \tag{1}$$

Q_1 and Q_2 are the magnitudes of the point charges, R the separation, and k is a proportionality constant. If the mks (meter-kilogram-second) system of units is used, Q is measured in coulombs, R in meters, and the force is in newtons.

All the mks units are not as familiar to us as are the English units we use every day, but they are now standard in electrical engineering and physics. The newton is a unit of force which is equivalent to 0.2248 lb of force, or to 10^5 dynes, and is the force required to give a one-kilogram mass an acceleration of one meter per second per second. The coulomb is an extremely large unit of charge, for the smallest known quantity of charge is that of the electron (negative) or proton (positive), given in mks units as $(1.60206 \pm 0.00003) \times 10^{-19}$ coulomb, and hence a negative charge of one coulomb represents about 6×10^{18} electrons. The electron has a rest mass of $(9.1083 \pm 0.0003) \times 10^{-31}$ kg and has a radius of the order of magnitude of 3.8×10^{-15} m. This does not mean that the electron is spherical in shape, but merely serves to describe the size of the region in which a slowly moving electron has the greatest probability of being found. All other known charged particles, including the proton, have larger masses, larger radii, and occupy a probabilistic volume larger than does the electron.

The constant of proportionality in (1) is written as

$$k = \frac{1}{4\pi\epsilon}$$

where the factor 4π will now appear in the denominator of Coulomb's law but will not appear in the more useful equations (including Maxwell's equations) which we shall obtain with the help of Coulomb's law. The new constant ϵ is called the *permittivity*, or *inductive capacity*, of the homogeneous medium in which the charge is embedded and the force is being measured. The permittivity of free space, or a vacuum, is designated ϵ_0 and has the magnitude

$$\epsilon_0 = 8.854 \times 10^{-12} \doteq \frac{1}{36\pi} 10^{-9} \text{ farad/m} \qquad (2)$$

The quantity ϵ_0 is not dimensionless, for Coulomb's law shows that it has the label coulombs² /(newton)(m²). We shall later define the *farad* and show that it has the dimensions of coulombs²/(newton)(m), and we anticipate this definition by using the unit farad/m in (2) above.

The permittivity of a material is usually given relative to that of a vacuum by defining

$$\epsilon_R = \frac{\epsilon}{\epsilon_0}$$

where $\epsilon_R = relative\ permittivity.$

Coulomb's law is now

$$F = \frac{Q_1 Q_2}{4\pi\epsilon R^2} \qquad (3)$$

and may be used to give numerical results, such as showing that the force between two charges of one coulomb each separated by one meter is 9×10^9 newtons, or about one million tons.[1]

In order to write the vector form of (3) we need the additional information (furnished also by Colonel Coulomb) that the force acts along the line joining the two charges and is repulsive if the charges are alike in sign and attractive if they are of opposite sign. Let the vector $\mathbf{R}_{12}$ represent the directed line segment from Q_1 to Q_2, and let $\mathbf{F}_2$ be the

[1] The explosive force of the atomic bomb is due almost entirely to Coulomb forces. Fission results in the separation of the positive nucleus into several parts, which are then subject to these extremely large forces.

force on Q_2. Then

$$\mathbf{F}_2 = \frac{Q_1 Q_2}{4\pi\epsilon R_{12}{}^2}\, \mathbf{a}_{R12} \tag{4}$$

where $\mathbf{a}_{R12}$ = a unit vector in the direction of $\mathbf{R}_{12}$, or

$$\mathbf{a}_{R12} = \frac{\mathbf{R}_{12}}{|\mathbf{R}_{12}|} = \frac{\mathbf{R}_{12}}{R_{12}} \tag{5}$$

As an example of the use of the vector form of Coulomb's law, consider a charge of 3×10^{-4} coulomb at $P(1,2,3)$ and a charge of -10^{-4} coulomb at $Q(2,0,5)$ in a vacuum. Then

$$Q_1 = 3 \times 10^{-4} \qquad Q_2 = -10^{-4}$$
$$\mathbf{R}_{12} = (2 - 1)\mathbf{a}_x + (0 - 2)\mathbf{a}_y + (5 - 3)\mathbf{a}_z = \mathbf{a}_x - 2\mathbf{a}_y + 2\mathbf{a}_z$$
$$\mathbf{a}_{R12} = \frac{\mathbf{a}_x - 2\mathbf{a}_y + 2\mathbf{a}_z}{3}$$
$$\mathbf{F}_2 = \frac{3 \times 10^{-4}(-10^{-4})}{4\pi \frac{1}{36\pi} 10^{-9} \times 9}\left(\frac{\mathbf{a}_x - 2\mathbf{a}_y + 2\mathbf{a}_z}{3}\right)$$
$$= -30\left(\frac{\mathbf{a}_x - 2\mathbf{a}_y + 2\mathbf{a}_z}{3}\right) \qquad \text{newtons}$$

The magnitude of the force is 30 newtons (or about 7 lb), and the direction is specified by the unit vector, which has been left in the parentheses in order to display the magnitude of the force. The force on Q_2 may also be considered as three component forces:

$$\mathbf{F}_2 = -10\mathbf{a}_x + 20\mathbf{a}_y - 20\mathbf{a}_z$$

The force expressed by Coulomb's law is a mutual force, for each of the two charges experiences a force of the same magnitude, although of opposite direction. We might equally well have written

$$\mathbf{F}_1 = -\mathbf{F}_2 = \frac{Q_1 Q_2}{4\pi\epsilon R_{12}{}^2}\, \mathbf{a}_{R21} = -\frac{Q_1 Q_2}{4\pi\epsilon R_{12}{}^2}\, \mathbf{a}_{R12}$$

Coulomb's law is linear, for if we multiply Q_1 by a factor n, the force is also multiplied by the same factor n. It is also true that the force on a charge in the presence of several other charges is the sum of the forces on that charge due to each of the other charges acting alone.

D2.1. Three charges, Q_1, Q_2, Q_3, are located at the origin, 10 cm from the origin on the positive y axis, and 10 cm from the origin on the positive x axis, respectively, and have charges of $10^{-9}/18\pi$, $-\sqrt{2} \times 10^{-9}/9\pi$, and 4π coulombs, also respectively. Find the force in a vacuum (expressed in terms of its cartesian components):

(a) On Q_3 due only to Q_1.

(b) On Q_3 due only to Q_2.

(c) On Q_3 due to both Q_1 and Q_2.

Ans. 400a$_y$ newtons.

2.2. Electric Field Intensity. If we now consider one charge fixed in position, say Q_1, and move a second charge slowly around, we note that there exists everywhere a force on this second charge. Calling this second charge a test charge, Q_t, the force on it is given by Coulomb's law:

$$\mathbf{F}_t = \frac{Q_1 Q_t}{4\pi\epsilon R_{1t}{}^2}\, \mathbf{a}_{R1t}$$

Writing this force as a force per unit charge,

$$\frac{\mathbf{F}_t}{Q_t} = \frac{Q_1}{4\pi\epsilon R_{1t}{}^2}\, \mathbf{a}_{R1t} \tag{1}$$

We now have an expression which does not involve the size or sign of the test charge, for as the test charge increases or decreases in magnitude, so does the force on it. As the test charge changes sign, the force obediently changes direction, and their ratio is still constant. The quantity on the right side of (1) is a function only of Q_1 and the directed line segment from Q_1 to the position of the test charge. This describes a vector field and is called the *electric field intensity.*

We define the electric field intensity as the vector force on a unit positive test charge. We would not *measure* it experimentally by finding the force on a 1-coulomb test charge, however, for this would probably cause such a force on Q_1 as to change the position of that charge.

Electric field intensity must be measured by the unit newtons per coulomb, force per unit charge. Again anticipating a new dimensional quantity, the *volt*, to be presented in the fourth chapter and having the label of joules per coulomb or newton-meters per coulomb, we shall at once measure electric field intensity in the practical units of volts per meter. Using a capital letter **E** for electric field intensity, we have finally

$$\mathbf{E} = \frac{\mathbf{F}_t}{Q_t} \tag{2}$$

$$= \frac{Q_1}{4\pi\epsilon R_{1t}{}^2}\, \mathbf{a}_{R1t} \tag{3}$$

Equation (2) is the defining expression for electric field intensity, and (3) is the expression for the electric field intensity due to a single point charge Q_1. In the succeeding sections we shall obtain and interpret expressions for the electric field intensity due to more complicated arrangements of charge, but now let us see what information we can obtain from (3), the field of a single point charge.

First, let us dispense with the subscripts in (3), reserving the right to use them again any time there is a possibility of misunderstanding:

$$E = \frac{Q}{4\pi\epsilon R^2} a_R \qquad (4)$$

We should remember that R is the magnitude of the vector $\mathbf{R}$, the directed line segment from the point at which the point charge Q is located to the point at which $\mathbf{E}$ is desired, and a_R is a unit vector in the $\mathbf{R}$ direction.[1]

Let us arbitrarily locate Q_1 at the center of a spherical coordinate system. The unit vector a_R then becomes the radial unit vector a_r, and R is r. Hence

$$E = \frac{Q_1}{4\pi\epsilon r^2} a_r \qquad (5)$$

or

$$E_r = \frac{Q_1}{4\pi\epsilon r^2}$$

The field has a single radial component, and its inverse-square-law relationship is quite obvious.

In cartesian coordinates we should write $\mathbf{R} = x a_x + y a_y + z a_z$, $a_R = (x a_x + y a_y + z a_z)/\sqrt{x^2 + y^2 + z^2}$, and then

$$E = \frac{Q}{4\pi\epsilon(x^2 + y^2 + z^2)} \left(\frac{x}{\sqrt{x^2 + y^2 + z^2}} a_x + \right.$$
$$\left. \frac{y}{\sqrt{x^2 + y^2 + z^2}} a_y + \frac{z}{\sqrt{x^2 + y^2 + z^2}} a_z \right) \qquad (6)$$

This expression no longer shows immediately the simple nature of the field, and its complexity is the price we pay for solving a problem having spherical symmetry in a coordinate system with which we may (temporarily) have more familiarity.

Without using vector analysis, the information contained in (6) would have to be expressed in three equations, one for each component, and in order to obtain the equations we should have to break up the magnitude of the electric field intensity into the three components by finding the projection on each coordinate axis. Using vector notation, this is done automatically when we write the unit vector.

---

[1] We firmly intend to avoid confusing r and a_r with R and a_R. The first two refer specifically to the spherical or cylindrical coordinate systems, whereas R and a_R do not refer to any coordinate system—the choice is still available to us.

The solution in cylindrical coordinates is called for in one of the problems at the end of the chapter.

If we consider a charge which is *not* at the origin of our coordinate system, the field no longer possesses spherical symmetry (nor cylindrical symmetry unless the charge lies on the z axis), and we might as well use cartesian coordinates. For a charge Q located at a, b, c, we obtain

$$\mathbf{E} = \frac{Q[(x - a)\mathbf{a}_x + (y - b)\mathbf{a}_y + (z - c)\mathbf{a}_z]}{4\pi\epsilon[(x - a)^2 + (y - b)^2 + (z - c)^2]^{3/2}} \tag{7}$$

Equation (6) is merely a special case of (7), where $a = b = c = 0$.

2.3. Field of n Point Charges. Since the Coulomb forces are linear, the electric field intensity due to two point charges Q_1 and Q_2 is the sum of the forces on Q_t caused by Q_1 and Q_2 acting alone, or

$$\mathbf{E} = \frac{Q_1}{4\pi\epsilon R_1{}^2}\,\mathbf{a}_{R1} + \frac{Q_2}{4\pi\epsilon R_2{}^2}\,\mathbf{a}_{R2}$$

The distances R_1 and R_2 and the unit vectors $\mathbf{a}_{R1}$ and $\mathbf{a}_{R2}$ are of course different.

As soon as we add this second charge, the spherical symmetry disappears and it becomes simplest to solve the problem in cartesian coordinates. The field due to each charge is obtained in terms of cartesian components, and these may be added to find the total field. This is the same procedure

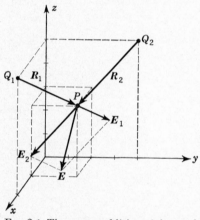

FIG. 2.1. The vector addition of the total electric field intensity at $P(1,2,3)$ due to Q_1 at $(2,0,5)$ and Q_2 at $(0,4,5)$.

as is used in Prob. D2.1c to find the force on a charge due to two other charges.

As an example of this method, let us find the electric field intensity at $P(1,2,3)$ in a vacuum due to $Q_1 = 3 \times 10^{-8}$ coulomb at $(2,0,5)$ and $Q_2 = 6 \times 10^{-8}$ coulomb at $(0,4,5)$ (Fig. 2.1).

The directed line segments $\mathbf{R}_1$ and $\mathbf{R}_2$ are found first, and the two unit vectors obtained from them:

$$\mathbf{R}_1 = (1 - 2)\mathbf{a}_x + (2 - 0)\mathbf{a}_y + (3 - 5)\mathbf{a}_z = -\mathbf{a}_x + 2\mathbf{a}_y - 2\mathbf{a}_z$$
$$\mathbf{R}_2 = (1 - 0)\mathbf{a}_x + (2 - 4)\mathbf{a}_y + (3 - 5)\mathbf{a}_z = \mathbf{a}_x - 2\mathbf{a}_y - 2\mathbf{a}_z$$
$$\mathbf{a}_{R1} = \frac{-\mathbf{a}_x + 2\mathbf{a}_y - 2\mathbf{a}_z}{3}$$
$$\mathbf{a}_{R2} = \frac{\mathbf{a}_x - 2\mathbf{a}_y - 2\mathbf{a}_z}{3}$$

We then find the field intensity due to each charge acting alone:

$$\mathbf{E}_1 = \frac{3 \times 10^{-8}}{4\pi \frac{1}{36\pi} 10^{-9} \times 9} \frac{-\mathbf{a}_x + 2\mathbf{a}_y - 2\mathbf{a}_z}{3} = -10\mathbf{a}_x + 20\mathbf{a}_y - 20\mathbf{a}_z$$

$$\mathbf{E}_2 = \frac{6 \times 10^{-8}}{4\pi \frac{1}{36\pi} 10^{-9} \times 9} \frac{\mathbf{a}_x - 2\mathbf{a}_y - 2\mathbf{a}_z}{3} = 20\mathbf{a}_x - 40\mathbf{a}_y - 40\mathbf{a}_z$$

and add vectorially:

$$\mathbf{E} = \mathbf{E}_1 + \mathbf{E}_2 = 10\mathbf{a}_x - 20\mathbf{a}_y - 60\mathbf{a}_z$$

The magnitude of the total electric field intensity is

$$E = \sqrt{10^2 + 20^2 + 60^2} = 64.0 \text{ volts/m}$$

and the direction is shown by the components of **E** just as well as by specifying a unit vector, which, however, would be

$$\mathbf{a}_E = \frac{10\mathbf{a}_x - 20\mathbf{a}_y - 60\mathbf{a}_z}{64.0} = 0.156\mathbf{a}_x - 0.312\mathbf{a}_y - 0.938\mathbf{a}_z$$

If we now add additional charges at other positions, the field due to n point charges is

$$\mathbf{E} = \frac{Q_1}{4\pi\epsilon R_1^2} \mathbf{a}_{R1} + \frac{Q_2}{4\pi\epsilon R_2^2} \mathbf{a}_{R2} + \cdots + \frac{Q_n}{4\pi\epsilon R_n^2} \mathbf{a}_{Rn} \qquad (1)$$

This expression takes up less space when we use a summation sign Σ and a summing integer m which takes on all integral values between 1 and n:

$$\mathbf{E} = \sum_{m=1}^{n} \frac{Q_m}{4\pi\epsilon R_m^2} \mathbf{a}_{Rm} \qquad (2)$$

When expanded, (2) is identical with (1), and those unfamiliar with summation signs and series should check that result.

D2.2. If $Q_1 = 343$ μcoulombs and $Q_2 = -81$ μcoulombs, and Q_1 is located at the origin and Q_2 at (0,2,4), find the electric field intensity at (2,3,6) in cartesian components in free space due to:

(a) Q_1 alone.

(b) Q_2 alone.

(c) Q_1 and Q_2.

Ans. $-72,000\mathbf{a}_x$ volts/m.

D2.3. Evaluate the sums:

(a) $\displaystyle\sum_{m=1}^{5} \frac{1}{m+1}$.

(b) $\displaystyle\sum_{m=1}^{3} \frac{1}{m^2 + 1}$.

(c) $\displaystyle\sum_{m=1}^{4} (-1)^{m+1} \tan\left[(2m - 1)\frac{\pi}{4}\right]$.

Ans. $2\frac{5}{4}$.

2.4. Field Due to a Continuous Volume Charge Distribution. If we now visualize a region of space filled with a tremendous number of charges separated by minute distances, such as the space between grid and cathode in a vacuum tube operating with space charge, we see that we can replace this distribution of very small particles with a smooth continuous distribution described by a *volume charge density*, just as we describe water as having a density of one gram per cubic centimeter even though it consists of atomic- and molecular-sized particles. We are able to do this only if we are uninterested in the small irregularities (or ripples) in the field as we move from electron to electron, of if we care little that the mass of the water actually increases in small but finite steps as each new molecule is added.

This is really no limitation at all, for our end results are almost always in terms of a current in a receiving antenna, a voltage in a vacuum-tube plate circuit, a charge on a capacitor, or, in general, in some large-scale *macroscopic* result. It is very seldom that we must know a current, electron by electron.

We denote volume charge density by the Greek letter *rho* (ρ), and it is of course measured in coulombs per cubic meter.

The small amount of charge ΔQ in a small volume Δv is

$$\Delta Q = \rho \, \Delta v \tag{1}$$

and the total charge within some finite volume is obtained by integrating throughout that volume:

$$Q = \int_{\text{vol}} dQ = \int_{\text{vol}} \rho \, dv \tag{2}$$

Only one integral sign is customarily indicated, but the differential dv signifies integration throughout a volume, and hence a triple integration. Fortunately, we may content ourselves for the most part with no more than the indicated integration, for multiple integrals are very difficult to evaluate in all but the most symmetrical problems.

The small contribution to the electric field intensity produced by ΔQ is

$$\Delta \mathbf{E} = \frac{\Delta Q}{4\pi\epsilon R^2} \, \mathbf{a}_R = \frac{\rho \, \Delta v}{4\pi\epsilon R^2} \, \mathbf{a}_R$$

If we sum the contributions of all the volume charge in a given region,

$$E = \sum_{m=1}^{n} \frac{\rho \, \Delta v}{4\pi\epsilon R^2} \, a_R$$

and then let the volume element Δv approach zero as the number of these elements n becomes infinite, the summation becomes an integral:

$$E = \int_{vol} \frac{\rho \, dv}{4\pi\epsilon R^2} \, a_R \qquad (3)$$

This is again a triple integral, and we shall do our best to avoid actually performing the integration.

The significance of the various quantities under the integral sign of (3) has not changed from their interpretation in Sec. 2.2, Eq. (4). The unit vector a_R is in the direction of R, which extends from the position of the element of charge $\rho \, dv$ to the point at which we are determining the electric field intensity. In general, we must expect that ρ, a_R, and R are functions of the variables of integration, say x, y, and z.

D2.4. Find the total charge in the specified volume:

(a) Volume: cube, edges 2 m long and parallel to axes, center at $(1,1,1)$; $\rho = 5xyz$.

(b) Volume: cylinder, radius of 1 m, height of 2 m, center at origin, axis on z axis; $\rho = \dfrac{20r^2(z+1)}{\pi}$.

(c) Volume: sphere, radius of 1 m, center at origin; $\rho = \dfrac{4\sin\theta(1+\cos\phi)}{\pi^2 r}$.

Ans. 62 coulombs.

2.5. Field of a Line Charge.

Up to this point we have considered two types of charge distribution, the point charge and charge distributed throughout a volume with a density of ρ coulombs/m³. The point charge we should recognize as volume charge density existing in only a very small region, at least until we consider dimensions of the order of magnitude of the "diameter" of an electron. The modern theories of physics state that an electron may be viewed as either a particle or a wave but that its position and momentum cannot both be known exactly. As a matter of fact, the more knowledge we have about momentum, the less we know about the position. It is better to use probability, or statistics, to describe the most probable momentum or to define the region in which we are most likely to find our electron. This theory leads to a "diameter" of about 3.8×10^{-15} m for an electron.

If we now consider a filament-like distribution of volume charge density, such as a very fine sharp beam in a cathode-ray tube or a charged conductor of very small radius, we find it convenient to treat the charge as a line charge of density ρ_L coulombs/m. In the case of the electron beam, the charges are in motion and it is true that we do not have an electrostatic problem. However, if the electron motion is steady and uniform (a d-c beam) and if we ignore for the moment the magnetic field which is produced, the electron beam may be considered as composed of stationary electrons, for snapshots taken at any time will show the same charge distribution.

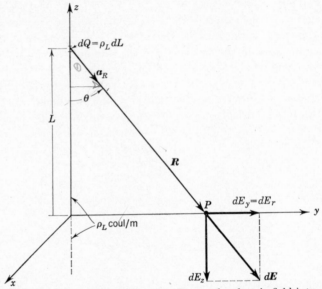

Fig. 2.2. The contribution $d\mathbf{E} = dE_y\mathbf{a}_y + dE_z\mathbf{a}_z$ to the electric field intensity produced by an element of charge $dQ = \rho_L \, dL$ located a distance L from the origin. The linear charge density is uniform and extends along the entire z axis.

Let us assume a straight line charge extending along the z axis in a cylindrical coordinate system from $-\infty$ to ∞, as shown in Fig. 2.2. We desire the electric field intensity $\mathbf{E}$ at any and every point resulting from a *uniform* line charge density of ρ_L coulombs/m.

Symmetry should always be considered first in order to determine two specific items: (1) with which coordinates the field does *not* vary, and (2) which components of the field are *not* present. The answers to these questions then tell us which components are present and with which coordinates they vary.

Referring to Fig. 2.2, we realize that as we move around the line charge, varying ϕ while keeping r and z constant, the line charge appears the same from every angle. In other words, azimuthal symmetry is present and no field component may vary with ϕ.

Again, if we maintain r and ϕ constant while moving up and down the line charge by changing z, the line charge still recedes into infinite distance in both directions and the problem is unchanged. This is axial symmetry and leads to fields which are not functions of z.

If we maintain ϕ and z constant and vary r, the problem changes and Coulomb's law leads us to expect the field to become weaker as r increases. Hence, by a process of elimination we are led to the fact that the field varies only with r.

Now, which components are present? Each incremental length of line charge acts as a point charge and produces an incremental contribution to the electric field intensity which is directed away from the bit of charge (assuming a positive line charge). No element of charge produces a ϕ component of electric field intensity; E_ϕ is zero. However, each element does produce an E_r and E_z component, but the contribution to E_z by elements of charge which are equal distances above and below the point at which we are determining the field will cancel.

We therefore have found that we have only an E_r component and it varies only with r. Now to find this component.

We choose a point P on the y axis at which to determine the field. This is a perfectly general point in view of the lack of variation of the field with ϕ and z. Applying Sec. 2.2, Eq. (4), to find the incremental field at P due to the incremental charge $dQ = \rho_L \, dL$, we have

$$d\mathbf{E} = \frac{\rho_L \, dL}{4\pi\epsilon R^2} \mathbf{a}_R \tag{1}$$

or
$$dE_y = dE_r = \frac{\rho_L \, dL \sin\theta}{4\pi\epsilon R^2} = \frac{\rho_L \, dL}{4\pi\epsilon R^2} \frac{y}{R} = \frac{\rho_L \, dL \, r}{4\pi\epsilon R^3}$$

Replacing R^2 by $L^2 + r^2$ or $L^2 + y^2$ and summing the contributions from every element of charge,

$$E_r = \int_{-\infty}^{\infty} \frac{\rho_L r \, dL}{4\pi\epsilon(L^2 + r^2)^{3/2}}$$

Integrating by integral tables or change of variable, $L = r \cot\theta$, we have

$$E_r = \frac{\rho_L}{4\pi\epsilon} r \left[\frac{1}{r^2} \frac{L}{\sqrt{L^2 + r^2}} \right]_{-\infty}^{\infty}$$

$$= \frac{\rho_L}{2\pi\epsilon r} \tag{2}$$

This is the desired answer, but there are many other ways of obtaining it. We might have used the angle θ as our variable of integration, for $L = r \cot \theta$ from Fig. 2.2 and $dL = -r \csc^2 \theta \, d\theta$. Since $R = r \csc \theta$, our integral becomes, simply,

$$dE_r = \frac{\rho_L \, dL}{4\pi\epsilon R^2} \sin \theta = -\frac{\rho_L \sin \theta \, d\theta}{4\pi\epsilon r}$$

$$E_r = -\frac{\rho_L}{4\pi\epsilon r} \int_{180°}^{0°} \sin \theta \, d\theta = \frac{\rho_L}{4\pi\epsilon r} \cos \theta \bigg]_{180°}^{0°}$$

$$= \frac{\rho_L}{2\pi\epsilon r}$$

Here the integration was simpler, but some experience with problems of this type is necessary before we can unerringly choose the simplest variable of integration at the beginning of the problem.

We might also have considered Sec. 2.4, Eq. (3), as our starting point:

$$\mathbf{E} = \int_{vol} \frac{\rho \, dv}{4\pi\epsilon R^2} \mathbf{a}_R$$

letting $\rho \, dv = \rho_L \, dL$ and integrating along the line which is now our "volume" containing all the charge. Suppose we do this and forget everything we have learned from the symmetry of the problem. Choose point P now at a general location (r,ϕ,z) (Fig. 2.3) and write:

$$\mathbf{R} = r\mathbf{a}_r - (L - z)\mathbf{a}_z$$
$$R = \sqrt{r^2 + (L - z)^2}$$
$$\mathbf{a}_R = \frac{r\mathbf{a}_r - (L - z)\mathbf{a}_z}{\sqrt{r^2 + (L - z)^2}}$$
$$\mathbf{E} = \int_{-\infty}^{\infty} \frac{\rho_L \, dL \, [r\mathbf{a}_r - (L - z)\mathbf{a}_z]}{4\pi\epsilon[r^2 + (L - z)^2]^{3/2}}$$
$$= \frac{\rho_L}{4\pi\epsilon} \left\{ \int_{-\infty}^{\infty} \frac{r \, dL \, \mathbf{a}_r}{[r^2 + (L - z)^2]^{3/2}} - \int_{-\infty}^{\infty} \frac{(L - z) \, dL \, \mathbf{a}_z}{[r^2 + (L - z)^2]^{3/2}} \right\}$$

Before integrating a vector expression, it is necessary to know whether or not the vector under the integral sign (here, the unit vectors $\mathbf{a}_r$ and $\mathbf{a}_z$) varies with the variable of integration (here dL). If it does not, then it is a constant and may be removed from within the integral, leaving a scalar which may be integrated by normal methods. Our unit vectors of course cannot change in magnitude, but a change in direction is just as troublesome. Fortunately, the direction of $\mathbf{a}_r$ does not change with L (nor with r, but it does change with ϕ), and $\mathbf{a}_z$ is constant always.

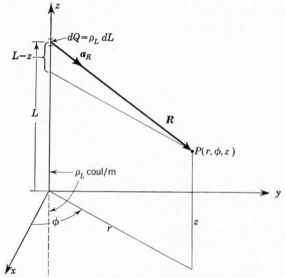

FIG. 2.3. The geometry of the problem for the field about an infinite line charge if symmetry is ignored.

Hence, we remove the unit vectors from the integrals and again integrate with tables or by changing variables:

$$\mathbf{E} = \frac{\rho_L}{4\pi\epsilon} \left\{ \mathbf{a}_r \int_{-\infty}^{\infty} \frac{r \, dL}{[r^2 + (L-z)^2]^{3/2}} - \mathbf{a}_z \int_{-\infty}^{\infty} \frac{(L-z) \, dL}{[r^2 + (L-z)^2]^{3/2}} \right\}$$

$$= \frac{\rho_L}{4\pi\epsilon} \left\{ \left[\mathbf{a}_r r \, \frac{1}{r^2} \, \frac{L-z}{\sqrt{r^2 + (L-z)^2}} \right]_{-\infty}^{\infty} - \left[\mathbf{a}_z \frac{1}{\sqrt{r^2 + (L-z)^2}} \right]_{-\infty}^{\infty} \right\}$$

$$= \frac{\rho_L}{4\pi\epsilon} \left[\mathbf{a}_r \frac{2}{r} + \mathbf{a}_z(0) \right] = \frac{\rho_L}{2\pi\epsilon r} \mathbf{a}_r$$

Again we obtain the same answer, as we should, for there is nothing wrong with the method except that the integration was harder and there were two integrations to perform. This is the price we pay for neglecting the consideration of symmetry and plunging doggedly ahead with mathematics. Look before you integrate.

Other methods for solving this basic problem will be discussed later after we introduce Gauss's law and the concept of potential.

Now let us consider the answer itself:

$$E_r = \frac{\rho_L}{2\pi\epsilon r}$$

We note that the field falls off inversely with the distance to the charged line, as compared with the point charge where the field decreased with the square of the distance. Moving ten times as far from a point charge leads to a field only 1 per cent the previous strength, but moving ten times as far from a line charge only reduces the field to 10 per cent of its former value. An analogy can be drawn with a source of illumination, for the light intensity from a point source of light also falls off inversely as the square of the distance to the source. The field of an infinitely long fluorescent tube thus decays inversely as the first power of the radial distance to the tube, and we should expect the light intensity about a finite-length tube to obey this law near the tube. As our point recedes farther and farther from a finite-length tube, however, it eventually looks like a point source and the field obeys the inverse-square relationship.

In Sec. 2.7 we shall describe how fields may be sketched and use the field of the line charge as one example.

2.6. Field of a Sheet of Charge. Another basic charge configuration is the infinite sheet of charge having a uniform density of ρ_s coulombs/m^2. The charge-distribution family now is complete: point, line, sheet, and volume, or Q, ρ_L, ρ_s, ρ.

Let us place this sheet in the yz plane and again consider symmetry (Fig. 2.4). We see first that the field cannot vary with y or with z, and then that the y and z components arising from differential elements of charge symmetrically located with respect to the point at which we wish the field will cancel. Hence, only E_x is present, and this component is a function of x alone. To evaluate this component, we are again faced with many methods from which to choose, and this time we shall use but one method and leave others for the problems at the end of this chapter.

Let us use the field of the infinite line charge [Sec. 2.5, Eq. (2)] by dividing the infinite sheet up into differential width strips. One such strip is shown in Fig. 2.4. The line charge density, or charge per unit length, is $\rho_L = \rho_s \, dy$, and the distance to our general point P on the x axis from this line charge is $r = \sqrt{x^2 + y^2}$. The contribution to E_x at P from this differential width strip is, then,

$$dE_x = \frac{\rho_s \, dy}{2\pi\epsilon \sqrt{x^2 + y^2}} \cos\theta = \frac{\rho_s}{2\pi\epsilon} \frac{x \, dy}{x^2 + y^2}$$

Adding the effects of all the strips,

$$E_x = \frac{\rho_s}{2\pi\epsilon} \int_{-\infty}^{\infty} \frac{x \, dy}{x^2 + y^2} = \frac{\rho_s}{2\pi\epsilon} \tan^{-1}\frac{y}{x} \Big]_{-\infty}^{\infty}$$

$$= \frac{\rho_s}{2\epsilon} \tag{1}$$

If the point P were chosen on the negative x axis, then

$$E_x = -\frac{\rho_s}{2\epsilon}$$

for the field is always directed away from the positive charge. This difficulty in sign is usually overcome by specifying a unit vector $\mathbf{a}_n$, which is normal to the sheet and directed outward, or away from it. Then

$$\mathbf{E} = \frac{\rho_s}{2\epsilon}\mathbf{a}_n \tag{2}$$

This is a startling answer, for the field is constant in magnitude and direction. It is just as strong a million miles away from the sheet as

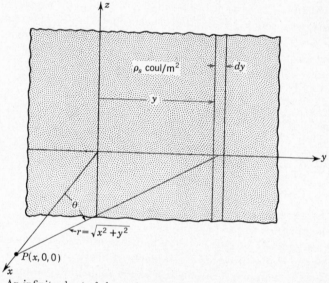

FIG. 2.4. An infinite sheet of charge in the yz plane, a general point P on the x axis. and the differential width line charge used as the element in determining the field at P.

it is right off the surface. Returning to our light analogy, we see that a uniform source of light on the ceiling of a very large room leads to just as much illumination on a square foot on the floor as it does on a square foot 1 in. below the ceiling. If you desire greater illumination on this subject, it will do you no good to hold the book closer to this source.

If a second infinite sheet of charge, having a *negative* charge density of $-\rho_s$ coulombs/m², is located in the plane $x = a$, we may find the total field by adding the contribution of each sheet. In the region $x > a$,

$$\mathbf{E}_+ = \frac{\rho_s}{2\epsilon}\,\mathbf{a}_x \qquad \mathbf{E}_- = -\frac{\rho_s}{2\epsilon}\,\mathbf{a}_x \qquad \mathbf{E} = \mathbf{E}_+ + \mathbf{E}_- = 0$$

and for $x < 0$,

$$\mathbf{E}_+ = -\frac{\rho_s}{2\epsilon}\,\mathbf{a}_x \qquad \mathbf{E}_- = \frac{\rho_s}{2\epsilon}\,\mathbf{a}_x \qquad \mathbf{E} = \mathbf{E}_+ + \mathbf{E}_- = 0$$

and when $0 < x < a$,

$$\mathbf{E}_+ = \frac{\rho_s}{2\epsilon}\,\mathbf{a}_x \qquad \mathbf{E}_- = \frac{\rho_s}{2\epsilon}\,\mathbf{a}_x \qquad \mathbf{E} = \mathbf{E}_+ + \mathbf{E}_- = \frac{\rho_s}{\epsilon}\,\mathbf{a}_x \qquad (3)$$

This is an important practical answer, for it is the field between the parallel plates of a capacitor, provided the linear dimensions of the plates are very much greater than their separation and provided also that we are considering a point well removed from the edges. The field outside the capacitor, while not zero as we found for the ideal case above, is usually negligible.

D2.5. A sheet of charge of density $10^{-9}/6\pi$ coulomb/m² and a line charge of density $2 \times 10^{-9}/9$ coulomb/m are parallel and separated 1 m in a vacuum. Find the magnitude of the electric field intensity at a point 1 m distant from both the sheet and line:

(a) Due to the sheet of charge alone.
(b) Due to the line charge alone.
(c) Due to both.

Ans. 12 volts/m.

2.7. Streamlines and Sketches of Fields. We now have vector equations for the electric field intensity resulting from several different charge configurations, and we have had little difficulty in interpreting the magnitude and direction of the field from the equations. Unfortunately, this simplicity cannot last much longer for we have solved most of the simple cases and our new charge distributions now must lead to more complicated expressions for the fields and more difficulty in visualizing the fields through the equations. However, it is true that one picture is worth about a thousand words if we just know what picture to draw.

Consider the field about the line charge:

$$\mathbf{E} = \frac{\rho_L}{2\pi\epsilon r}\,\mathbf{a}_r$$

Figure 2.5a shows a cross-sectional view of the line charge and on it is shown what might be our first effort at picturing the field, short line segments drawn here and there having a length proportional to the magnitude of **E** and pointing in the direction of **E**.   The sketch fails to show the symmetry with respect to ϕ, so we try again in Fig. 2.5*b* with a symmetrical location of the line segments.   The real trouble now appears—the longest lines must be drawn in the most crowded region, and this also plagues us if we use line segments of equal length but of a thickness which is proportional to E (Fig. 2.5*c*).   Other schemes which have been suggested include drawing shorter lines to represent stronger fields (inherently misleading) and using intensity of color to represent stronger fields (difficult and uneconomical).

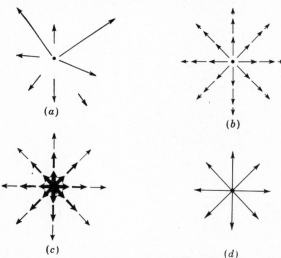

Fig. 2.5. One very poor (*a*), two fair (*b*, *c*), and the usual (*d*) forms of streamline sketch.

For the present, then, let us be content to show only the *direction* of **E** by drawing continuous lines from the charge which are everywhere tangent to **E**.   Figure 2.5*d* shows this compromise.   A symmetrical distribution of lines (one every 45°) indicates azimuthal symmetry, and arrowheads should be used to show direction.

These lines are usually called *streamlines*, although other terms such as flux lines and direction lines are also used.   A small positive test charge placed at any point in this field and free to move would accelerate in the direction of the streamline passing through that point. If the field represented the velocity of a liquid or a gas (which, incidentally, would have to have a source at $r = 0$), small suspended particles in the liquid or gas would trace out the streamlines.

We shall find out later that a bonus accompanies this streamline sketch, for the magnitude of the field can be shown to be inversely proportional to the spacing of the streamlines. The closer they are together, the stronger is the field. At that time we shall also find an easier, more accurate method of making the streamline sketch.

A sketch of the field of the point charge turns out to be identical with that of the line charge, for in the plane of the sketch the field is also directed radially outward. The spacing between the streamlines is also (apparently) the same, yet one field is inverse-distance and the other is inverse-square law. When we consider the spacing of lines behind and in front of our sketch, however, we see that this spacing is less in the case of the point charge, for all the lines diverge from a single point.

SUGGESTED REFERENCES

1. Boast, W. B.: "Principles of Electric and Magnetic Fields," 2d ed., Harper & Brothers, New York, 1956. Treats electrostatics with several simple numerical examples. Does not use vector analysis throughout.
2. Rogers, W. E.: "Introduction to Electric Fields," McGraw-Hill Book Company, Inc., New York, 1954. Discusses an experimental method and a mathematical method of obtaining the streamlines.

PROBLEMS

1. Newton's law of gravity may be written $F = Gm_1m_2/R^2$, where m_1 and m_2 are point masses separated a distance R, and G is the gravitational constant. Using mks units, $G = 6.664 \times 10^{-11}$ m³/(kg)(sec²). Show why the gravitational force between charges may be neglected by computing the ratio between the gravitational and Coulomb forces on two electrons separated R m.

2. A uniform line charge of ρ_L coulombs/m is distributed in the shape of a ring of radius a. The electric field intensity is desired at a point on the axis of the ring h m from the plane of the ring. (a) What coordinate system should be used? (b) With which coordinates does the field vary? (c) Which components are present at the point in question? (d) Using Sec. 2.5, Eq. (1), with appropriate expressions for dL, a_R, and R, set up the integral and find the desired electric field intensity.

3. Repeat Prob. 2 for a disk of radius a carrying a uniform surface charge density of ρ_s coulombs/m². The form of Sec. 2.5, Eq. (1), must be changed slightly to apply to a differential element of surface charge.

4. Two point charges of Q_1 coulombs each are located at $(0,0,1)$ and $(0,0,-1)$. Determine the locus of the possible positions of a third charge Q_2, where Q_2 may have any desired positive or negative value, such that $\mathbf{E} = 0$ at $(0,1,0)$. What is the locus if the two original charges are Q_1 and $-Q_1$?

5. A crude device for measuring charge consists of two pith balls, one fixed in position and the other movable and subject to a restraining force kx, where k is a spring constant. The uncharged pith balls are located at $x = 0$ and $x = d$, the latter fixed. If the balls are given equal and opposite charges of Q coulombs, obtain the expression by which Q may be found as a function of x. Determine the maximum charge which may be measured in terms of ϵ_0, k, and d, and state the separation of the balls then. What happens if a larger charge is applied?

6. A point charge Q is located at the origin of a cylindrical coordinate system. Determine the electric field intensity in cylindrical coordinates at a general point (r,ϕ,z). Compare the result with Sec. 2.2, Eqs. (5) and (6).

7. Show for the ring and disk of charge (Probs. 2 and 3 above) that the field approaches that of a point charge as h becomes very large. The answer should be expressed in terms of the total charge on the ring or disk.

8. Assume a semi-infinite uniform line charge lying on the negative z axis. Use symmetry to determine the components and variables involved in the electric field intensity at a general point and also at any point lying on the positive z axis. Find the field at $z = h$ on the z axis.

9. The semi-infinite line of Prob. 8 now carries a nonuniform linear charge density of $\rho_L = -a/(1 - z)$ coulombs/m. Determine the field at $z = h$ on the z axis.

10. A finite line charge, 10 m long and having a uniformly distributed total charge of $10^{-8}/9$ coulomb, lies on the x axis between $x = 2$ and $x = 12$. (a) Find the electric field intensity at the origin by an exact integration. (b) Assume the line charge may be represented by five point charges of $10^{-8}/45$ coulomb each, located at $x = 3, 5, 7, 9, 11$, and find the electric field intensity at the origin by summing the fields due to each charge alone. Compare the results.

11. Find the field of a uniform sheet of charge by starting with the equation
$$\mathbf{E} = \int_s \rho_s \mathbf{a}_R \, dS/4\pi\epsilon R^2.$$
Compare the result with Sec. 2.6, Eq. (1).

12. Again find the field of a uniform sheet of charge, using the field of the ring of charge obtained in Prob. 2.

13. Again find the field of a uniform sheet of charge, using the field of the disk of charge obtained in Prob. 3.

14. Two uniform sheets of charge are perpendicular to each other, the $x = 0$ plane with $\rho_s = 10^{-9}/6\pi$ coulomb/m^2, and the $y = 0$ plane with $\rho_s = 2 \times 10^{-9}/6\pi$ coulomb/m^2. Obtain the expression for the total electric field intensity in the quadrant $x > 0$, $y > 0$. Sketch the streamlines in the $z = 0$ plane.

15. In a two-dimensional field $\mathbf{E} = E_x\mathbf{a}_x + E_y\mathbf{a}_y$, where E_x and E_y are functions only of x and y, show that the equations of the streamlines may be obtained by solving the differential equation $E_y/E_x = dy/dx$.

16. Use the results of Prob. 15 to find and sketch in the quadrant $x > 0$, $y > 0$, the streamlines of the field $\mathbf{E} = x\mathbf{a}_x - y\mathbf{a}_y$.

17. A line charge lies on the z axis between $z = -1$ and $z = 1$. The nonuniform line charge density is given by $\rho_L = |z|$. In the plane $z = 0$: (a) What components of $\mathbf{E}$ are present? (b) Of which variables are these components a function? (c) Obtain the integral expression for $\mathbf{E}$ at a general point in the $z = 0$ plane. The integral should be in a form suitable for evaluation by someone knowing nothing about vector analysis or electrostatics.

18. Determine $\mathbf{E}$ at $(0,0,1)$ if a sheet of charge in the $z = 0$ plane contains a charge density $\rho_s = (x^2 + y^2 + 1)^{3/2}$. The sheet extends between $x = \pm 2$ and $y = \pm 2$.

CHAPTER 3

ELECTRIC FLUX DENSITY, GAUSS'S LAW, AND DIVERGENCE

After drawing a few of the fields described in the previous chapter and becoming familiar with the concept of the streamlines which show the direction of the force on a test charge at every point, it is difficult to avoid giving these lines a physical significance and thinking of them as *flux* lines. No physical particle is projected radially outward from the point charge, and there are no steel tentacles reaching out to attract or repel an unwary test charge, but as soon as the streamlines are drawn on paper there seems to be a picture showing "something" is present.

It is very helpful to invent an *electric flux* which streams away symmetrically from a point charge and is coincident with the streamlines and to visualize this flux wherever an electric field is present.

This chapter introduces and uses the concept of electric flux and electric flux density to solve again several of the problems presented in the last chapter. The work here turns out to be much easier, and this is due to the extremely symmetrical problems which we are solving.

3.1. Electric Flux Density. About 1837 the Director of the Royal Society in London, Michael Faraday, became very much interested in static electric fields and the effect of various insulating materials on these fields. This problem had been bothering him during the past ten years when he was engaged experimentally in his now famous work on induced electromotive force, which we shall discuss in Chap. 10. With that subject completed he had a pair of concentric spheres constructed, the outer one consisting of two hemispheres which could be firmly clamped together.

His experiment then consisted essentially of the following steps:

1. With the equipment dismantled, the inner sphere was given a known positive charge.

2. The hemispheres were then clamped together around the charged sphere with about ¾ in. of insulating, or dielectric, material between them.

46

3. The outer sphere was discharged by connecting it momentarily to ground.

4. The outer sphere was separated carefully, using tools made of insulating material in order not to disturb the induced charge on it, and the negative induced charge on each hemisphere measured.

Faraday found that the total charge[1] on the outer sphere was equal in magnitude to the original charge placed on the inner sphere and that this was true regardless of the dielectric material separating the two spheres. He concluded that there was some sort of "displacement" from the inner sphere to the outer which was independent of the medium, and we now refer to this flux as *displacement, displacement flux*, or simply *electric flux*.

Faraday's experiments also showed, of course, that a larger positive charge on the inner sphere induced a correspondingly larger negative charge on the outer sphere, leading to a direct proportionality between the electric flux and the charge on the inner sphere. The constant of proportionality is dependent on the system of units involved, and we are fortunate in our use of the mks system of units because the constant is unity. If electric flux is denoted by Ψ and the total charge on the inner sphere by Q, then for Faraday's experiment

$$\Psi = Q$$

and the electric flux Ψ is measured in coulombs.

We can obtain more quantitative information by considering an inner sphere of radius a and an outer sphere of radius b, with charges of Q and $-Q$, respectively (Fig. 3.1). The electric flux Ψ extending from the inner sphere to the outer sphere is indicated by the symmetrically distributed lines (flux lines) drawn between the spheres.

At the surface of the inner sphere, Ψ lines of electric flux are produced by the charge $Q = \Psi$ coulombs distributed uniformly over a surface having an area of $4\pi a^2$ m². The density of the flux at this surface is $\Psi/4\pi a^2$, or $Q/4\pi a^2$ coulombs/m², and this is an important new quantity.

Electric flux density, measured in coulombs per square meter (sometimes described as "lines per square meter," for each line is due to one coulomb), is given the letter **D**, which was originally chosen because of the alternate names of *displacement flux density*, or *displacement density*. Electric flux density is more descriptive, and we shall use that term consistently.

---

[1] This charge was not measured in any standard unit, but in degrees of twist of a quartz fiber supporting a radial arm carrying a charged pith ball, in the torsion balance invented by Coulomb.

The electric flux density **D** is a vector field and is a member of the "flux density" class of vector fields as opposed to the "force fields" class which includes the electric field intensity **E**.   The direction of **D** at a point is the direction of the flux lines at that point, and the magnitude is given by the number of flux lines crossing a surface normal to the lines divided by the surface area.

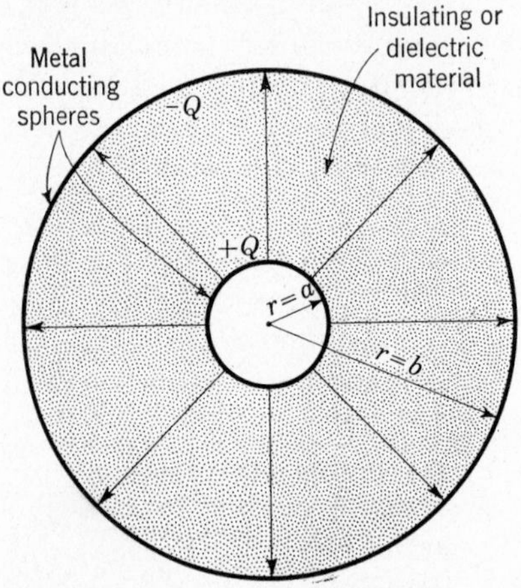

Referring again to Fig. 3.1, the electric flux density is in the radial direction and has a value of

Metal conducting spheres

Insulating or dielectric material

$$\mathbf{D}\Big|_{r=a} = \frac{Q}{4\pi a^2}\mathbf{a}_r \qquad \text{(inner sphere)}$$

$$\mathbf{D}\Big|_{r=b} = \frac{Q}{4\pi b^2}\mathbf{a}_r \qquad \text{(outer sphere)}$$

and at a radial distance r, where $a \leq r \leq b$,

$$\mathbf{D} = \frac{Q}{4\pi r^2}\mathbf{a}_r$$

FIG. 3.1. The electric flux in the region between a pair of charged concentric spheres.

If we now let the inner sphere become smaller and smaller, while still retaining a charge of Q coulombs, it becomes a point charge in the limit, but the electric flux density at a point r m from the point charge is still given by

$$\mathbf{D} = \frac{Q}{4\pi r^2}\mathbf{a}_r$$

for Q lines of flux are symmetrically directed outward from the point and pass through an imaginary spherical surface of area $4\pi r^2$.

This result should be compared with Sec. 2.2, Eq. (4), the radial electric field intensity of a point charge,

$$\mathbf{E} = \frac{Q}{4\pi \epsilon r^2}\mathbf{a}_r$$

from which the relationship

$$\mathbf{D} = \epsilon\mathbf{E} \tag{1}$$

is apparent.

This proportionality between **D** and **E** is not just an accidental result in a specific problem.   We have chosen to develop gradually the concept of electric flux and electric flux density and to show that **D** = ϵ**E** for the specific case of a point charge.   Now let us consider this relationship as the definition of **D** and use the point-charge illustration as an aid in obtaining a physical understanding of the electric flux density.

Throughout this text we shall restrict our attention to dielectric materials which are linear (ϵ is not a function of $|\mathbf{E}|$) and isotropic (ϵ is not a function of the direction of $\mathbf{E}$). Nonhomogeneous materials, in which ϵ is a function of position, are considered only occasionally. For an anisotropic medium, **D** and **E** need not be parallel, and ϵ is a tensor, which must be described by nine components, as compared to a vector, which is describable by three.

D3.1. A uniform electric flux density of 10 coulombs/m² is directed in the positive x direction. Determine the magnitude of the electric flux crossing a surface 1 m²:

(a) Lying in the yz plane.
(b) Lying in the xy plane.
(c) Lying in the plane $x = z$.

Ans. 17.1 coulombs.

D3.2. Find the numerical value of the electric flux density in free space:

(a) 4 m from a point charge of 128π coulombs.
(b) 3 m from a line charge of 24π coulombs/m.
(c) 1,234.56789 m from a surface charge of 6 coulombs/m².

Ans. 9 coulombs/m².

3.2. Gauss's Law. If we return to Faraday's experiments with the concentric spheres, we could sum up his results as an experimental law by stating that the electric flux passing through any imaginary spherical surface lying between the two conducting spheres is equal to the charge enclosed by this imaginary spherical surface. This enclosed charge is distributed on the surface of the inner sphere, or it might be concentrated as a point charge at the center of the imaginary sphere. However, since one line of electric flux is produced by one coulomb of charge, the inner conductor might just as well have been a cube or a brass door key and the total induced charge on the outer sphere would still be the same. Certainly the flux density would change from its previous uniform value to some unknown distribution, but $+Q$ coulombs on any inner conductor would produce an induced charge of $-Q$ coulombs on the surrounding sphere. Going one step farther, we could now replace the two outer hemispheres by an empty (but completely closed) soup can. Q coulombs on the brass door key would produce $\Psi = Q$ lines of electric flux and would induce $-Q$ coulombs on the tin can. If it were a perfect insulator, the soup could even be left in the can without changing the results.

These generalizations of Faraday's experiment lead to the following statement, which is known as *Gauss's law*. *The electric flux passing through any closed surface is equal to the total charge enclosed.* The contribution of Gauss, one of the greatest mathematicians the world has ever produced, was actually not in stating the law as we have above, but in providing a mathematical form for this statement. This statement we shall now obtain.

Let us imagine a distribution of charge, shown as a cloud of point charges in Fig. 3.2, surrounded by a closed surface of any shape. If the total charge is Q, then Q lines of electric flux will pass through the enclosing surface. At every point on the surface the electric flux density vector $\mathbf{D}$ will have some value $\mathbf{D}_s$, where the subscript s merely reminds us that $\mathbf{D}$ must be evaluated at the surface, and $\mathbf{D}_s$ will in general vary in magnitude and direction from one point on the surface to another.

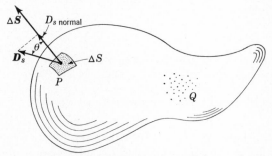

Fɪɢ. 3.2. The electric flux density $\mathbf{D}_s$ at P due to charge Q.

We must now consider the nature of an incremental element of the surface. An incremental element of area ΔS is very nearly a portion of a plane surface, and the complete description of this surface element requires not only a statement of its magnitude, ΔS, but also of its orientation in space. In other words, the incremental surface element is a vector quantity. The only unique direction which may be associated with ΔS (the vector incremental surface element) is the direction of the normal to the plane tangent to the surface at the point of tangency. There are, of course, two such normals, and the ambiguity is removed by specifying the outward normal whenever the surface is closed and "outward" has a specific meaning.

At any point P consider an incremental element of surface ΔS and let $\mathbf{D}_s$ make an angle of θ with ΔS, as shown in Fig. 3.2. The flux crossing ΔS is then the product of the normal component of $\mathbf{D}_s$ and ΔS:

$$\Delta \Psi = \text{flux crossing } \Delta S = D_{s,\text{normal}} \, \Delta S = D_s \cos \theta \, \Delta S = \mathbf{D}_s \cdot \Delta \mathbf{S}$$

where we are able to apply the definition of the dot product developed in the first chapter.

The total flux passing through the closed surface is obtained by adding the differential contributions crossing each surface element $\Delta \mathbf{S}$:

$$\Psi = \int d\Psi = \oint_{\text{closed surface}} \mathbf{D}_s \cdot d\mathbf{S}$$

The resultant integral is a *closed surface integral*, and since the surface element $d\mathbf{S}$ always involves the differentials of two coordinates, such as $dx \, dy$, $r \, d\phi \, dr$, or $r^2 \sin \theta \, d\theta \, d\phi$, the integral is a double integral. Usually only one integral sign is used for brevity, and we shall always place an s below the integral sign to indicate a surface integral, although this is not actually necessary because the differential $d\mathbf{S}$ is automatically the signal for a surface integral. One last convention is to place a small circle on the integral sign itself to indicate that the integration is to be performed over a *closed* surface. Such a surface is often called a *Gaussian surface*. We then have the mathematical formulation of Gauss's law:

$$\Psi = \oint_s \mathbf{D}_s \cdot d\mathbf{S} = \text{charge enclosed} = Q$$

The charge enclosed might be several point charges, in which case

$$Q = \Sigma Q_n$$

or a line charge,

$$Q = \int \rho_L \, dL$$

or a surface charge,

$$Q = \int_s \rho_s \, dS$$

or a volume charge distribution,

$$Q = \int_{\text{vol}} \rho \, dv$$

The last form is usually used, and we should agree now that it represents any or all of the other forms. With this understanding, Gauss's law may be written in terms of the charge distribution:

$$\oint_s \mathbf{D}_s \cdot d\mathbf{S} = \int_{\text{vol}} \rho \, dv \tag{1}$$

a mathematical statement meaning simply that the total electric flux through any closed surface is equal to the charge enclosed.

To illustrate the application of Gauss's law, let us check the results of Faraday's experiment by placing a point charge of Q coulombs at the origin of a spherical coordinate system (Fig. 3.3) and by choosing

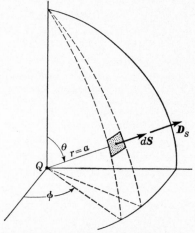

our closed surface as a sphere of radius a. The electric field intensity of the point charge has been found to be

$$E = \frac{Q}{4\pi \epsilon r^2} \mathbf{a}_r$$

and since

$$D = \epsilon E$$

we have, as before,

$$D = \frac{Q}{4\pi r^2} \mathbf{a}_r$$

At the surface of the sphere,

$$D_s = \frac{Q}{4\pi a^2} \mathbf{a}_r$$

FIG. 3.3. Application of Gauss's law to the field of a point charge Q on a spherical closed surface of radius a.

The differential element of area on a spherical surface is, in spherical coordinates from Chap. 1,

$$dS = r^2 \sin \theta \, d\phi \, d\theta = a^2 \sin \theta \, d\phi \, d\theta$$

or $\qquad\qquad d\mathbf{S} = a^2 \sin \theta \, d\phi \, d\theta \, \mathbf{a}_r$

The integrand is

$$\mathbf{D}_s \cdot d\mathbf{S} = \frac{Q}{4\pi a^2} a^2 \sin \theta \, d\phi \, d\theta \, \mathbf{a}_r \cdot \mathbf{a}_r = \frac{Q}{4\pi} \sin \theta \, d\phi \, d\theta$$

leading to the closed surface integral

$$\int_{\theta=0}^{\theta=\pi} \int_{\phi=0}^{\phi=2\pi} \frac{Q}{4\pi} \sin \theta \, d\phi \, d\theta$$

where the limits on the integrals have been chosen so that the integration is carried over the entire surface of the sphere once.[1] Integrating,

$$\int_{\theta=0}^{\theta=\pi} \frac{Q}{4\pi} \sin \theta \, (2\pi) \, d\theta = \frac{Q}{2} \left. (-\cos \theta) \right]_0^\pi = Q$$

and we obtain a result showing Q lines of electric flux cross the surface, as we should.

[1] Note that if θ and ϕ both cover the range from 0 to 2π, the spherical surface is covered twice.

The following four sections contain examples of the application of Gauss's law to problems of a simple, symmetrical geometry with the object of finding the electric field intensity. The first application is essentially the same as the example above, except that the problem is worked backward.

D3.3. Several types of charge are located as follows: (1) point charge, 2 coulombs at origin; (2) point charge, 3 coulombs at $(0,0,10)$; (3) line charge on entire z axis, 4 coulombs/m; (4) sheet of charge at entire $z = 0$ plane, 5 coulombs/m². Determine the charge enclosed by each of these closed surfaces:

(a) A sphere of 1 m radius centered at $(0,0,10)$.

(b) A cylinder of 1 m radius, the axis being the z axis and extending from $z = 1$ to $z = 11$.

(c) A cube, centered at the origin, 3 m on a side, edges parallel to coordinate axes.

Ans. 113 coulombs.

D3.4. Evaluate $\oint_s \mathbf{D} \cdot d\mathbf{S}$ where $\mathbf{D}$ and the surface are given as:

(a) $\mathbf{D} = 10x\mathbf{a}_x$; surface, cube, 1 m on a side centered at the origin, edges parallel to the coordinate axes.

(b) $\mathbf{D} = r \sin z \, \mathbf{a}_z$; surface, cylinder, 2-m radius with axis on the z axis and extending from $z = -\pi/2$ to $\pi/2$.

(c) $\mathbf{D} = r \, (\ln r) \sin \theta \, \mathbf{a}_r$; surface, sphere, 2-m radius, centered at origin.

Ans. 98.2 coulombs.

3.3. Gauss's-law Application—Field of a Point Charge.

Let us now consider how we may use Gauss's law,

$$Q = \oint_s \mathbf{D}_s \cdot d\mathbf{S}$$

to determine $\mathbf{D}_s$ if the charge distribution is known. This is an example of an integral equation in which the unknown quantity to be determined appears under the integral sign.

The solution is easy if we are able to choose a closed surface which satisfies two conditions:

1. $\mathbf{D}_s$ is everywhere either normal or tangential to the closed surface so that $\mathbf{D}_s \cdot d\mathbf{S}$ becomes either $D_s \, dS$ or zero, respectively.

2. On that portion of the closed surface for which $\mathbf{D}_s \cdot d\mathbf{S}$ is not zero, $D_s = $ constant.

This allows us to replace the dot product with the product of the scalar magnitudes and then to bring D_s outside of the integral sign. The remaining integral is then $\int_s dS$ over that portion of the closed surface which $\mathbf{D}_s$ crosses normally, and this is simply the area of this section of that surface.

Only a knowledge of the symmetry of the problem enables us to choose such a closed surface, and this knowledge is obtained easily by remembering that the electric field intensity due to a positive point charge is directed radially outward from the point charge.

Let us consider a point charge Q at the origin of a spherical coordinate system and decide on a suitable closed surface which will meet the two requirements listed above. The surface in question is obviously a spherical surface, centered at the origin and of any radius r. D_s is everywhere normal to the surface; D_s has the same value at all points on the surface.

Then we have, in order,

$$Q = \oint_s \mathbf{D}_s \cdot d\mathbf{S} = \oint_{\substack{\text{sphere,}\\ \text{center at origin,}\\ \text{radius } r}} D_s \, dS$$

$$= D_s \oint_{\substack{\text{sphere,}\\ \text{center at origin,}\\ \text{radius } r}} dS = D_s \int_{\phi=0}^{\phi=2\pi} \int_{\theta=0}^{\theta=\pi} r^2 \sin\theta \, d\theta \, d\phi$$

$$= 4\pi r^2 D_s$$

and hence

$$D_s = \frac{Q}{4\pi r^2}$$

Since r may have any value and since $\mathbf{D}_s$ is directed radially outward,

$$\mathbf{D} = \frac{Q}{4\pi r^2} \mathbf{a}_r \qquad \mathbf{E} = \frac{Q}{4\pi \epsilon r^2} \mathbf{a}_r$$

which agrees with the results of Chap. 2. The example is a trivial one, and the objection could be raised that we had to know that the field was symmetrical and directed radially outward before we could obtain an answer. This is true, and that leaves the inverse-square-law relationship as the only check obtained from Gauss's law. The example does, however, serve to illustrate a method which we may apply to other problems, including several to which Coulomb's law is almost incapable of supplying an answer.

Are there any other surfaces which would have satisfied our two conditions? The student should satisfy himself that such simple surfaces as a cube or a cylinder do not meet the requirements.

3.4. Gauss's-law Application—Field of a Line Charge. Let us start now with a uniform-line-charge distribution of ρ_L coulombs/m lying on the z axis and extending from $-\infty$ to $+\infty$ (Fig. 3.4). We first must obtain a knowledge of the symmetry of the field, and we may consider this knowledge complete when the answers to these two questions are known:

1. With which coordinates does the field vary (or of what variables is D a function)?

2. Which components of **D** are present?

These same questions were asked when the problem of the infinite line charge was considered earlier in Sec. 2.5, from the standpoint of Coulomb's law. We found then that the knowledge obtained from answering them enabled us to make a much simpler integration. The problem could have been (and was) worked without any consideration of symmetry, but it was more difficult.

In using Gauss's law, however, it is not a question of using symmetry to simplify the solution, for the application of Gauss's law depends on symmetry, and if we cannot show that symmetry exists then we cannot use Gauss's law to obtain a solution. The two questions above now become "musts."

Although these two questions were asked and answered for this problem before, the main points of the argument will bear repetition. With the object of obtaining the simplest answers to question 1, we select a cylindrical coordinate system. Then D is not a function of z, for at whatever point we stand to inspect the field, a change in our z coordinate value does not change the

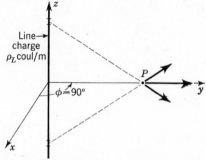

FIG. 3.4. An infinite line charge of ρ_L coulombs/m lying along the z axis.

appearance of the line. It still is just as far away and extends to infinity in either direction. If we vary ϕ by proceeding around the line, keeping r constant of course, again there is no change in the aspect of the line and D cannot be a function of ϕ. Changing r does result in the point being generally farther from the line, leading us to suspect that the field varies with r and probably decreases with increasing r.

The answer to the first question is, therefore, that D is not a function of z or ϕ, but probably is a function of r.

In order to answer the second question let us apply our knowledge of the field of a point charge by investigating the field at the point P (Fig. 3.4) located at $(r,90°,0)$. This is a perfectly general point in view of the answers obtained to the first question. The field due to any small element of the line charge contains a z and an r component, but the z component produced by an element of line charge located at some positive value of z is exactly canceled by that due to an element at an equivalent negative value of z. The answer to the second question is, then, simply that only the D_r component is present.

Collecting these results, we have

$$\mathbf{D} = D_r \mathbf{a}_r$$
$$D_r = f(r)$$

The choice of a closed surface is now simple, for a cylindrical surface is the only surface to which D_r is everywhere normal and it may be closed by plane surfaces normal to the z axis. A closed right circular cylinder of radius r extending from $z = 0$ to $z = L$ is shown in Fig. 3.5. We apply Gauss's law:

$$Q = \oint_{\text{cyl}} \mathbf{D}_s \cdot d\mathbf{S} = D_s \int_{\text{sides}} dS + 0 \int_{\text{top}} dS + 0 \int_{\text{bottom}} dS$$
$$= D_s \int_{z=0}^{L} \int_{\phi=0}^{2\pi} r \, d\phi \, dz = D_s 2\pi r L$$

and obtain

$$D_s = D_r = \frac{Q}{2\pi r L}$$

In terms of the charge density ρ_L, the total charge enclosed is

$$Q = \rho_L L$$

giving

$$D_r = \frac{\rho_L}{2\pi r}$$

or

$$E_r = \frac{\rho_L}{2\pi \epsilon r}$$

Comparison with Sec. 2.5, Eq. (2), shows that the correct result has been obtained and with much less work. Once the appropriate surface has been chosen, the integration usually amounts only to writing down the area of the surface at which $\mathbf{D}$ is normal.

The problem of a coaxial capacitor is almost identical with that of the line charge and is an example which is extremely difficult to solve from the standpoint of Coulomb's law. Suppose that we have two coaxial cylindrical conductors, the inner of radius a and the outer of radius b, each infinite in extent (Fig. 3.6). We shall assume a charge distribution of ρ_s coulombs/m² on the outer surface of the inner conductor.

Symmetry considerations show us that only the D_r component is present and that it can be a function only of r. A right circular cylinder of length L and radius r, where $a < r < b$, is necessarily chosen as the Gaussian surface, and we quickly have

$$Q = D_s 2\pi r L$$

The total charge on a length L of the inner conductor is

$$Q = \int_{z=0}^{L} \int_{\phi=0}^{2\pi} \rho_s a \, d\phi \, dz = 2\pi a L \rho_s$$

from which we have

$$D_s = \frac{a\rho_s}{r} \qquad \mathbf{D} = \frac{a\rho_s}{r} \mathbf{a}_r \qquad a < r < b$$

This result might be expressed in terms of charge per unit length,

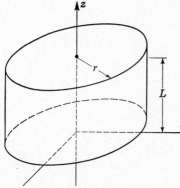

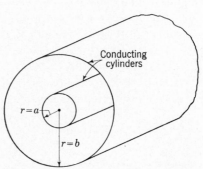

FIG. 3.5. The Gaussian surface for an infinite line charge is a right circular cylinder of length L, radius r.

FIG. 3.6. The two coaxial cylindrical conductors forming a coaxial capacitor.

because the inner conductor has $2\pi a \rho_s$ coulombs on a meter length, and hence, letting $\rho_L = 2\pi a \rho_s$,

$$\mathbf{D} = \frac{\rho_L}{2\pi r} \mathbf{a}_r$$

and the solution has a form identical with that of the infinite line charge.

Since every line of electric flux starting from the charge on the inner cylinder must terminate on a negative charge on the inner surface of the outer cylinder, the total charge on that surface must be

$$Q_{\text{outer cyl}} = -2\pi a L \rho_{s_{\text{inner cyl}}}$$

and the surface charge on the outer cylinder is found as

$$2\pi b L \rho_{s_{\text{outer cyl}}} = -2\pi a L \rho_{s_{\text{inner cyl}}}$$

or

$$\rho_{s_{\text{outer cyl}}} = -\frac{a}{b} \rho_{s_{\text{inner cyl}}}$$

What would happen if we should use a cylinder of radius r, $r > b$, for the Gaussian surface? The total charge enclosed would then be zero, for there are equal and opposite charges on each conducting cylinder.   Hence

$$0 = D_s 2\pi r L \qquad r > b$$
$$D_s = 0 \qquad r > b$$

An identical result would be obtained for $r < a$, showing that this coaxial capacitor has no external field (we have proved that the outer conductor is a "shield") and that there is no field within the center conductor.

If we complicate our problem slightly by placing a layer of dielectric material about the inner cylinder so that we have a permittivity ϵ_1 from $r = a$ to $r = R_1$ and a permittivity ϵ_2 from $r = R_1$ to $r = b$, as sketched in Fig. 3.7, while still retaining a charge of $\rho_L = 2\pi a \rho_s$ coulombs/m, it is evident that:

1. D still varies only with r.
2.   Only the D_r component is present as before.
3.   The same cylinder may be used as the closed surface.
4.   The value of D_r is the same!

The presence of the other dielectric does not affect our solution until we apply the equation $\mathbf{D} = \epsilon\mathbf{E}$ to find $\mathbf{E}$, for

$$D_r = \frac{\rho_L}{2\pi r}$$
$$= \epsilon E_r$$

and since $\epsilon = \epsilon_1$ for $a < r < R_1$,

$$E_r = \frac{\rho_L}{2\pi\epsilon_1 r} \qquad a < r < R_1$$

and similarly,

$$E_r = \frac{\rho_L}{2\pi\epsilon_2 r} \qquad R_1 < r < b$$

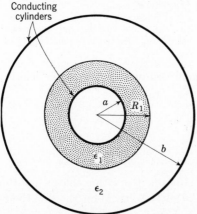

Fig. 3.7. A coaxial capacitor containing two different dielectrics.   The relative dielectric constant is ϵ_1 for $a < r < R_1$ and ϵ_2 for $R_1 < r < b$.

We have two different expressions for $\mathbf{E}$, each valid only in a restricted range of r.   At the surface $r = R_1$ the electric field intensity is discontinuous and jumps by a factor of ϵ_1/ϵ_2.   The electric flux density, however, is continuous at this surface.

The variation of D_r and E_r with r is shown in Fig. 3.8 for the case in which $\epsilon_2 = \epsilon_1/2$, $b = 3a$, $R_1 = 2a$.

Additional cylindrical layers of dielectric could be added with no difficulty, and we may consider the problem of the infinite line charge

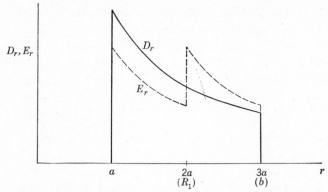

FIG. 3.8. Relative electric field intensity and electric flux density in a coaxial capacitor for which $\epsilon_2 = \frac{1}{2}\epsilon_1$, $b = 3a$, and $R_1 = 2a$.

or coaxial capacitor finished until we discuss potential in the next chapter.

3.5. Gauss's-law Application—Volume Charge Distribution. A continuous volume charge distribution raises one additional problem, that of finding the total charge within the chosen closed surface. Suppose that a distribution with spherical symmetry is assumed in which ρ varies with r:

$$\rho = \rho_0 \sqrt{\frac{a}{r}} \quad \text{coulombs/m}^3$$

where ρ_0 and a are constants, such that $\rho = \rho_0$ at $r = a$.

The symmetry indicates that the field does not vary with ϕ or θ and that only the D_r component is present. A spherical surface is therefore selected as the Gaussian surface, and we have

$$Q = \oint_s \mathbf{D}_s \cdot d\mathbf{S} = D_r 4\pi r^2$$

where Q = total charge within the spherical surface. This may be obtained by integrating

$$Q = \int_{\text{vol}} \rho \, dv = \int_{\theta=0}^{\pi} \int_{\phi=0}^{2\pi} \int_{r=0}^{r} \rho_0 \sqrt{\frac{a}{r}} \, r^2 \sin\theta \, dr \, d\phi \, d\theta$$
$$= \frac{8\pi}{5} \rho_0 \sqrt{a} \, r^{5/2}$$

The field is then

$$D_r = \frac{2}{5} \rho_0 \sqrt{ar}$$

Both the electric flux density D_r and the volume charge density ρ are plotted as a function of the radius r in Fig. 3.9. It should be noted from this sketch that although the charge density is infinite at the origin, this does not lead to an infinite field strength at that point. More generally, if we had let ρ vary as $1/r^k$, we would have found that the field at the origin is zero when $k < 1$, infinite when $k > 1$, and some nonzero finite value when $k = 1$.

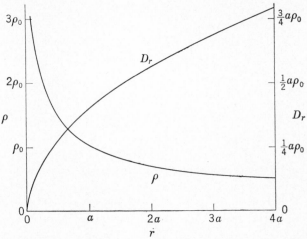

Fig. 3.9. Sketch of the variation of electric flux density D_r with radius r for a volume-charge-density distribution decreasing as $1/\sqrt{r}$.

3.6. Gauss's-law Application—Differential Volume Element.

We are now going to apply the methods of Gauss's law to a slightly different type of problem, one which does not possess any symmetry at all. At first glance it might seem that our case is hopeless, for without symmetry a simple Gaussian surface cannot be chosen such that the normal component of $\mathbf{D}$ is constant or zero everywhere on the surface. Without such a surface, the integral cannot be evaluated. There is only one way to circumvent these difficulties, and that is to choose such a very small closed surface that $\mathbf{D}$ is *almost* constant over the surface, and the small change in $\mathbf{D}$ may be adequately represented by using the first two terms of the Taylor's-series expansion for $\mathbf{D}$. The result will become more nearly correct as the volume enclosed by the Gaussian surface decreases, and we intend eventually to allow this volume to approach zero.

This example also differs from the preceding ones in that we shall not obtain the value of $\mathbf{D}$ as our answer, but instead receive some extremely valuable information about the way $\mathbf{D}$ varies in the region of our small surface. This leads directly to one of Maxwell's four equations, which are basic to all electromagnetic theory.

Let us consider any point P, shown in Fig. 3.10, located by a cartesian coordinate system. The value of $\mathbf{D}$ at the point P may be expressed in cartesian components, $\mathbf{D}_0 = D_{x0}\mathbf{a}_x + D_{y0}\mathbf{a}_y + D_{z0}\mathbf{a}_z$. We choose as our closed surface the small rectangular box, centered at P, having sides of length Δx, Δy, and Δz, and apply Gauss's law,

$$\oint_s \mathbf{D} \cdot d\mathbf{S} = Q$$

In order to evaluate the integral over the closed surface, the integral must be broken up into six integrals, one over each face:

$$\oint_s \mathbf{D} \cdot d\mathbf{S} = \int_{\text{front}} + \int_{\text{back}} + \int_{\text{left}} + \int_{\text{right}} + \int_{\text{top}} + \int_{\text{bottom}}$$

Consider the first of these in detail. Since the surface element is

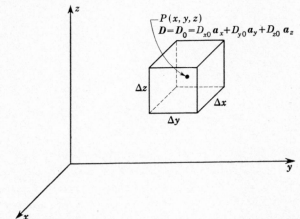

FIG. 3.10. A Gaussian surface of differential size about the point P.

very small, $\mathbf{D}$ is essentially constant (over *this* portion of the entire closed surface) and

$$\int_{\text{front}} \doteq \mathbf{D}_{\text{front}} \cdot \Delta\mathbf{S}_{\text{front}}$$
$$\doteq \mathbf{D}_{\text{front}} \cdot \Delta y\,\Delta z\mathbf{a}_x$$
$$\doteq D_{x_{\text{front}}} \Delta y\,\Delta z$$

where we have only to approximate the value of D_x at this front face. The front face is at a distance of $\Delta x/2$ from P, and hence

$$D_{x_{\text{front}}} \doteq D_{x0} + \frac{\Delta x}{2} \times (\text{rate of change of } D_x \text{ with } x)$$

$$\doteq D_{x0} + \frac{\Delta x}{2} \frac{\partial D_x}{\partial x}$$

where D_{x0} is the value of D_x at P, and where a partial derivative must be used to express the rate of change of D_x with x since D_x in general also varies with y and z. This expression could have been obtained more formally by using the constant term and the term involving the first derivative in the Taylor's-series expansion for D_x in the neighborhood of P.

We have now

$$\int_{\text{front}} \doteq \left(D_{x0} + \frac{\Delta x}{2} \frac{\partial D_x}{\partial x} \right) \Delta y \, \Delta z$$

Consider now the integral over the back surface:

$$\int_{\text{back}} \doteq \mathbf{D}_{\text{back}} \cdot \Delta \mathbf{S}_{\text{back}}$$
$$\doteq \mathbf{D}_{\text{back}} \cdot (-\Delta y \, \Delta z \, \mathbf{a}_x)$$
$$\doteq - D_{x_{\text{back}}} \Delta y \, \Delta z$$

and

$$D_{x_{\text{back}}} \doteq D_{x0} - \frac{\Delta x}{2} \frac{\partial D_x}{\partial x}$$

giving

$$\int_{\text{back}} \doteq \left(-D_{x0} + \frac{\Delta x}{2} \frac{\partial D_x}{\partial x} \right) \Delta y \, \Delta z$$

If we combine these two integrals,

$$\int_{\text{front}} + \int_{\text{back}} \doteq \frac{\partial D_x}{\partial x} \Delta x \, \Delta y \, \Delta z$$

By exactly the same process we find that

$$\int_{\text{right}} + \int_{\text{left}} \doteq \frac{\partial D_y}{\partial y} \Delta x \, \Delta y \, \Delta z$$

and

$$\int_{\text{top}} + \int_{\text{bottom}} \doteq \frac{\partial D_z}{\partial z} \Delta x \, \Delta y \, \Delta z$$

and these results may be collected to yield

$$\oint_s \mathbf{D} \cdot d\mathbf{S} \doteq \left(\frac{\partial D_x}{\partial x} + \frac{\partial D_y}{\partial y} + \frac{\partial D_z}{\partial z} \right) \Delta x \, \Delta y \, \Delta z$$

or

$$\oint_s \mathbf{D} \cdot d\mathbf{S} = Q \doteq \left(\frac{\partial D_x}{\partial x} + \frac{\partial D_y}{\partial y} + \frac{\partial D_z}{\partial z} \right) \Delta v \tag{1}$$

The expression is an approximation which becomes better as Δv becomes smaller, and in the following section we shall let the volume Δv approach zero. For the moment, we have applied Gauss's law to the closed surface surrounding the volume element Δv and have as a result the approximation (1) stating that

$$\text{Charge enclosed in volume } \Delta v \doteq \left(\frac{\partial D_x}{\partial x} + \frac{\partial D_y}{\partial y} + \frac{\partial D_z}{\partial z} \right) \times \text{volume } \Delta v$$

D3.5. How much charge is contained in the small volume of 1 mm³ centered at the origin if:

   (a) $\mathbf{D} = 10xa_x + 20y^2a_y + (\cos z)a_z$?
   (b) $\mathbf{D} = 10a_x + 3a_y + 4\pi a_z$?
   (c) $\mathbf{D} = (\sin x)a_x + (z + 1)e^y a_y + e^y a_z$?

Ans. 0.012 µcoulomb.

3.7. Divergence. We shall now obtain an exact relationship from Sec. 3.6, Eq. (1), by allowing the volume element Δv to shrink to zero. We write (1) as

$$\frac{\partial D_x}{\partial x} + \frac{\partial D_y}{\partial y} + \frac{\partial D_z}{\partial z} \doteq \frac{\oint_s \mathbf{D} \cdot d\mathbf{S}}{\Delta v} = \frac{Q}{\Delta v} = \rho \quad \text{Knon}$$

or

$$\frac{\partial D_x}{\partial x} + \frac{\partial D_y}{\partial y} + \frac{\partial D_z}{\partial z} = \lim_{\Delta v \to 0} \frac{\oint_s \mathbf{D} \cdot d\mathbf{S}}{\Delta v} = \lim_{\Delta v \to 0} \frac{Q}{\Delta v}$$

where the approximation has been replaced by an equality. It is evident that the last term is the volume charge density ρ, and hence that

$$\frac{\partial D_x}{\partial x} + \frac{\partial D_y}{\partial y} + \frac{\partial D_z}{\partial z} = \lim_{\Delta v \to 0} \frac{\oint_s \mathbf{D} \cdot d\mathbf{S}}{\Delta v} = \rho \qquad (1)$$

This equation contains too much information to discuss all at once, and we shall write (1) as two separate equations:

$$\frac{\partial D_x}{\partial x} + \frac{\partial D_y}{\partial y} + \frac{\partial D_z}{\partial z} = \lim_{\Delta v \to 0} \frac{\oint_s \mathbf{D} \cdot d\mathbf{S}}{\Delta v} \qquad (2)$$

$$\frac{\partial D_x}{\partial x} + \frac{\partial D_y}{\partial y} + \frac{\partial D_z}{\partial z} = \rho \qquad (3)$$

where we shall save (3) for consideration in the next section.

Equation (2) does not involve charge density, and the methods of the previous section could have been used on any vector $\mathbf{A}$ to find $\oint_s \mathbf{A} \cdot d\mathbf{S}$ for a small closed surface, leading to

$$\frac{\partial A_x}{\partial x} + \frac{\partial A_y}{\partial y} + \frac{\partial A_z}{\partial z} = \lim_{\Delta v \to 0} \frac{\oint_s \mathbf{A} \cdot d\mathbf{S}}{\Delta v} \qquad (4)$$

where $\mathbf{A}$ could represent velocity, temperature gradient, force, or any other vector field.

This operation appeared so many times in physical investigations in the last century that it received a descriptive name, *divergence*. The divergence of **A** is defined by

$$\text{Divergence of } \mathbf{A} = \lim_{\Delta v \to 0} \frac{\oint_s \mathbf{A} \cdot d\mathbf{S}}{\Delta v} \tag{5}$$

and is usually abbreviated div **A**. The physical interpretation of the divergence of a vector is obtained by describing carefully the operations implied by the right-hand side of (5), where we shall consider **A** as a member of the flux-density family of vectors in order to aid the physical interpretation.

The divergence of the vector flux density **A** *is the outflow of flux from a small closed surface per unit volume as the volume shrinks to zero.*

The physical interpretation of divergence afforded by this statement is often useful in obtaining qualitative information about the divergence of a vector field without resorting to a mathematical investigation. For instance, let us consider the divergence of the velocity of water in a bathtub after the drain has been opened. The net outflow of water through *any* closed surface lying entirely within the water must be zero, for water is essentially incompressible and the water entering and leaving different regions of the closed surface must be equal. Hence, the divergence of this velocity is zero.

If, however, we consider the velocity of the air in an inner tube which has just been punctured by a nail, we realize that the air is expanding as the pressure drops and that consequently there is a net outflow from any closed surface lying within the inner tube. The divergence of this velocity is therefore greater than zero.

A positive divergence for any vector quantity indicates a *source* of that vector quantity at that point. Similarly, a negative divergence indicates a *sink*. Since the divergence of the water velocity above is zero, no source or sink exists.[1] The expanding air, however, produces a positive divergence of the velocity, and each interior point may be considered a source.

Writing (4) with our new term, we have

$$\text{div } \mathbf{D} = \frac{\partial D_x}{\partial x} + \frac{\partial D_y}{\partial y} + \frac{\partial D_z}{\partial z} \tag{6}$$

[1] Having chosen a differential element of volume within the water, the gradual decrease in water level with time will eventually cause the volume element to lie above the surface of the water. At the instant the surface of the water intersects the volume element, the divergence is positive and the small volume is a source. This complication is avoided above by specifying an internal point.

This expression is again of a form which does not involve the charge density and which could be written for any vector **A**. It is the result of applying the definition of divergence (5) to a differential volume element in *cartesian coordinates*.

If a differential volume unit $r\, dr\, d\phi\, dz$ in cylindrical coordinates or $r^2 \sin \theta\, dr\, d\theta\, d\phi$ in spherical coordinates had been chosen, expressions for divergence involving the components of the vector in the particular coordinate system and involving partial derivatives with respect to the variables of that system would have been obtained. These expressions are obtained in Appendix A and are given here for convenience:

$$\text{div } \mathbf{D} = \frac{1}{r}\frac{\partial}{\partial r}(rD_r) + \frac{1}{r}\frac{\partial D_\phi}{\partial \phi} + \frac{\partial D_z}{\partial z} \quad \text{(cylindrical)} \tag{7}$$

$$= \frac{1}{r^2}\frac{\partial}{\partial r}(r^2 D_r) + \frac{1}{r \sin \theta}\frac{\partial}{\partial \theta}[(\sin \theta)D_\theta] + \frac{1}{r \sin \theta}\frac{\partial D_\phi}{\partial \phi}$$
$$\text{(spherical)} \tag{8}$$

It should be noted that the divergence is an operation which is performed on a vector, but that the result is a scalar. In a somewhat similar way, we should recall that the dot, or scalar, product was a multiplication of two vectors which yielded a scalar product.

For some reason, it is a common mistake on meeting divergence for the first time to impart a vector quality to the operation by scattering unit vectors around in the partial derivatives. Divergence merely tells us *how much* flux is leaving a small volume on a per-unit-volume basis and does not describe the "direction" of this flux at all.

D3.6. Obtain the divergence of each of these vectors at the origin:

(a) $\mathbf{A} = 10(\sin x)\mathbf{a}_x + (x + y)\mathbf{a}_y + x^2 y^2 z^2 \mathbf{a}_z$.

(b) $\mathbf{r} = x\mathbf{a}_x + y\mathbf{a}_y + z\mathbf{a}_z$.

(c) $\mathbf{B} = 3r^2(\sin \phi)\mathbf{a}_r + 2r(\sin \phi)\mathbf{a}_\phi + 2z(1 - \cos \phi)\mathbf{a}_z$.

Ans. 16.

3.8. Maxwell's First Equation (Electrostatics). We now wish to consolidate the gains of the last two sections and to provide an interpretation of the divergence operation as it relates to electric flux density. The expressions developed there may be written

$$\text{div } \mathbf{D} = \lim_{\Delta v \to 0} \frac{\oint_s \mathbf{D} \cdot d\mathbf{S}}{\Delta v} \tag{1}$$

$$= \frac{\partial D_x}{\partial x} + \frac{\partial D_y}{\partial y} + \frac{\partial D_z}{\partial z} \tag{2}$$

and $$= \rho \tag{3}$$

where the first equation is the definition of divergence, the second is the result of applying the definition to a differential volume element in cartesian coordinates, giving us an equation by which the divergence of a vector expressed in cartesian coordinates may be evaluated, and the third is merely (3) of the last section, written using the new term div **D**. Equation (3) is almost an obvious result if we have achieved any familiarity at all with the concept of divergence as defined by (1), for given Gauss's law,

$$\oint_s \mathbf{D} \cdot d\mathbf{S} = Q$$

per unit volume

$$\frac{\oint_s \mathbf{D} \cdot d\mathbf{S}}{\Delta v} = \frac{Q}{\Delta v}$$

as the volume shrinks to zero,

$$\lim_{\Delta v \to 0} \frac{\oint_s \mathbf{D} \cdot d\mathbf{S}}{\Delta v} = \lim_{\Delta v \to 0} \frac{Q}{\Delta v}$$

we should see div **D** on the left and volume charge density on the right:

$$\text{div } \mathbf{D} = \rho_v$$

This is the first of Maxwell's four equations, as they apply to electrostatics and steady magnetic fields, and it states that the electric flux per unit volume leaving a vanishingly small volume unit is exactly equal to the volume charge density there. This equation (3) is aptly called the *point form of Gauss's law*. Gauss's law relates the flux leaving any closed surface to the charge enclosed, and Maxwell's first equation makes an identical statement on a per-unit-volume basis for a vanishingly small volume, or at a point. Remembering that the divergence may be expressed as the sum of three partial derivatives, Maxwell's first equation is also described as the differential-equation form of Gauss's law, and, conversely, Gauss's law is recognized as the integral form of Maxwell's first equation.

As a specific illustration, consider the divergence of **D** qualitatively in the region about a line charge (but not on the line charge). In any small closed region, just as many lines of electric flux enter the surface as leave it, since there is no charge within the region on which a flux line may terminate, and the divergence of **D** must be zero. At every point in space surrounding this isolated line charge, div **D** = 0. (If a point on the line charge is selected, we find div **D** is infinite, for a finite amount of charge per unit length on a line involves an infinite charge per unit volume.)   The simple mathematical proof that the divergence is zero is a part of the drill problem below.

D3.7. Find the volume charge density ρ which gives rise to the three expressions for the electric flux density given below:

(a) In spherical coordinates, $\mathbf{D} = \dfrac{Q}{4\pi r^2}\, \mathbf{a}_r$.

(b) In cylindrical coordinates, $\mathbf{D} = \dfrac{\rho_L}{2\pi r}\, \mathbf{a}_r$.

(c) In cartesian coordinates, $\mathbf{D} = \rho_s \mathbf{a}_x$.

Ans. 0.

3.9. The Vector Operator ∇ and the Divergence Theorem. If we remind ourselves again that divergence is an operation on a vector yielding a scalar result, just as the dot product of two vectors gives a scalar result, it seems possible that we can find something which may be dotted with **D** to yield the scalar

$$\frac{\partial D_x}{\partial x} + \frac{\partial D_y}{\partial y} + \frac{\partial D_z}{\partial z}$$

Obviously, this cannot be accomplished by using a dot product; the process must be a *dot operation.*

Let us define the *del operator*, **∇**, as a *vector operator:*

$$\mathbf{\nabla} = \frac{\partial}{\partial x}\, \mathbf{a}_x + \frac{\partial}{\partial y}\, \mathbf{a}_y + \frac{\partial}{\partial z}\, \mathbf{a}_z \tag{1}$$

Similar *scalar operators* appear in several methods of solving differential equations, where we often let D replace d/dx, D^2 replace d^2/dx^2, and so forth.[1] We agree on defining **∇** (pronounced "del") that it shall be treated in every way as an ordinary vector with the one important exception that partial derivatives result instead of products of scalars.

Consider **∇ · D**, signifying

$$\mathbf{\nabla} \cdot \mathbf{D} = \left(\frac{\partial}{\partial x}\, \mathbf{a}_x + \frac{\partial}{\partial y}\, \mathbf{a}_y + \frac{\partial}{\partial z}\, \mathbf{a}_z \right) \cdot (D_x \mathbf{a}_x + D_y \mathbf{a}_y + D_z \mathbf{a}_z)$$

We first consider the dot products of the unit vectors, discarding the six zero terms and having left

$$\mathbf{\nabla} \cdot \mathbf{D} = \frac{\partial}{\partial x}\, (D_x) + \frac{\partial}{\partial y}\, (D_y) + \frac{\partial}{\partial z}\, (D_z)$$

---

[1] This scalar operator D, which will not appear again, is not to be confused with the electric flux density.

where the parentheses are now removed by operating or differentiating:

$$\mathbf{\nabla} \cdot \mathbf{D} = \frac{\partial D_x}{\partial x} + \frac{\partial D_y}{\partial y} + \frac{\partial D_z}{\partial z}$$

This is recognized as the divergence of $\mathbf{D}$, so that we have

$$\text{div } \mathbf{D} = \mathbf{\nabla} \cdot \mathbf{D} = \frac{\partial D_x}{\partial x} + \frac{\partial D_y}{\partial y} + \frac{\partial D_z}{\partial z}$$

The use of $\mathbf{\nabla} \cdot \mathbf{D}$ is much more prevalent than that of div $\mathbf{D}$, although both usages have their advantages. Writing $\mathbf{\nabla} \cdot \mathbf{D}$ allows us to obtain simply and quickly the correct partial derivatives, but only in cartesian coordinates, as we shall see below. On the other hand, div $\mathbf{D}$ is an excellent reminder of the physical interpretation of divergence. We shall use the operator notation $\mathbf{\nabla} \cdot \mathbf{D}$ from now on to indicate the divergence operation.

The vector operator $\mathbf{\nabla}$ not only is used with divergence, but will appear in several other very important operations later. One of these is $\mathbf{\nabla}u$, where u is any scalar, and leads to

$$\mathbf{\nabla}u = \left(\frac{\partial}{\partial x} \mathbf{a}_x + \frac{\partial}{\partial y} \mathbf{a}_y + \frac{\partial}{\partial z} \mathbf{a}_z \right) u = \frac{\partial u}{\partial x} \mathbf{a}_x + \frac{\partial u}{\partial y} \mathbf{a}_y + \frac{\partial u}{\partial z} \mathbf{a}_z \quad (2)$$

The operator $\mathbf{\nabla}$ does not have a specific form in other coordinate systems. If we are considering $\mathbf{D}$ in cylindrical coordinates, then $\mathbf{\nabla} \cdot \mathbf{D}$ still indicates the divergence of $\mathbf{D}$, or

$$\mathbf{\nabla} \cdot \mathbf{D} = \frac{1}{r} \frac{\partial}{\partial r} (rD_r) + \frac{1}{r} \frac{\partial D_\phi}{\partial \phi} + \frac{\partial D_z}{\partial z}$$

where this expression has been taken from Sec. 3.7. We have no form for $\mathbf{\nabla}$ itself to help us obtain this sum of partial derivatives. This means that $\mathbf{\nabla}u$, as yet unnamed but easily written above in cartesian coordinates, cannot be expressed by us at this time in cylindrical coordinates. Such an expression will be obtained when $\mathbf{\nabla}u$ is defined in the following chapter.

We shall close our discussion of divergence by presenting a theorem which will be needed several times in later chapters, *Gauss's theorem*, or the *divergence theorem*. We have actually obtained it already and now have little more to do than point it out and name it, for starting from Gauss's law,

$$\oint_s \mathbf{D} \cdot d\mathbf{S} = Q$$

and letting

$$Q = \int_{\text{vol}} \rho \, dv$$

and then replacing ρ by its equal,

$$\nabla \cdot \mathbf{D} = \rho$$

we have

$$\oint_s \mathbf{D} \cdot d\mathbf{S} = Q = \int_{\text{vol}} \rho \, dv = \int_{\text{vol}} \nabla \cdot \mathbf{D} \, dv$$

The first and last expressions constitute the divergence theorem:

$$\oint_s \mathbf{D} \cdot d\mathbf{S} = \int_{\text{vol}} \nabla \cdot \mathbf{D} \, dv \tag{3}$$

which may be stated:

The integral of the normal component of any vector field over a closed surface is equal to the integral of the divergence of this vector field throughout the volume enclosed by the closed surface.

It should be noted that the divergence theorem is true for any vector field, although we have obtained it specifically for the electric flux

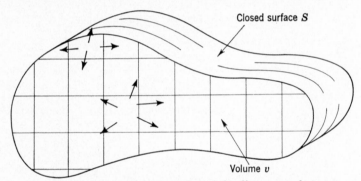

Closed surface S

Volume v

Fig. 3.11. A physical interpretation of the divergence theorem.

density $\mathbf{D}$. In general, its greatest use results from the fact that it relates a triple integration throughout some volume to a simpler double integration over the surface of that volume.

The divergence theorem becomes obvious physically if we consider a volume v, shown in cross section in Fig. 3.11, which is surrounded by a closed surface S. Division of the volume into a number of small compartments of differential size and consideration of one cell shows that the flux diverging from such a cell *enters*, or *converges* on, the adjacent cells unless the cell contains a portion of the outer surface. Summing up, the divergence of the flux density throughout a volume leads then to the same result as determining the net flux crossing the enclosing surface.

As a simple check on the validity of the theorem, consider a field $\mathbf{D} = x\mathbf{a}_x$ and the surface of a unit cube centered at the origin. Evaluating the surface integral first, we see that $\mathbf{D}$ is parallel to four of the six faces, and the remaining two give

$$\oint_s \mathbf{D} \cdot d\mathbf{S} = \int_{-\frac{1}{2}}^{\frac{1}{2}} \int_{-\frac{1}{2}}^{\frac{1}{2}} (-\tfrac{1}{2}\mathbf{a}_x) \cdot (-dy\, dz\, \mathbf{a}_x)$$

$$+ \int_{-\frac{1}{2}}^{\frac{1}{2}} \int_{-\frac{1}{2}}^{\frac{1}{2}} (\tfrac{1}{2}\mathbf{a}_x) \cdot (dy\, dz\, \mathbf{a}_x)$$

$$= 1$$

Since $\nabla \cdot \mathbf{D} = \dfrac{\partial}{\partial x}(x) = 1$, the volume integral becomes

$$\int_{\text{vol}} \nabla \cdot \mathbf{D}\, dv = \int_{-\frac{1}{2}}^{\frac{1}{2}} \int_{-\frac{1}{2}}^{\frac{1}{2}} \int_{-\frac{1}{2}}^{\frac{1}{2}} 1\, dx\, dy\, dz = 1$$

and the check is accomplished. Remembering Gauss's law, we see that we have also determined that a total charge of 1 coulomb lies within this unit cube.

SUGGESTED REFERENCES

1. Skilling, H. H.: "Fundamentals of Electric Waves," 2d ed., John Wiley & Sons, Inc., New York, 1948. The operations of vector calculus are well illustrated. Divergence is discussed on pages 22 and 38. Chapter 1 is interesting reading.
2. Winch, R. P.: "Electricity and Magnetism," Prentice-Hall, Inc., Englewood Cliffs, N.J., 1955. The presentation is very descriptive and is given with the viewpoint of the physicist, but at an introductory level. Pages 250–277 are most appropriate here.

PROBLEMS

1. Compare the electric field intensity due to a point charge of Q coulombs with that of a uniform distribution of volume charge density within a spherical surface of radius a if the total charge is again Q coulombs. Specifically, compare the fields at points for which $r > a$ and $r < a$.

2. Use Gauss's law to show that an inverse distance field in spherical coordinates, $\mathbf{D} = \mathbf{a}_r/r$, requires every spherical shell of 1 m thickness to contain 4π coulombs of charge. Does this indicate a continuous volume charge distribution? If so, how does the charge density vary with r?

3. Find the total charge contained within a cube centered at the origin and having sides of length L parallel to the coordinate axes. The electric flux density is $\mathbf{D} = \sin \pi x\, \mathbf{a}_x$. Find the average charge density within the cube for $L = 1, 0.5, 0.1$, and 0.01 m. Take the limit as L approaches zero, and find the exact volume charge density at the origin.

4. Three point charges are located as follows: $Q_1 = 10^{-6}$ at $(1,0,0)$, $Q_2 = 2 \times 10^{-6}$ at $(0,1,0)$, and $Q_3 = -10^{-6}$ at $(0,0,0)$. Use Gauss's law to obtain approximate expressions for $\mathbf{D}$ and $\mathbf{E}$ at a distant point $P(x,y,z)$ where $r = \sqrt{x^2 + y^2 + z^2} \gg 1$.

5. A coaxial capacitor having an inner radius a and an outer radius b contains three different dielectric layers, ϵ_1 for $a < r < R_1$, ϵ_2 for $R_1 < r < R_2$, and ϵ_3 for

$R_2 < r < b$. What must be the relative values of ϵ_1, ϵ_2, and ϵ_3 if the maximum electric field intensities at $r = a$, $r = R_1$, and $r = R_2$ are to be equal? This prob- lem indicates a method whereby the electric field intensity may be maintained more uniform throughout the capacitor, allowing more economical use of dielectric materials having a specific value of maximum electric field intensity before voltage breakdown.

6. If we could specify a material to be used as the dielectric in a coaxial capacitor for which the permittivity varied continuously with the radius, what variation with r should be used in order to maintain a uniform value of the electric field intensity?

7. An infinite line charge on the z axis carries a uniform charge density of 1 cou- lomb/m. Without using any involved integrations, determine the electric flux cutting each of these surfaces: (a) the portion of the $x = 1$ plane bounded by the lines $z = \pm 1$, $y = \pm \infty$; (b) the portion of the $x = 1$ plane bounded by the lines $z = \pm 1$, $y = \pm 1$; (c) the portion of the cylinder $r = 1$ between $z = 1$ and $z = -1$; (d) the outer part ($r > 2$) of the toroid whose axis lies on the z axis and whose cross section in the $x = 0$ plane consists of two unit radius circles centered at $z = 0$, $y = \pm 2$.

8. The field of a uniform ring of charge is obtained in Chap. 2, Prob. 2, for a point on the axis of the ring only. Use the concept of Gauss's law to obtain an approximate expression for the electric field intensity very close to the ring itself.

9. Describe a suitable Gaussian surface (if any exists) for the charge distribu- tions specified below: (a) A long electron beam of finite radius, having a uniform charge per unit length and given charge-density variation with radius. (b) A right circular cylinder of height h containing a uniform volume charge density. (c) The distant field of two closely spaced, parallel, identical, uniform line charges.

10. A uniform infinite sheet of charge of density ρ_s coulombs/m^2 occupies the $x = 0$ plane. Select a suitable Gaussian surface and determine **D** and **E** for $x > 0$ and $x < 0$.

11. A uniform surface charge of ρ_s coulombs/m^2 is in the form of a spherical surface of radius a. Obtain expressions for **D** at points for which $r > a$ and $r < a$. If the sheet is now considered a uniform-volume-charge distribution in a thin spherical shell of thickness t, describe the field in the charge-free regions outside and inside of the shell and also in the region within the shell of charge itself.

12. Show that the last sentence of Sec. 3.5 is true.

13. Volume charge density varies in spherical coordinates as $\rho = (\rho_0 \sin \pi r)/r^2$. Find the surfaces on which **D** = 0.

14. Construct an incremental volume element in cylindrical coordinates of sides Δr, $r\,\Delta\phi$, and Δz centered at a general point r_0, ϕ_0, z_0 at which $\mathbf{D}_0 = D_{r0}\mathbf{a}_r + D_{\phi 0}\mathbf{a}_\phi + D_{z0}\mathbf{a}_z$. Compute the flux passing through each face, and show that the charge enclosed is $\left[\dfrac{1}{r}\dfrac{\partial}{\partial r}(rD_r) + \dfrac{1}{r}\dfrac{\partial D_\phi}{\partial \phi} + \dfrac{\partial D_z}{\partial z}\right] r\,\Delta r\,\Delta\phi\,\Delta z$.

15. Assuming a region of space in which only an x component of **D** is present and that this component varies only with y and z, show that no volume charge density can exist there. If this single component present does vary with x, what must be the requirements on D_x to ensure zero charge density at a specific point? Show that volume charge density may exist at a point even though D_x, D_y, and D_z equal zero at that point. *(rate of change of D field is necessary)*

16. Use Maxwell's first equation to describe the variation of the electric field intensity with x in a region in which no charge density exists and in which a non-

trap! $D_x = 0$, but $\dfrac{\partial D_x}{\partial x}$ not necessarily zero

$D_x = K\sin x$ $D_y = 0$ $D_z = 0$

@ $x = 0$

$D_x = 0 (!)$ but $\dfrac{\partial D_x}{\partial x} = K\cos x \neq 0$

homogeneous dielectric has a permittivity that increases exponentially with x. The field has an x component only.

17. Suppose that we live in a two-dimensional "Flatland"[1] where the concept of volume does not exist as we know it. What definition of divergence should we use in place of Sec. 3.7, Eq. (5)? Explain the significance of the integral, and state in words the definition of two-dimensional divergence.

18. Using the definition of the vector operator ∇, obtain expressions in cartesian coordinates for $\nabla \cdot \nabla u$ and $\nabla(\nabla \cdot \mathbf{A})$.

19. State whether the divergence of the following vector fields is positive, negative, or zero: (a) the thermal energy flow in joules/(sec)/(m²) at any point in a freezing ice cube; (b) the current density in amp/m² within a bus bar carrying direct current; (c) the insect velocity in bugs/(sec)/(m²) on a freshly set picnic table; (d) the magnetic flux density in webers/m².

20. The density at a certain point in a region of expanding gas is decreasing by a factor of 2 every second. If the density is 5×10^{-4} kg/m³ at $t = 0$, find the divergence of the rate of flow $\mathbf{U}$ kg/(sec)(m²) of the gas at $t = 0$.

21. Find the total charge within the cylindrical surface $r = 6$, $z = \pm 2$, if $\mathbf{D} = 3(6 - r)\mathbf{a}_r + 2[\cos(\pi z/4)]\mathbf{a}_z$. This problem should be worked by two methods, one involving a volume integral and the other a surface integral.

[1] This two-dimensional land is the subject of an interesting little book by Edwin A. Abbott, "Flatland: A Romance of Many Dimensions," Roberts Brothers, Boston, 1885.

CHAPTER 4

ENERGY AND POTENTIAL

In the previous two chapters we have become acquainted with Coulomb's law and its use in finding the electric field about several simple distributions of charge and also Gauss's law and its application in determining the field about some symmetrical charge arrangements. The use of Gauss's law was invariably easier, for the problem of integration always disappeared when the proper closed surface was chosen.

However, if we had attempted to find a slightly more complicated field such as that of two unlike point charges separated by a small distance, we would have found it impossible to choose a suitable Gaussian surface and obtain an answer. Coulomb's law, however, is more powerful and enables us to solve problems for which Gauss's law is not applicable. The application of Coulomb's law is laborious, detailed, and often quite complex, the reason for this being precisely the fact that the electric field intensity, a vector field, must be found directly from the charge distribution. Three different integrations are needed in general, one for each component, and the resolution of the vector into components usually adds to the complexity of the integrals.

Certainly it would be desirable if we could find some as yet undefined scalar function with a single integration and then determine the electric field from this scalar by some simple straightforward procedure, such as differentiation.

This scalar function does exist and is known as the potential, or potential field. We shall find that it has a very real physical interpretation and is more familiar to most of us than is the electric field which it will be used to find.

We should expect, then, to be equipped soon with a third method of finding electric fields—a single scalar integration, although not always as simple as we might wish, followed by a pleasant differentiation.

The remaining difficult portion of the task, the integration, we intend to remove in Chap. 7.

4.1. Energy Expended in Moving a Point Charge in an Electric Field. The electric field intensity was defined as the force on a unit

73

test charge at that point where we wish to find the value of this vector field. If we attempt to move this test charge around in the electric field, we have to exert an equal and opposite force to that exerted by the field, and this requires us to expend energy, or do work. If we are fortunate, the force due to the field is in the direction in which we wish to move the charge, and our energy expenditure turns out to be negative; we do not do the work, the field does.

Suppose we wish to move a charge Q a distance $d\mathbf{L}$ in an electric field $\mathbf{E}$. The force on Q due to the electric field is

$$\mathbf{F}_E = Q\mathbf{E}$$

where the subscript reminds us that this force is due to the field, and the component of this force in the direction $d\mathbf{L}$ which we must overcome is

$$F_{LE} = \mathbf{F}_E \cdot \mathbf{a}_L = Q\mathbf{E} \cdot \mathbf{a}_L$$

where $\mathbf{a}_L = $ a unit vector in the direction of $d\mathbf{L}$.

The force which we must apply is equal and opposite to the force due to the field:

$$F_{\text{applied}} = -Q\mathbf{E} \cdot \mathbf{a}_L$$

and our expenditure of energy is the product of the force and distance:

Work done by external source moving $Q = -Q\mathbf{E} \cdot \mathbf{a}_L \, dL = -Q\mathbf{E} \cdot d\mathbf{L}$

or

$$dW = -Q\mathbf{E} \cdot d\mathbf{L} \qquad \text{joules} \qquad (1)$$

where we have replaced $\mathbf{a}_L \, dL$ by the simpler expression $d\mathbf{L}$.

This differential amount of work required may be zero under several conditions determined easily from (1). There are the trivial conditions for which $\mathbf{E}$, Q, and $d\mathbf{L}$ are zero and a much more important case in which $\mathbf{E}$ and $d\mathbf{L}$ are perpendicular. Here the charge is moved always in a direction at right angles to the electric field. We can draw on a good analogy between the electric field and the gravitational field, where again energy must be expended to move against the field. Sliding a mass around on a frictionless uneven surface is an effortless process if the mass is moved along a constant elevation contour; positive or negative work must be done in moving it to a higher or lower elevation, respectively.

Returning to the charge in the electric field, the work required to move the charge a finite distance must be determined by integrating:

$$W = -Q \int_{\text{initial position}}^{\text{final position}} \mathbf{E} \cdot d\mathbf{L} \qquad (2)$$

where the path must be specified before the integral can be evaluated.

This definite integral is very basic to field theory, and we shall devote the following section to its interpretation and evaluation.

D4.1. How much work is done in moving a charge of 3 coulombs in a uniform electric field, $\mathbf{E} = -10\mathbf{a}_x + 12\mathbf{a}_y + 5\mathbf{a}_z$, a distance of 1 mm (which may be taken as an incremental length) along the line joining:

    (a) (0,0,0) to (0,0,1)?
    (b) (0,1,0) to (2,0,0)?
    (c) (3,0,5) to (2,2,6)?

Ans. −0.0198 joule.

4.2. The Line Integral. The integral expression for the work done in moving a point charge of Q coulombs from one position to another [Sec. 4.1, Eq. (2)] is an example of a line integral, which in vector-analysis notation always takes the form of the integral along some prescribed path of the dot product of a vector field and a differential vector-path length $d\mathbf{L}$. Without using vector analysis we should have to write

$$W = -Q \int_{\text{initial}}^{\text{final}} E_L \, dL$$

where E_L = component of $\mathbf{E}$ along $d\mathbf{L}$.

A line integral is like many other integrals which appear in advanced analysis, including the surface integral appearing in Gauss's law, in that it is essentially descriptive. We like to look at it much more than we like to work it out. It tells us to choose a path, break it up into a large number of very small segments, multiply the component of the field along each segment by the length of the segment, and then add the results for all the segments. This is a summation, of course, and the integral is only obtained exactly when the number of segments becomes infinite.

This procedure is indicated in Fig. 4.1, where a path has been chosen from an initial position A to a final position B and a *uniform electric field* selected for simplicity. The path is divided into six segments, $\Delta \mathbf{L}_1, \Delta \mathbf{L}_2, \ldots, \Delta \mathbf{L}_6$, and the components of $\mathbf{E}$ along each segment denoted by $E_{L1}, E_{L2}, \ldots, E_{L6}$. The work involved in moving a charge Q from A to B is then approximately

$$W = -Q(E_{L1} \Delta L_1 + E_{L2} \Delta L_2 + \cdots + E_{L6} \Delta L_6)$$

or, using vector notation,

$$W = -Q(\mathbf{E}_1 \cdot \Delta \mathbf{L}_1 + \mathbf{E}_2 \cdot \Delta \mathbf{L}_2 + \cdots + \mathbf{E}_6 \cdot \Delta \mathbf{L}_6)$$

and since we have assumed a uniform field,

$$\mathbf{E}_1 = \mathbf{E}_2 = \cdots = \mathbf{E}_6$$
$$W = -Q\mathbf{E} \cdot (\Delta \mathbf{L}_1 + \Delta \mathbf{L}_2 + \cdots + \Delta \mathbf{L}_6)$$

What is this sum of vector segments in the parentheses above? Vectors add by the parallelogram law, and the sum is just the vector directed from the initial point A to the final point B, $\mathbf{L}_{AB}$. Therefore

$$W = -Q\mathbf{E} \cdot \mathbf{L}_{AB} \tag{1}$$

Remembering the summation interpretation of the line integral, this

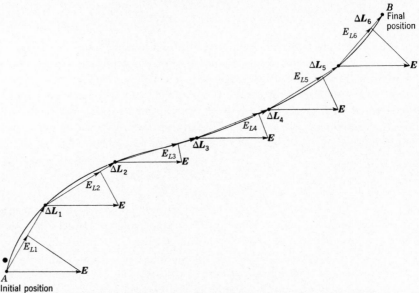

FIG. 4.1. Graphical interpretation of a line integral in a uniform field.

result for the uniform field can be obtained rapidly now from the integral expression

$$W = -Q \int_A^B \mathbf{E} \cdot d\mathbf{L}$$

for dc fields only

as applied to a uniform field

$$W = -Q\mathbf{E} \cdot \int_A^B d\mathbf{L}$$

where the last integral becomes $\mathbf{L}_{AB}$ and

$$W = -Q\mathbf{E} \cdot \mathbf{L}_{AB}$$

Even though this result applies only to the special case of a uniform-electric-field intensity, we should note that the work involved in moving the charge depends only on Q, $\mathbf{E}$, and $\mathbf{L}_{AB}$, a vector drawn from the initial to the final point of the path chosen. It does not depend on the particular path we have selected along which to carry the charge. We may proceed from A to B on a straight line or via the Old Chisholm Trail; the answer is the same.

Merely to illustrate the mechanics of setting up a line integral for evaluation along a specific path, let us carry a charge of 1 coulomb from the origin to $(1,1,0)$ in a uniform field of $\mathbf{E} = -100\mathbf{a}_x$. The expected result is first determined by (1) as

$$W = -Q\mathbf{E} \cdot \mathbf{L}_{AB} = -(1)(-100\mathbf{a}_x) \cdot (1\mathbf{a}_x + 1\mathbf{a}_y)$$
$$= 100 \text{ joules}$$

and we now select two different paths, perform the indicated integrations, and obtain 100 joules each time.

1. Path: straight line from origin to $(1,1,0)$. In cartesian coordinates $d\mathbf{L} = dx\,\mathbf{a}_x + dy\,\mathbf{a}_y + dz\,\mathbf{a}_z$, where the relations between dx, dy, and dz depend on the path. The equation of the path must be the equation of a straight line in the $z = 0$ plane and is given by

$$y = x \qquad z = 0$$

from which we have

$$dy = dx \qquad dz = 0$$

and therefore

$$d\mathbf{L} = dx\,(\mathbf{a}_x + \mathbf{a}_y)$$
$$W = -Q \int_{x=0}^{x=1} (-100\mathbf{a}_x) \cdot (\mathbf{a}_x + \mathbf{a}_y)\,dx$$
$$= 100 \int_0^1 dx = 100$$

We could equally as well have used y as our variable:

$$d\mathbf{L} = dy\,(\mathbf{a}_x + \mathbf{a}_y)$$
$$W = -Q \int_{y=0}^{y=1} (-100\mathbf{a}_x) \cdot (\mathbf{a}_x + \mathbf{a}_y)\,dy = 100$$

2. Path: parabola $y = x^2$, $z = 0$ from origin to $(1,1,0)$. We now find

$$dy = 2x\,dx \qquad dz = 0$$
$$W = -Q \int_{x=0}^{x=1} (-100\mathbf{a}_x) \cdot (\mathbf{a}_x + 2x\mathbf{a}_y)\,dx = 100$$

or, using y as the variable, with a little more difficulty:

$$W = -Q \int_{y=0}^{y=1} (-100\mathbf{a}_x) \cdot \left(\frac{\mathbf{a}_x}{2x} + \mathbf{a}_y\right) dy$$
$$= 100 \int_0^1 \frac{dy}{2x} = 100 \int_0^1 \frac{dy}{2\sqrt{y}} = 100\sqrt{y}\Big]_0^1 = 100$$

Note that the expression for $d\mathbf{L}$ is always $dx\ \mathbf{a}_x + dy\ \mathbf{a}_y + dz\ \mathbf{a}_z$ and the specified path serves to determine the relationships between the several differentials. The integration is then finally performed with respect to whichever variable is most convenient. In cylindrical or spherical coordinates the differential elements of length are seen from the first chapter to be $d\mathbf{L} = dr\ \mathbf{a}_r + r\ d\phi\ \mathbf{a}_\phi + dz\ \mathbf{a}_z$ and $d\mathbf{L} = dr\ \mathbf{a}_r + r\ d\theta\ \mathbf{a}_\theta + r\sin\theta\ d\phi\ \mathbf{a}_\phi$, respectively.

As a final example illustrating the evaluation of the line integral, let us investigate several paths which we might take near an infinite line charge. The field has been obtained several times and is entirely in the radial direction:

$$\mathbf{E} = E_r\mathbf{a}_r = \frac{\rho_L}{2\pi\epsilon r}\ \mathbf{a}_r$$

Let us first find the work done in carrying the positive charge of Q coulombs about a circular path of radius r_1, centered at the line charge, as illustrated in Fig. 4.2a. Without lifting a pencil, we see

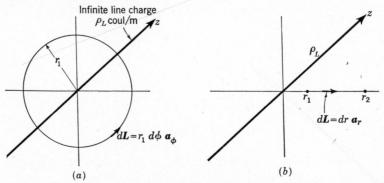

FIG. 4.2. (a) A circular path and (b) a radial path along which a charge of Q coulombs is carried in the field of an infinite line charge.

that the work must be nil, for the path is always perpendicular to the electric field intensity, or the force on the charge is always exerted at right angles to the direction in which we are moving it. For practice, however, let us set up the integral and obtain the answer.

The differential element $d\mathbf{L}$ is chosen in cylindrical coordinates, and the circular path selected demands that dr and dz be zero, so $d\mathbf{L} = r_1\ d\phi\ \mathbf{a}_\phi$. The work is then

$$W = -Q \int_{\text{initial}}^{\text{final}} \frac{\rho_L}{2\pi\epsilon r_1}\ \mathbf{a}_r \cdot r_1\ d\phi\ \mathbf{a}_\phi$$
$$= -Q \int_0^{2\pi} \frac{\rho_L}{2\pi\epsilon}\ d\phi\ \mathbf{a}_r \cdot \mathbf{a}_\phi = 0$$

Let us now carry the charge from r_1 to r_2 along a radial path (Fig. 4.2b). Here, $d\mathbf{L} = dr\,\mathbf{a}_r$ and

$$W = -Q \int_{\text{initial}}^{\text{final}} \frac{\rho_L}{2\pi\epsilon r}\,\mathbf{a}_r \cdot dr\,\mathbf{a}_r = -Q \int_{r_1}^{r_2} \frac{\rho_L\,dr}{2\pi\epsilon r}$$

or

$$W = -\frac{Q\rho_L}{2\pi\epsilon} \ln \frac{r_2}{r_1}$$

Since r_2 is larger than r_1, $\ln(r_2/r_1)$ is positive, and we see that the work done is negative, indicating that the external source moving the charge receives energy.

One of the pitfalls in evaluating line integrals is a tendency to use too many minus signs when a charge is moved in the direction of a *decreasing* coordinate value. This is taken care of completely by the limits on the integral, and no misguided attempt should be made to change the sign of $d\mathbf{L}$. Suppose we carry Q coulombs from r_2 to r_1 (Fig. 4.2b). We still have $d\mathbf{L} = dr\,\mathbf{a}_r$ and show the different direction by recognizing $r = r_2$ as the initial point and $r = r_1$ as the final point:

$$W = -Q \int_{r_2}^{r_1} \frac{\rho_L}{2\pi\epsilon} \frac{dr}{r} = \frac{Q\rho_L}{2\pi\epsilon} \ln \frac{r_2}{r_1}$$

This is the negative of the previous answer and is obviously correct.

D4.2. Find the work done in moving a unit positive charge in the field $\mathbf{E} = -y\mathbf{a}_x - x\mathbf{a}_y$ along a straight line from the origin to:
(a) $(0,1,0)$.
(b) $(1,0,0)$.
(c) $(1,1,0)$.

Ans. 1 joule.

D4.3. Repeat Prob. D4.2c using the path:
(a) Parabola, $y = x^2$.

(b) Sine curve, $y = \sin \dfrac{\pi x}{2}$.

(c) $y = 2\left(1 - \dfrac{1}{1 + x^2}\right)$.

Ans. 3 joules.

4.3. Definition of Potential Difference and Potential. We are now ready to define a new concept from the expression for the work done by an external source in moving a charge Q from one point to another in an electric field $\mathbf{E}$:

$$W = -Q \int_{\text{initial}}^{\text{final}} \mathbf{E} \cdot d\mathbf{L}$$

In much the same way as we defined the electric field intensity as the force on a *unit* test charge, we now define *potential difference* as the work done (by an external source) in moving a *unit* positive charge from one point to another in an electric field:

$$\text{Potential difference} = -\int_{\text{initial}}^{\text{final}} \mathbf{E} \cdot d\mathbf{L}$$

We shall have to agree on the direction of movement, as implied by our language, and we do this by stating that the potential difference between points A and B is represented by V_{AB} and is the work done in moving the unit charge from B (last-named) to A (first-named).

Potential difference is measured in joules per coulomb, for which the *volt* is defined as a more common unit, represented by V. Hence the potential difference between points A and B is

$$V_{AB} = -\int_{B}^{A} \mathbf{E} \cdot d\mathbf{L} \qquad \text{volts} \tag{1}$$

and V_{AB} is positive if work is done in carrying the positive charge from B to A.

From the line-charge example of the last section, we found the work done in taking the charge from r_2 to r_1 was

$$W = \frac{Q\rho_L}{2\pi\epsilon} \ln \frac{r_2}{r_1}$$

and the potential difference between points at r_1 and r_2 is

$$V_{12} = \frac{W}{Q} = \frac{\rho_L}{2\pi\epsilon} \ln \frac{r_2}{r_1}$$

We can try out this definition by finding the potential difference between points A and B at radial distances r_A and r_B from a point charge of Q coulombs. Choosing a spherical coordinate system centered at Q,

$$\mathbf{E} = E_r \mathbf{a}_r = \frac{Q}{4\pi\epsilon r^2} \mathbf{a}_r$$

and
$$d\mathbf{L} = dr \, \mathbf{a}_r$$
we have

$$V_{AB} = -\int_{B}^{A} \mathbf{E} \cdot d\mathbf{L} = -\int_{r_B}^{r_A} \frac{Q}{4\pi\epsilon r^2} \, dr = \frac{Q}{4\pi\epsilon} \left(\frac{1}{r_A} - \frac{1}{r_B} \right) \tag{2}$$

If $r_B > r_A$, the potential difference V_{AB} is positive, indicating energy is expended by the external source in bringing the positive charge from r_B to r_A. This agrees with the physical picture showing the two like charges repelling each other.

It is often convenient to speak of the *potential,* or *absolute potential,* of a point, rather than the potential difference between two points, but this means only that we agree to measure every potential difference with respect to a specified reference point which we consider to have zero potential. Common agreement must be reached on the zero reference before a statement of the potential has any significance. A person having one hand on the deflection plates of a cathode-ray tube which are "at a potential of 50 volts" and his other hand on the cathode terminal would probably be too shaken up to understand that the cathode is not the zero reference, but that all potentials in that circuit are customarily measured with respect to the metallic shield about the tube.

Perhaps the most universal zero reference point in experimental or physical potential measurements is "ground," by which we mean the potential of the surface region of the earth itself. Theoretically, we usually represent this surface by an infinite plane at zero potential, although some large-scale problems, such as those involving propagation across the Atlantic Ocean, require a spherical surface at zero potential.

Another widely used reference "point" is infinity. This usually appears in theoretical problems approximating a physical situation in which the earth is relatively far removed from the region in which we are interested, such as the static field near the wing tip of an airplane which has acquired a charge in flying through a thunderhead, or the field near two closely spaced wires connecting a television set to its antenna.

A cylindrical surface of some definite radius may occasionally be used where cylindrical symmetry is present and infinity proves inconvenient. And, of course, some special problems fit none of these zero references, but anyone trying to establish the field of an antenna in a rectangular cavity or of an electron inside of an ellipsoid should be ready for anything.

If the potential at point A is V_A and that at B is V_B, then

$$V_{AB} = V_A - V_B$$

where we necessarily agree that V_A and V_B shall have the same zero reference point.

D4.4. If the potential difference between points $A(1,0,0)$ and $B(2,0,0)$ is 10 volts, find the potential difference between points $B(2,0,0)$ and $C(3,0,0)$:

(a) In the field of a point charge located at the origin.
(b) In the field of an infinite line charge on the z axis.
(c) In a uniform field.

Ans. 19.2 volts.

Test for conservative field. $\longrightarrow \oint E \cdot dL = 0$

4.4. The Potential Field of a Point Charge. In the previous section we found an expression [Eq. (2)] for the potential difference between two points located at $r = r_A$ and $r = r_B$ in the field of a point charge of Q coulombs placed at the origin:

$$V_{AB} = \frac{Q}{4\pi\epsilon}\left(\frac{1}{r_A} - \frac{1}{r_B}\right) = V_A - V_B \tag{1}$$

It was assumed there that the two points lay on the same radial line or had the same θ and ϕ coordinate values, allowing us to set up a simple path on this radial line along which to carry our positive charge. We now should ask whether different θ and ϕ coordinate values for the initial and final position will affect our answer and whether we could choose more complicated paths between the two points without changing the results.

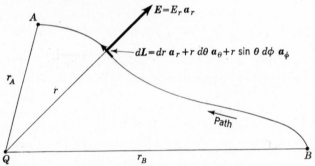

FIG. 4.3. A general path between general points A and B in the field of a point charge Q.

Let us answer both questions at once by choosing two general points A and B (Fig. 4.3) at radial distances of r_A and r_B and any values for the other coordinates.

The differential path length $d\mathbf{L}$ has r, θ, and ϕ components, and the electric field has only a radial component. Taking the dot product leaves us then only

$$V_{AB} = -\int_{r_B}^{r_A} E_r \, dr = -\int_{r_B}^{r_A} \frac{Q}{4\pi\epsilon r^2} \, dr = \frac{Q}{4\pi\epsilon}\left(\frac{1}{r_A} - \frac{1}{r_B}\right)$$

We obtain the same answer and see, therefore, that the potential difference between two points in the field of a point charge depends only on the distance of each point from the charge and does not depend on the particular path used to carry our unit charge from one point to the other.

How might we conveniently define a zero reference for potential? The simplest possibility is to let $V = 0$ at infinity. If we let the point at $r = r_B$ recede to infinity, the potential at r_A becomes

$$V_A = \frac{Q}{4\pi\epsilon r_A}$$

and since there is no need specially to identify this point with the A subscript,

$$V = \frac{Q}{4\pi\epsilon r} \tag{2}$$

This expression defines the potential at any point r m from a point charge of Q coulombs, the potential at infinite radius being taken as the zero reference. Returning to a physical interpretation, we may say that $Q/4\pi\epsilon r$ joules of work must be done in carrying a one-coulomb charge from infinity to any point r m from the charge of Q coulombs.

The potential is a scalar field and does not involve any unit vectors.

Let us now define an *equipotential surface* as a surface composed of all those points having the same value of potential. No work is involved in moving a unit charge around on an equipotential surface, for, by definition, there is no potential difference between any two points on this surface.

The equipotential surfaces in the potential field of a point charge are spheres centered at the point charge.

We may choose a different zero reference for this field by merely stating that the potential is zero at $r = r_0$. Equation (2) is no longer correct, and we return to (1), letting r_B be r_0, where r_A is our general point r:

$$V = \frac{Q}{4\pi\epsilon}\left(\frac{1}{r} - \frac{1}{r_0}\right) \tag{3}$$

The potential at infinity now turns out to be a finite negative value, and this value appears as a constant difference between the potential values given by (2) and (3). Adding or subtracting a constant amount from a potential expression is equivalent to a change in the zero reference, and we may recognize this by expressing the potential of a point charge by

$$V = \frac{Q}{4\pi\epsilon r} + C_1 \tag{4}$$

where C_1 may be evaluated as soon as the point is specified at which V is to be zero.

Finally, we might choose not to have a *zero* reference explicitly named, but instead choose a reference of 100 volts, or V_0 volts.   Letting $V = V_0$ at $r = r_1$, we solve for C_1:

$$C_1 = V_0 - \frac{Q}{4\pi\epsilon r_1}$$

and then write the potential:

$$V = \frac{Q}{4\pi\epsilon r} - \frac{Q}{4\pi\epsilon r_1} + V_0 \tag{5}$$

The zero reference can, of course, now be determined, and we see that it occurs when

$$r = \frac{r_1}{1 - \dfrac{4\pi\epsilon V_0 r_1}{Q}}$$

Presumably, however, we are more interested in the point at which $V = V_0$ and have chosen this point in the simplest manner.

It should be noted that expressions (2) to (5) for the potential of a point charge using various potential references will all yield the same expression (1) for the *potential difference* between two points, which allows for no choice of an arbitrary reference level.

An inspection of the form of the potential field of a point charge shows that it is an inverse-distance field, whereas the electric field intensity was found to be an inverse-square-law relationship.   A similar result occurs for the gravitational force field of a point mass (inverse-square law) and the gravitational potential field (inverse distance).   The gravitational force exerted on an object one million miles from the earth is four times that exerted on the same object two million miles away.   The kinetic energy given to a freely falling object starting from the end of the universe with zero velocity, however, is only twice as much at one million miles as it is at two million miles.

D4.5. Four point charges, each $Q = 10^{-9}/9$ coulomb, are located at the corners of a square 1 cm on a side.   Find the potential:

(a) At the center of the square if the potential at infinity is taken as zero.

(b) At the mid-point of any side if the zero reference is at infinity.

(c) At a point 2 cm from every charge if the potential at the center of the square is taken as the zero reference.

Ans. 779 volts.

4.5. The Potential Field of a System of Charges—Conservative Property.   We have an expression for the potential field of a single point charge, which we shall call Q_1, involving only the distance from Q_1 to the point in question.   If this distance is designated R_1, the capital letter reminding us that no special coordinate system is necessary,

 Next (See page 82)

then the potential is

$$V = \frac{Q_1}{4\pi\epsilon R_1}$$

Suppose that now there is also a second charge Q_2, located a distance R_2 from the point at which we are establishing the value of the potential. Can we simply say that the total potential is the sum of the potentials of each charge acting alone?

$$V \overset{?}{=} \frac{Q_1}{4\pi\epsilon R_1} + \frac{Q_2}{4\pi\epsilon R_2}$$

Retracing our steps, we may find the potential by evaluating the line integral, choosing the initial position at infinity to agree with our zero reference and calling the final position A:

$$V = -\int_{\infty}^{A} \mathbf{E} \cdot d\mathbf{L}$$

The total electric field intensity we know is the sum of the contributions by each charge:

$$V = -\int_{\infty}^{A} (\mathbf{E}_1 + \mathbf{E}_2) \cdot d\mathbf{L}$$

and the dot product obeys the associative law:

$$V = -\int_{\infty}^{A} (\mathbf{E}_1 \cdot d\mathbf{L} + \mathbf{E}_2 \cdot d\mathbf{L})$$

Finally, the integral of a sum is the sum of the integrals:

$$V = -\int_{\infty}^{A} \mathbf{E}_1 \cdot d\mathbf{L} - \int_{\infty}^{A} \mathbf{E}_2 \cdot d\mathbf{L}$$

The first integral is the potential due to Q_1 alone, the second is that due to Q_2 alone, and we may therefore remove our question mark above and write

$$V = \frac{Q_1}{4\pi\epsilon R_1} + \frac{Q_2}{4\pi\epsilon R_2}$$

Now that this step has been shown to be correct, we may add as many additional charges as we wish. The potential due to n point charges is

$$V = \frac{Q_1}{4\pi\epsilon R_1} + \frac{Q_2}{4\pi\epsilon R_2} + \cdots + \frac{Q_n}{4\pi\epsilon R_n}$$

$$= \sum_{m=1}^{n} \frac{Q_m}{4\pi\epsilon R_m} \tag{1}$$

and if each point charge is now represented as a small element of a continuous volume charge distribution, $\rho \, \Delta v$, then

$$V = \frac{\rho_1 \, \Delta v_1}{4\pi\epsilon R_1} + \frac{\rho_2 \, \Delta v_2}{4\pi\epsilon R_2} + \cdots + \frac{\rho_n \, \Delta v_n}{4\pi\epsilon R_n}$$

As we allow the number of elements to become infinite, we obtain the integral expression

$$V = \int_{\text{vol}} \frac{\rho \, dv}{4\pi\epsilon R} \tag{2}$$

We have come quite a distance from the potential field of the single point charge, and it might be helpful to examine (2) and refresh ourselves as to the meaning of each term. The potential V is determined with respect to a zero reference potential at infinity and is an exact measure of the work done in bringing a unit charge from infinity to the point, say A, at which we are finding the potential. The volume charge density ρ and differential volume element dv combine to represent a differential amount of charge $\rho \, dv$ located at some point in general different from A. The distance R is that distance from the element of charge $\rho \, dv$ to the point at which the potential is to be determined, A. The integral is a multiple (volume) integral.

If the charge distribution takes the form of a line charge or a surface charge, the integration is along the line or over the surface:

$$V = \int_L \frac{\rho_L \, dL}{4\pi\epsilon R} \tag{3}$$

$$V = \int_s \frac{\rho_s \, dS}{4\pi\epsilon R} \tag{4}$$

These integral expressions for potential in terms of the charge distribution should be compared with similar expressions for the electric field intensity, such as Sec. 2.4, Eq. (3):

$$\mathbf{E} = \int_{\text{vol}} \frac{\rho \, dv}{4\pi\epsilon R^2} \, \mathbf{a}_R$$

The potential again is inverse-distance, and the electric field intensity, inverse-square law. The latter, of course, is also a vector field.

We are prepared now to show the existence of a very important property of the electrostatic field. This property is the simple result of the following already known facts:

1. The potential due to a single point charge is the work done in carrying a unit positive charge from infinity to the point at which we desire the potential, and the work is independent of the path chosen between those two points.

2. The potential field in the presence of a number of point charges is the sum of the individual potential fields arising from each charge.

3. The potential due to a number of point charges or any continuous charge distribution may, therefore, be found by carrying a unit charge from infinity to the point in question along any path we choose.

In other words, the expression for potential (zero reference at infinity),

$$V_A = - \int_\infty^A \mathbf{E} \cdot d\mathbf{L}$$

or potential difference,

$$V_{AB} = V_A - V_B = - \int_B^A \mathbf{E} \cdot d\mathbf{L}$$

is not dependent on the path chosen for the line integral regardless of the source of the **E** field.

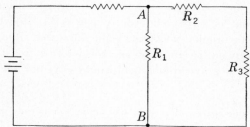

Fig. 4.4. A simple d-c-circuit problem which must be solved by applying $\oint \mathbf{E} \cdot d\mathbf{L} = 0$.

This result is often stated concisely by recognizing that no work is done in carrying the unit charge around any *closed path*, or

$$\oint \mathbf{E} \cdot d\mathbf{L} = 0 \qquad (5)$$

A small circle is placed on the integral sign to indicate the closed nature of the path. This symbol also appeared in the formulation of Gauss's law where a closed *surface* integral was used. Where could a closed *volume* integral be found?

Equation (5) is true for static fields, but we shall see much later that Faraday demonstrated it was incomplete when time-varying magnetic fields were present. One of Maxwell's greatest contributions to electromagnetic theory was in showing that a time-varying electric field produced a magnetic field, and therefore we should expect to find later that (5) is then not correct when either **E** or **H** varies with time.

Restricting our attention to the static case where **E** does not change with time, consider the d-c circuit shown in Fig. 4.4. Some familiarity with circuit concepts is assumed from more elementary studies; we shall not discuss the restrictions under which circuit theory is developed from field theory until a much later time.

Two points, A and B, are marked, and (5) says that no work is involved in carrying a unit charge from A through R_2 and R_3 to B and back to A through R_1, or that the sum of the potential differences around any closed path is zero.

Equation (5) is therefore just a more general form of Kirchhoff's circuital law for voltages, more general in that we can apply it to any region where an electric field exists and we are not restricted to a conventional circuit composed of wires, resistances, and batteries.

Any field that satisfies an equation of the form of (5), i.e., the closed line integral of the field is zero, is said to be a *conservative field*. The name arises from the fact that no work is done (or that energy is *conserved*) around a closed path. The gravitational field is also conservative, for any energy expended in moving (raising) an object against the field is recovered exactly when the object is returned (lowered) to its original location. The fact that jumping up and down tires a body out is caused by an energy return in a different form. A nonconservative gravitational field would solve our energy problems forever.

D4.6. A finite line charge, 10 m long and having a uniformly distributed total charge of $10^{-8}/9$ coulomb, lies on the x axis between $x = 2$ and 12.

(*a*) Find the potential at the origin using Eq. (3).

(*b*) Assume the line charge may be represented by five point charges of $10^{-8}/45$ coulomb each, located at $x = 3, 5, 7, 9, 11$, and find the potential at the origin using Eq. (1).

(*c*) Repeat (*b*), using 10 charges, $10^{-9}/9$ coulomb each, at $x = 2.5, 3.5, 4.5$, . . . , 11.5.

Ans. 5.330 volts.

4.6. Potential Gradient. We now have two methods of determining potential, one directly from the electric field intensity by means of a line integral, and another from the basic charge distribution itself by a volume integral. Neither method is very helpful in determining the fields in most practical problems, however, for, as we shall see later, neither the electric field intensity nor the charge distribution is very often known. Preliminary information is much more apt to consist of a description of two equipotential surfaces, such as the statement that we have two parallel conductors of circular cross section at potentials of 100 and -100 volts. Perhaps we wish to find the capacitance between the conductors, or the charge and current distribution on the conductors from which losses may be calculated.

These quantities may be easily obtained from the potential field, and our immediate goal will be a simple method of finding the electric field intensity from the potential.

We already have the general line-integral relationship between these quantities:

$$V = -\int \mathbf{E} \cdot d\mathbf{L} \tag{1}$$

but this is much easier to use in the reverse direction: given $\mathbf{E}$, find V.

However, (1) may be applied to a very short element of length ΔL along which $\mathbf{E}$ is essentially constant, leading to an incremental potential difference ΔV:

$$\Delta V \doteq -\mathbf{E} \cdot \Delta \mathbf{L} \tag{2}$$

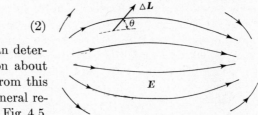

Let us see first if we can determine any new information about the relation of V to $\mathbf{E}$ from this equation. Consider a general region of space, as shown in Fig. 4.5, in which $\mathbf{E}$ and V both change as we move from point to point. Equation (2) tells us to choose an incremental vector element of

FIG. 4.5. A vector incremental element of length ΔL is shown making an angle of θ with an $\mathbf{E}$ field, shown by its streamlines. The sources of the field are not shown.

length $\Delta \mathbf{L} = \Delta L\, \mathbf{a}_L$ and multiply it by the component of $\mathbf{E}$ in the direction of $\mathbf{a}_L$ (one interpretation of the dot product) to obtain the small potential difference between the final and initial points of $\Delta \mathbf{L}$.

If we call the angle between $\Delta \mathbf{L}$ and $\mathbf{E}$, θ, then

$$\Delta V \doteq -E\, \Delta L \cos \theta$$

which becomes an exact expression in terms of the derivative dV/dL:

$$\frac{dV}{dL} = -E \cos \theta$$

In which direction should $\Delta \mathbf{L}$ be placed to obtain a maximum value of ΔV? Remember that $\mathbf{E}$ is a definite value at the point at which we are working and is independent of the direction of $\Delta \mathbf{L}$. The magnitude ΔL is also constant, and our variable is $\mathbf{a}_L$, the unit vector showing the direction of $\Delta \mathbf{L}$. It is obvious that the maximum positive increment of potential, $\Delta V_{\max}$, will occur when $\cos \theta$ is -1, or $\Delta \mathbf{L}$ points in the direction opposite to $\mathbf{E}$. For this condition,

$$\frac{dV}{dL}\bigg|_{\max} = E$$

This little exercise shows us two characteristics of the relationship between **E** and V at any point:

1. The magnitude of the electric field intensity is given by the maximum value of the rate of change of potential with distance.

2. This maximum value is obtained when the direction of the distance increment is opposite to **E** or, in other words, the direction of **E** is opposite to the direction in which the potential is increasing the most rapidly.

Let us illustrate these relationships in terms of potential now. Figure 4.6 is intended to show the information we have been given about some potential field. It does this by showing the equipotential surfaces (shown as lines in the two-dimensional sketch). We desire information about the electric field intensity at point P. Starting at P we lay off a small incremental distance $\Delta\mathbf{L}$ in various directions,

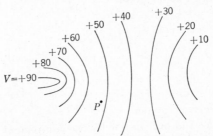

Fig. 4.6. A potential field is shown by its equipotential surfaces.

hunting for that direction in which the potential is changing (increasing) the most rapidly. From the sketch, this direction appears to be to the left. From our second characteristic above, the electric field intensity is, therefore, oppositely directed, or to the right at P. Its magnitude is given by dividing the small increase in potential by the small element of length.

It seems likely that the direction in which the potential is increasing the most rapidly is perpendicular to the equipotentials (in the direction of *increasing* potential), and this is correct, for, if $\Delta\mathbf{L}$ is directed along an equipotential, $\Delta V = 0$ by our definition of an equipotential surface. But then

$$\Delta V = -\mathbf{E} \cdot \Delta\mathbf{L} = 0$$

and since neither **E** nor $\Delta\mathbf{L}$ is zero, **E** must be perpendicular to this $\Delta\mathbf{L}$ or perpendicular to the equipotentials.

Since the potential-field information is more apt to be determined first, let us describe the direction of $\Delta\mathbf{L}$ which leads to a maximum increase in potential mathematically in terms of the potential field rather than the electric field intensity. We do this by letting a_N be a unit vector normal to the equipotential surface and directed toward the higher potentials. The electric field intensity is then expressed in terms of the potential:

$$\mathbf{E} = -\left.\frac{dV}{dL}\right|_{max} a_N \tag{3}$$

which shows that the magnitude of $\mathbf{E}$ is given by the maximum space rate of change of V and the direction of $\mathbf{E}$ is *normal* to the equipotential surface (in the direction of *decreasing* potential).

Since $dV/dL\,|_{max}$ occurs when $\Delta \mathbf{L}$ is in the direction of a_N, we may remind ourselves of this fact by letting

$$\left.\frac{dV}{dL}\right|_{max} = \frac{dV}{dN}$$

and
$$\mathbf{E} = -\frac{dV}{dN} a_N \tag{4}$$

Equation (3) or (4) serves to provide a physical interpretation of the process of finding the electric field intensity from the potential. Both are descriptive of a general procedure, and we do not intend to use them directly to obtain quantitative information. This procedure leading from V to $\mathbf{E}$ is not unique to this pair of quantities, however, but has appeared as the relationship between a scalar and a vector field in hydraulics, thermodynamics, magnetics, and indeed in almost every field to which vector analysis has been applied.

The operation on V by which $-\mathbf{E}$ is obtained is known as the *gradient*, and the gradient of a scalar field T is defined as

$$\text{Gradient of } T = \text{grad } T = \frac{dT}{dN} a_N \tag{5}$$

where a_N is a unit vector directed normally to the equipotential surfaces and that normal is chosen which points in the direction of increasing values of T.

Using this new term, we now may write the relationship between V and $\mathbf{E}$ as

$$\mathbf{E} = -\text{grad } V \tag{6}$$

In order to obtain an expression which is convenient for the evaluation of the gradient, let us return to the electric field and (2). If $\Delta \mathbf{L}$ is taken in the x direction, $\Delta \mathbf{L} = \Delta x\, a_x$, and

$$\Delta V \doteq -(E_x a_x + E_y a_y + E_z a_z) \cdot \Delta x\, a_x = -E_x \Delta x$$

or
$$E_x \doteq -\frac{\Delta V}{\Delta x}$$

This expression is exact only as Δx approaches zero. Since no change is being made in y or z, the quotient of the increments becomes a partial derivative in the limit:

$$\lim_{\Delta x \to 0} \frac{\Delta V}{\Delta x}\bigg|_{y,z \text{ constant}} = \frac{\partial V}{\partial x}$$

and

$$E_x = -\frac{\partial V}{\partial x}$$

In a similar manner, we obtain

$$E_y = -\frac{\partial V}{\partial y}$$

$$E_z = -\frac{\partial V}{\partial z}$$

These results may be combined vectorially to yield

$$\mathbf{E} = -\left(\frac{\partial V}{\partial x}\mathbf{a}_x + \frac{\partial V}{\partial y}\mathbf{a}_y + \frac{\partial V}{\partial z}\mathbf{a}_z\right) \tag{7}$$

and comparison of (6) and (7) provides us with an expression which may be used to evaluate the gradient in cartesian coordinates:

$$\text{grad } V = \frac{\partial V}{\partial x}\mathbf{a}_x + \frac{\partial V}{\partial y}\mathbf{a}_y + \frac{\partial V}{\partial z}\mathbf{a}_z \tag{8}$$

The gradient of a scalar is a vector, and the author's experience has shown that the unit vectors which are often incorrectly added to the divergence expression appear to have been removed from the gradient. Once the physical interpretation of the gradient, expressed by (5), is grasped as showing the maximum space rate of change of a scalar quantity and *the direction in which this maximum occurs*, the vector nature of the gradient should be self-evident.

The vector operator

$$\boldsymbol{\nabla} = \frac{\partial}{\partial x}\mathbf{a}_x + \frac{\partial}{\partial y}\mathbf{a}_y + \frac{\partial}{\partial z}\mathbf{a}_z$$

may be used as an operator on a scalar T, $\boldsymbol{\nabla}T$, producing

$$\boldsymbol{\nabla}T = \frac{\partial T}{\partial x}\mathbf{a}_x + \frac{\partial T}{\partial y}\mathbf{a}_y + \frac{\partial T}{\partial z}\mathbf{a}_z$$

from which we see that

$$\boldsymbol{\nabla}T = \text{grad } T$$

This allows us to use a very compact expression to relate $\mathbf{E}$ and V:

$$\mathbf{E} = -\boldsymbol{\nabla}V \tag{9}$$

The gradient may be expressed in terms of partial derivatives in other coordinate systems through application of its definition (5). These expressions are derived in Appendix A and repeated below for convenience when dealing with problems having cylindrical or spherical symmetry:

$$\mathbf{\nabla} V = \frac{\partial V}{\partial r}\, \mathbf{a}_r + \frac{1}{r}\frac{\partial V}{\partial \phi}\, \mathbf{a}_\phi + \frac{\partial V}{\partial z}\, \mathbf{a}_z \qquad \text{(cylindrical)} \qquad (10)$$

$$= \frac{\partial V}{\partial r}\, \mathbf{a}_r + \frac{1}{r}\frac{\partial V}{\partial \theta}\, \mathbf{a}_\theta + \frac{1}{r \sin \theta}\frac{\partial V}{\partial \phi}\, \mathbf{a}_\phi \qquad \text{(spherical)} \qquad (11)$$

As a simple example of the use of the gradient in finding the electric field intensity from the potential, let us start with the potential field of a point charge in spherical coordinates [Sec. 4.4, Eq. (2)]:

$$V = \frac{Q}{4\pi\epsilon r}$$

The gradient in spherical coordinates is given by (11), and we see that since V is a function only of r, the only component of $\mathbf{E}$ will be the radial component. Taking the partial derivative as indicated by (11), we obtain

$$\mathbf{E} = -\mathbf{\nabla} V = \frac{Q}{4\pi\epsilon r^2}\, \mathbf{a}_r$$

D4.7. A two-dimensional electric field ($E_z = 0$) is investigated at the origin by noting the change (increase) in potential along a 1-mm line segment extending outward from the origin and making an angle α with the x axis. Find the approximate value of $\mathbf{E}$ at the origin if the potential change is:
(a) $\Delta V = 0.05 \cos \alpha$.
(b) $\Delta V = 0.1 \sin (\alpha + 45°)$.
(c) $\Delta V = 0.075[\cos (\alpha + 36.8°) + \sin (\alpha + 53.2°)]$.

Ans. $-(241\mathbf{a}_x + 71\mathbf{a}_y)$.

D4.8. Find the electric field intensity at $(1,0,0)$ which must be associated with the given potential field. Express each answer in cartesian components:
(a) $V = x^2 - y^2$.
(b) $V = \dfrac{\cos \phi}{r}$ (cylindrical coordinates).
(c) $V = \frac{1}{2}(1 + \frac{1}{2}r \sin \theta \sin \phi)$.

Ans. $-\mathbf{a}_x - 0.25\mathbf{a}_y$.

4.7. The Dipole. In this section we are going to consider a new problem from several different aspects in order to show the value of the potential approach, the use of the gradient, and in general to correlate the information and physical concepts presented in this chapter.

An electric dipole, or simply a dipole, is the name given to two point charges of opposite sign, separated by a distance which is small compared to the distance to the point P at which we want to know the electric and potential fields. The dipole is shown in Fig. 4.7. The distant point P is described by the spherical coordinates r, θ, and $\phi = 90°$, in view of the azimuthal symmetry. The positive and negative point charges are separated d m and located at $(0,0,\tfrac{1}{2}d)$ and $(0,0,-\tfrac{1}{2}d)$, respectively.

So much for the geometry. What should we do next? Should we find the total electric field intensity by adding the known fields of each point charge? Would it be easier to find the total potential field first? In either case, having found one, we shall find the other from it before calling the problem solved.

If we choose to find **E** first, we shall have two components to keep track of in spherical coordinates (symmetry shows E_ϕ is zero), and

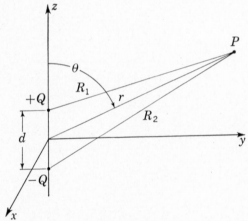

Fig. 4.7. The geometry of the problem of an electric dipole.

then the only way to find V from **E** is by use of the line integral. This last step includes establishing a suitable zero reference for potential, since the line integral gives us only the potential difference between the two points at the ends of the integral path.

On the other hand, the determination of V first, which is a single quantity, not a vector, and has a slightly simpler expression in the case of one point charge, followed by the gradient operation to find **E**, seems like a much easier problem.

Choosing this simpler method, we let the distances from Q and $-Q$ to P be R_1 and R_2, respectively, and write the total potential as

$$V = \frac{Q}{4\pi\epsilon}\left(\frac{1}{R_1} - \frac{1}{R_2}\right) = \frac{Q}{4\pi\epsilon}\frac{R_2 - R_1}{R_1 R_2}$$

For a distant point, $R_1 \doteq R_2$, and the $R_1 R_2$ product in the denominator may be replaced by r^2. The approximation may not be made in the numerator, however, without obtaining the trivial answer that the potential field approaches zero as we go very far away from the dipole. Coming back a little closer to the dipole, we see from Fig. 4.7 that $R_2 - R_1$ may be approximated very easily if R_1 and R_2 are assumed to be parallel:

$$R_2 - R_1 \doteq d \cos \theta$$

The final result is, then,

$$V = \frac{Qd \cos \theta}{4\pi\epsilon r^2} \tag{1}$$

Using the gradient relationship in spherical coordinates,

$$\mathbf{E} = -\boldsymbol{\nabla} V = -\left(\frac{\partial V}{\partial r} \, \mathbf{a}_r + \frac{1}{r} \frac{\partial V}{\partial \theta} \, \mathbf{a}_\theta + \frac{1}{r \sin \theta} \frac{\partial V}{\partial \phi} \, \mathbf{a}_\phi \right)$$

we obtain

$$\mathbf{E} = -\left(-\frac{Qd \cos \theta}{2\pi\epsilon r^3} \, \mathbf{a}_r - \frac{Qd \sin \theta}{4\pi\epsilon r^3} \, \mathbf{a}_\theta \right)$$

$$= \frac{Qd}{4\pi\epsilon r^3} \, (2 \cos \theta \, \mathbf{a}_r + \sin \theta \, \mathbf{a}_\theta) \tag{2}$$

These are the desired distant fields of the dipole, obtained with a very small amount of work. Any student who has several hours to spend may try to work the problem in the reverse direction—the author considers the process too long and detailed to include even for effect.

We shall, however, work the last part of the reverse problem and try to find V by the line integral if we are given $\mathbf{E}$. This field intensity is given above by (2), and the general line integral is

$$V = -\int \mathbf{E} \cdot d\mathbf{L}$$

What path shall we choose? A single integration only will be required if our path lies entirely in the r or θ directions because only these components of $\mathbf{E}$ are present. Of these two choices a radial path appears simpler, for this allows us to set the zero reference condition at infinity by choosing the initial point of the path at infinity. We then have

$$V = -\int_\infty^r \frac{Qd}{4\pi\epsilon r^3} \, 2 \cos \theta \, dr = \frac{Qd \cos \theta}{4\pi\epsilon r^2}$$

which is in agreement with (1).

Turning our attention to the resultant fields, it is interesting to note that the potential field now decreases as the inverse *square* of the distance, and the electric field intensity decreases as the inverse *cube* of the distance from the dipole.   Each field falls off faster than the corresponding field for the point charge, but this is no more than we should expect, for the opposite charges appear to be closer together at greater distances and to act more like a single point charge of zero coulombs.

Symmetrical arrangements of a larger number of point charges produce distant fields decreasing as the inverse of higher and higher powers of r.

D4.9. A dipole has $Q = 10^{-9}/9$, $d = 1$ m.   For points on the z axis ($\theta = 0$), calculate the percentage error in finding the potential by Sec. 4.7, Eq. (1), as compared with the exact result for:
(a) $r = 1$.
(b) $r = 5$.
(c) $r = 10$.

Ans. 26.25 per cent low.

4.8. Energy Density in the Electrostatic Field.   We introduced the potential concept by considering the work done, or energy expended, in moving a point charge around in an electric field, and now we must tie up the loose ends of that discussion by tracing the energy flow one step farther.

Bringing a positive charge from infinity into the field of another positive charge requires work, the work being done by the external source moving the charge.   Let us imagine that the external source carries the charge up to a point near the fixed charge and then holds it there.   Energy must be conserved, and the energy expended in bringing this charge into position now represents potential energy, for if the external source released its hold on the charge it would accelerate away from the fixed charge, acquiring kinetic energy of its own and the capability of doing work.

In order to find the potential energy present in a system of charges, we must find the work done by an external source in positioning the charges.

We may start by visualizing an empty universe.   Bringing a charge Q_1 from infinity to any position requires no work, for there is no field present.[1]   The positioning of Q_2 at a point in the field of Q_1 requires an amount of work given by the product of the charge Q_2 and the potential at that point due to Q_1.   If we represent this potential as

[1] However, somebody in the workshop at infinity had to do an infinite amount of work to create the point charge in the first place!   How much energy is required to bring two half charges into coincidence to make a unit charge?

$V_2{}^1$, where the subscript indicates the location and the superscript the source, then

$$\text{Work to position } Q_2 = Q_2 V_2{}^1$$

Similarly, we may express the work required to position each additional charge in the field of all those already present:

$$\text{Work to position } Q_3 = Q_3 V_3{}^1 + Q_3 V_3{}^2$$
$$\text{Work to position } Q_4 = Q_4 V_4{}^1 + Q_4 V_4{}^2 + Q_4 V_4{}^3$$

and so forth. The total work is obtained by adding each contribution:

Total positioning work = potential energy of field = W_E
$$= Q_2 V_2{}^1 + Q_3 V_3{}^1 + Q_3 V_3{}^2 + Q_4 V_4{}^1 + Q_4 V_4{}^2 + Q_4 V_4{}^3 + \cdots \quad (1)$$

Noting the form of a representative term in the above equation,

$$Q_3 V_3{}^1 = Q_3 \left(\frac{Q_1}{4\pi\epsilon R_{13}} \right) = Q_1 \left(\frac{Q_3}{4\pi\epsilon R_{31}} \right)$$

we see that it might equally well have been written as $Q_1 V_1{}^3$. If each term of the total energy expression is replaced by its equal, we have

$$W_E = Q_1 V_1{}^2 + Q_1 V_1{}^3 + Q_2 V_2{}^3 + Q_1 V_1{}^4 + Q_2 V_2{}^4 + Q_3 V_3{}^4 + \cdots \quad (2)$$

Adding the two energy expressions (1) and (2) gives us a chance to simplify the result a little:

$$2W_E = Q_1(V_1{}^2 + V_1{}^3 + V_1{}^4 + \cdots)$$
$$+ Q_2(V_2{}^1 + V_2{}^3 + V_2{}^4 + \cdots)$$
$$+ Q_3(V_3{}^1 + V_3{}^2 + V_3{}^4 + \cdots)$$
$$+ \cdots$$

because each sum of potentials in parentheses is the combined potential due to all the charges, except for the charge at the point where this combined potential is being found. In other words,

$$V_1{}^2 + V_1{}^3 + V_1{}^4 + \cdots = V_1$$

the potential at the location of Q_1 due to the presence of Q_2, Q_3, ... We therefore have

$$W_E = \tfrac{1}{2}(Q_1 V_1 + Q_2 V_2 + Q_3 V_3 + \cdots) = \tfrac{1}{2} \sum_{m=1}^{m=N} Q_m V_m \quad (3)$$

In order to obtain an expression for the energy stored in a region of continuous charge distribution, each charge is replaced by $\rho \, dv$ and the summation becomes an integral:

$$W_E = \frac{1}{2} \int_{\text{vol}} \rho V \, dv \tag{4}$$

Equations (3) and (4) allow us to find the total potential energy present in a system of point charges or distributed volume charge density. Similar expressions may be easily written in terms of line or surface charge density. Usually, we prefer to use (4) and let it represent all the various types of charge which may have to be considered. Before we undertake any interpretation of this result, we should consider a few lines of more difficult vector analysis and obtain an expression equivalent to (4) but written in terms of the electric field intensity.

Using Maxwell's first equation, replace ρ by its equal $\boldsymbol{\nabla} \cdot \mathbf{D}$ and make use of a vector identity which is true for any scalar function V and any vector function $\mathbf{D}$:

$$\boldsymbol{\nabla} \cdot (V\mathbf{D}) \equiv V(\boldsymbol{\nabla} \cdot \mathbf{D}) + \mathbf{D} \cdot (\boldsymbol{\nabla} V) \tag{5}$$

the proof of which is naturally left as a problem. We then have, successively,

$$W_E = \frac{1}{2} \int_{\text{vol}} \rho V \, dv = \frac{1}{2} \int_{\text{vol}} (\boldsymbol{\nabla} \cdot \mathbf{D}) V \, dv$$
$$= \frac{1}{2} \int_{\text{vol}} [\boldsymbol{\nabla} \cdot (V\mathbf{D}) - \mathbf{D} \cdot (\boldsymbol{\nabla} V)] \, dv$$

Using the divergence theorem from the last chapter, the first volume integral of the last equation is changed into a closed surface integral, where the closed surface surrounds the volume considered. This volume, first appearing in (4), must contain *every* charge, and there can then be no charges outside of the volume. We may therefore consider the volume as *infinite* in extent if we wish. We have

$$W_E = \frac{1}{2} \oint_s (V\mathbf{D}) \cdot d\mathbf{S} - \frac{1}{2} \int_{\text{vol}} \mathbf{D} \cdot (\boldsymbol{\nabla} V) \, dv$$

The surface integral is equal to zero, for over this closed surface surrounding the universe we see that V is approaching zero at least as rapidly as $1/r$ (the charges look like a point charge from there), $\mathbf{D}$ is approaching zero at least as rapidly as $1/r^2$, while the differential element of surface, looking more and more like a portion of a sphere, is increasing only as r^2. Since the integrand is zero, the integral is zero. Substituting $\mathbf{E} = -\boldsymbol{\nabla} V$ in the remaining volume integral, we have our answer:

$$W_E = \tfrac{1}{2} \int_{\text{vol}} \mathbf{D} \cdot \mathbf{E} \, dv = \tfrac{1}{2} \int_{\text{vol}} \epsilon E^2 \, dv \tag{6}$$

Let us use (6) to calculate the energy stored in a section of a coaxial capacitor L m long. From the previous chapter we have

$$\mathbf{E} = \frac{a\rho_s}{\epsilon r} \, \mathbf{a}_r$$

and $\quad W_E = \tfrac{1}{2} \int_0^L \int_a^b \int_0^{2\pi} \epsilon \frac{a^2 \rho_s^2}{\epsilon^2 r^2} \, r \, d\phi \, dr \, dz = \pi L a^2 \rho_s^2 \frac{1}{\epsilon} \ln \frac{b}{a}$

This expression takes on a more familiar form if we recognize the total charge on the inner conductor as $Q = 2\pi a L \rho_s$ and also recognize the potential difference between the conductors as

$$V_{ab} = -\int_b^a \frac{a\rho_s}{\epsilon r} \, dr = \frac{a\rho_s}{\epsilon} \ln \frac{b}{a}$$

which may be substituted above to show that

$$W_E = \tfrac{1}{2} Q V_{ab}$$

which should be familiar as the energy stored in a capacitor.

The question of where the energy is stored in an electric field has not yet been answered. Potential energy can never be pinned down exactly and precisely as to its physical location. One lifts a pencil, and the pencil acquires potential energy. Is the energy stored in the molecules of the pencil, in the gravitational field between the pencil and the earth, or in some obscure place? Is the energy in a capacitor stored in the charges themselves, in the field, or where? No one can offer any proof for his own private opinion, and the matter of deciding may be left to the philosophers.

Electromagnetic field theory makes it easy to believe that the energy of an electric field or a charge distribution is stored in the field itself, for if we take (6), an exact and rigorously correct expression,

$$W_E = \tfrac{1}{2} \int_{\text{vol}} \mathbf{D} \cdot \mathbf{E} \, dv$$

and write it on a differential basis,

$$dW_E = \tfrac{1}{2} \mathbf{D} \cdot \mathbf{E} \, dv$$

or
$$\frac{dW_E}{dv} = \tfrac{1}{2} \mathbf{D} \cdot \mathbf{E}$$

we obtain a quantity, $\frac{1}{2}\mathbf{D} \cdot \mathbf{E}$, which has the dimensions of an energy density, or joules per cubic meter. We know that if we integrate this energy density over the entire field-containing volume, the result is truly the total energy present, but we have no justification for saying that the energy stored in each differential volume element dv is $\frac{1}{2}\mathbf{D} \cdot \mathbf{E} \, dv$. The picture is a convenient one, however, and we shall use it until proved wrong.

SUGGESTED REFERENCES

1. Attwood, S. S.: "Electric and Magnetic Fields," 3d ed., John Wiley & Sons, Inc., New York, 1949. There are a large number of well-drawn field maps of various charge distributions. Vector analysis is not used.
2. Boast, W. B.: (see Suggested References for Chap. 2).
3. Kraus, J. D.: "Electromagnetics," McGraw-Hill Book Company, Inc., New York, 1953. There are numerous illustrative examples which are clearly explained. An extensive bibliography is included.
4. Skilling, H. H.: (see Suggested References for Chap. 3). Gradient is described on pages 19–21.
5. Winch, R. P.: (see Suggested References for Chap. 3).

PROBLEMS

1. Suppose water is flowing with constant velocity in a canal in such a way that a force of 1 newton is exerted on a certain stationary object. Choose a coordinate system in which the origin is at the surface, z is upward, and water flows in the x direction. Find the work done by an external source in moving the object from $(0,0,1)$ to $(1,0,1)$, both points above the surface of the water, along these different paths: (*a*) direct path; (*b*) straight line segments from $(0,0,1)$ to $(0,0,-1)$ to $(1,0,-1)$ to $(1,0,1)$; (*c*) straight line segments from $(0,0,1)$ to $(0,0,2)$ to $(2,0,2)$ to $(2,0,-1)$ to $(1,0,-1)$ to $(1,0,1)$.

2. A unit positive charge is to be moved from $(1,0,0)$ to $(1,1,0)$ along the straight line segment connecting those points. The electric field intensity is $\mathbf{E} = -x^2\mathbf{a}_x + y^2\mathbf{a}_y$. Does volume charge density exist in this region? An approximate value of the energy expended is to be found without integration by dividing the path into two and then five equal sections. Use the value of $\mathbf{E}$ at the mid-point of each section.

3. Find the exact value of the energy expended in Prob. 2 above, and compare results.

4. Given $\mathbf{E} = -x\mathbf{a}_x + y\mathbf{a}_y$, use the line integral to find the work involved in moving a unit charge on a circular arc, the circle centered at the origin, from $x = a$ to $x = y = a/\sqrt{2}$. The vector $\mathbf{E}$ should be expressed in cylindrical coordinates to simplify the integration on a path of this form.

5. In cylindrical coordinates, $\mathbf{E} = 100r \cos \phi \, \mathbf{a}_r - 50r \sin \phi \, \mathbf{a}_\phi + 50z \, \mathbf{a}_z$. Find the potential difference between points $A(r = a, \phi = \alpha, z = 0)$ and $B(r = \phi = z = 0)$.

6. Given $\mathbf{E} = E_0$ (sin πx cos πy $\mathbf{a}_x$ + cos πx sin πy $\mathbf{a}_y$), find the difference in potential between $(\frac{1}{2},a,0)$ and $(b,c,0)$. Why is the answer independent of a?

7. The electric field intensity in spherical coordinates is given as $E_r = Ke^{-r/a}$, where K and a are constants. The expression is valid for all r. Find the potential at any point using a zero reference at infinity.

8. Express the potential field of an infinite line charge (a) with zero reference at $r = 1$; (b) with zero reference at $r = r_0$; (c) with $V = V_0$ at $r = r_0$. (d) Can the zero reference be placed at infinity? Why?

9. Two equal point charges of $Q = 2\pi\epsilon a$ coulombs are located on the z axis at $z = \pm a$. (a) Show that the potential on the z axis, for $|z| < a$, is $1/(1 - z^2/a^2)$. (b) Show that the potential on the x and y axes is $1/\sqrt{1 + x^2/a^2}$ and $1/\sqrt{1 + y^2/a^2}$, respectively. (c) Sketch the variation of potential along the x, y, and z axes, and describe the potential field near the origin.

10. Find the potential at the origin if volume charge density is given as $\rho = \rho_0 e^{-r}/r$. Choose a zero reference at infinity.

11. A filamentary conductor is formed into a ring of radius a and carries a linear charge density which varies with ϕ, $\rho_L = \rho_{L0} \sin(\phi/2)$. Find the potential at the center of the ring.

12. Use Sec. 4.5, Eq. (3), to find the potential at $(a,0,0)$ due to a uniform line charge of ρ_L coulombs/m on the z axis between $z = \pm L$. Show that the potential becomes infinite as $L \to \infty$. Why is this so?

13. Use the result of Prob. 12 for the finite line charge to find the difference in potential between points at $(a,0,0)$ and $(b,0,0)$. Let $L \to \infty$, and explain why this result is not infinite (compare with Prob. 12).

14. Use Sec. 4.5, Eq. (4), to find the potential at $r = 0$, $z = h$, due to a circular sheet of uniform surface charge, ρ_s coulombs/m², on the $z = 0$ plane of radius a. Show that the potential becomes infinite as $a \to \infty$ but that the potential difference between points at $z = h$ and $z = k$ remains finite.

15. The potential at any point in space is given in cylindrical coordinates by $V = (K/r^2) \cos b\phi$, where K and b are constants. (a) Where is the zero reference for potential? (b) Find the vector electric field intensity at any point (r,ϕ,z).

16. A point charge Q is located at the origin. Express the potential in both cartesian and cylindrical coordinates, and use the gradient operation in that coordinate system to find the electric field intensity. The result may be checked by conversion to spherical coordinates.

17. A certain potential field is given in spherical coordinates by $V = V_0(r/a)$ sin θ. Find the associated electric field intensity, electric flux density, and volume charge density.

18. Use the electric field intensity of the dipole [Sec. 4.7, Eq. (2)] to find the difference in potential between points at θ_a and θ_b, each point having the same r and ϕ coordinates. Under what conditions does the answer agree with Sec. 4.7, Eq. (1), for the potential at θ_a?

19. By expansion in cartesian coordinates prove the vector identity $\nabla \cdot (AB) \equiv A\nabla \cdot B + B \cdot \nabla A$.

20. A parallel-plane diode is operated in such a way that there are very few electrons in the region between the cathode and the plate. The plate-cathode potential drop is 200 volts, and the spacing is 4 mm. An electron is located at a point P midway between the plate and cathode. (a) What is the field intensity at P? (b) What is the force on the electron at P? (c) What energy is stored in this field if the plate and cathode areas are each 2 cm² and fringing fields are ignored? (d)

Express the energy expended in transferring the electron from the cathode to the plate as a percentage of the total stored energy.

21. Realizing that Sec. 4.8, Eq. (4), also infers integration over all surface, line, and point charges, show that this equation leads to an expression for the energy stored in a coaxial capacitor of length L which agrees with the value obtained in Sec. 4.8.

22. If $V = 5 \ln (x^2 + y^2)$, find $\mathbf{E}$. Determine the form of the equipotential surfaces and also of the streamlines of $\mathbf{E}$.

23. If the x axis points eastward and the y axis northward, find the gradient of the height h on a certain hillside which rises to the northwest in such a way that the height h increases 1 ft for every 2 ft on the horizontal.

24. Two infinite parallel sheets of charge, equal and opposite, are perpendicular to the x axis. Between the sheets the potential difference is $V_{ab} = 60(x_a - x_b)$. Express the absolute potential at x_a in terms of (a) a zero reference at x_0, (b) a reference level of 100 volts at $x = -1$.

CHAPTER 5

CONDUCTORS IN ELECTROSTATIC FIELDS; CAPACITANCE

In this chapter we intend to look at the application of the laws and methods of the previous chapters to conducting materials, to dielectric materials, and to capacitance problems. These latter are practical problems, and their solutions appear constantly in articles in the technical literature today. Of course, our examples have all been solved many times before; unsolved problems require a more advanced mathematical knowledge although not an appreciably more advanced knowledge of electromagnetic field theory.

We intend to define the terms *conductor* and *capacitance* carefully, but most of us should have an adequate idea of their meaning already. Certainly we have used conductors and capacitors in electric circuits, and perhaps even know the formulas for the computation of several capacitances having a simple geometry. We hope to extend this knowledge and to furnish a more exact understanding of the principles involved.

We shall also look at the physical nature and behavior of the dielectric materials used in capacitors and learn to describe these materials in a practical way.

5.1. Metallic Conductors. Physicists today describe the behavior of the electrons surrounding the positive atomic nucleus in terms of the relative energy possessed by the electron with respect to an arbitrary zero reference level which we shall assign to an electron in the orbital shell nearest the nucleus. Energy must be given to the electron to pull it away from the nucleus, and this energy can be imparted to the electron only in quanta, or certain discrete amounts, corresponding to positions in shells of larger radius which the electron may occupy. A normal atom has an electron occupying every one of the lower-energy shells, starting outward from the nucleus and continuing until the supply of electrons is exhausted.

In a crystalline solid, such as a metal or the diamond, atoms are packed closely together, many more electrons are present, and many more permissible energy levels are available because of the interaction forces between adjacent atoms. As a result, the energies which may be possessed by electrons are grouped into broad ranges, or "bands," each band consisting of very numerous, closely spaced, discrete levels. The normal solid has every level occupied, starting with the lowest and proceeding in order until all the electrons are located. If the electron with the greatest energy lies *within* a permissible band, i.e., not at the upper limit of the band, additional kinetic energy may be given to the electron and its neighbors by an external electric field, resulting in a current flow. The solid is called a metallic conductor.

If, however, the electron with the greatest energy occupies the top level in a band, no additional energy may be given to it, and the material is an insulator. If a very large amount of energy can be transferred to the electron, however, it may be sufficiently excited to jump the gap into the next band where conduction can again occur easily. Here the insulator breaks down.

An intermediate condition occurs when only a small "forbidden region" separates the two bands. Small amounts of thermal energy may raise the energy of the electrons at the top of the filled band and provide the basis for conduction. These materials are insulators which display many of the properties of conductors and are called *semiconductors*.

The flow of electrons constitutes a *current*, the unit of current being the ampere, defined as the rate of movement of charge passing a given reference point (or crossing a given reference plane) of one coulomb per second. Current is thus defined as the motion of positive charges, although conduction in metals takes place through the motion of electrons.

In field theory we are usually interested in events occurring at a point rather than within some large region, and we shall find the concept of current density, measured in amperes per square meter, more useful. Current density is a vector[1] represented by i.

The increment of current ΔI crossing an incremental surface ΔS perpendicular to the current density is

$$\Delta I = i \, \Delta S$$

[1] Current is not a vector, for it is easy to visualize a problem in which a total current of 1 amp in an irregularly shaped conductor (such as a sphere) may have a different direction at each point of a given cross section. Current in an exceedingly fine wire, or a *filamentary current*, may be defined as a vector, but we usually prefer to be consistent and give the direction to the filament, or path, and not to the current.

and in the case where the current density is not perpendicular to the surface,

$$\Delta I = \mathbf{i} \cdot \Delta \mathbf{S}$$

Total current is obtained by integrating:

$$I = \int_s \mathbf{i} \cdot d\mathbf{S} \tag{1}$$

Experimentally, the simple law relating the flow of conduction electrons to the impressed electric field was determined in its basic form many years before the underlying theory sketched above was understood. A high-school mathematics instructor in Cologne, following a carefully planned research program which he hoped would lead to a university professorship, decided electricity was a better research subject than mathematics, and after three years of work published in 1827 a small book containing the principle now known as *Ohm's law*. Professor Ohm, whose work was gradually accepted after early ridicule and led to his professorship six years later, arrived at the well-known conclusion that the potential difference across a conductor and the current through it are linearly related by a quantity he termed the *resistance:*

$$V = IR \tag{2}$$

The potential difference is that between the surface at which the current enters the conductor and that at which it leaves.

Resistance, appropriately measured in *ohms*, is a function of the conducting material and of the physical shape and dimensions of the conductor. For a small uniform sample Ohm showed the resistance was directly proportional to the length and inversely proportional to the cross-sectional area, the constant of proportionality being the *resistivity*, evidently having the dimensions of ohm-meters. The reciprocal of the resistance is termed conductance and carries the manufactured label of *mhos;* the reciprocal of the resistivity is the *conductivity* (mhos per meter). We shall find it more useful to work with the basic quantities, resistivity and conductivity, which do not depend on the dimensions of the sample.

In field theory the use of the conductivity leads to simpler expressions than does the resistivity. The conductivity σ (sigma) is related to the resistance by

$$R = \frac{L}{\sigma S}$$

or
$$\sigma = \frac{L}{RS} \qquad \text{mhos/m}$$

where L and S are the length and cross-sectional area of the small conductor sample, respectively.

We may easily generalize Ohm's law to apply to any small region within a conducting material by considering an incremental volume element having its faces parallel or perpendicular to the direction of current flow (Fig. 5.1). The current I entering the left face and leaving the right face may be written as the product of the current density i and area ΔS:

$$I = i\,\Delta S$$

and the potential difference across the length of the volume element may be expressed as the product of the electric field intensity E and the incremental length ΔL:

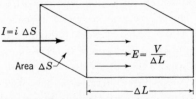

$$V = E\,\Delta L$$

Ohm's law is now

$$E\,\Delta L = i\,\Delta S\,R$$

FIG. 5.1. Current flow in an incremental volume element of length ΔL and cross-sectional area ΔS.   or $i = E\dfrac{\Delta L}{R\,\Delta S}$

and a glance at the conductivity definition shows that

$$i = \sigma E$$

Since the current flow is in the direction of the applied electric field, the vector expression is

$$\mathbf{i} = \sigma\mathbf{E} \tag{3}$$

This is known as the point form of Ohm's law.

This statement relates the current density due to the conduction electrons at a point in any conductor to the electric field intensity at that point. For copper, $\sigma = 5.8 \times 10^7$ mhos/m, and we see that a conduction current density of 5.8×10^7 amp/m^2 occurs wherever the field intensity is 1 volt/m. Fifty-eight amperes, or about 3.6×10^{20} electrons per second, then cross a surface area of 1 mm^2. Somebody watching this surface and counting the electrons would be even busier than this number implies, however, for the electron motion is a steady drift (in the direction *opposite* to the applied field) superimposed on a random motion of electrons from atom to atom as energy is exchanged by collisions between electrons and the remainder of the atom. In other words, electrons are crossing the surface in both directions and the *net* transfer of charge is 3.6×10^{20} electrons per second across each square millimeter in the direction opposite to the applied electric field.

The total charge density ρ at any point is zero, for each moving electron may still be associated with one atom which has lost an electron. We shall see the result of artificially injecting additional charged particles into the interior of a conductor in the next section.

D5.1. Find the current in amperes:

(a) Crossing the plane $z = -2$, if $\mathbf{i} = \dfrac{5e^{-r}\mathbf{a}_z}{\pi r}$ (cylindrical coordinates).

(b) Crossing a square centimeter in the xy plane, centered at the origin, edges parallel to the coordinate axes, if $\mathbf{i} = 3 \times 10^9(z^2\mathbf{a}_x + x^2\mathbf{a}_z)$.

(c) Flowing in a No. 10 AWG copper wire if $E = 0.1$ volt/m.

Ans. 42.9 amp.

D5.2. Find the current density (as a scalar magnitude) at a point within a conducting material where:

(a) $\sigma = 10^7$ mhos/m and the 1-mv equipotential surfaces are 10 cm apart.

(b) The sample is a copper cube, 1 mm on a side, with a potential difference of 1 μv between two opposite faces.

(c) The sample is a cylinder of 1 cm radius having a conductance of 10^3 mhos and a potential difference of 0.01 volt between end planes.

Ans. 1.9×10^5 amp/m^2.

5.2. Continuity of Current.   Although we are supposed to be studying static fields at this time, we must let time vary for a fraction of a microsecond to see what happens when the charge distribution is suddenly unbalanced within a conducting material.   Let us suppose, for the sake of the argument, that there suddenly appear a number of electrons in the interior of a conductor.   The electric fields set up by these electrons are not counteracted by any positive charges, and the electrons therefore begin to accelerate away from each other.   This continues until the electrons reach the surface of the conductor, or until a number of electrons equal to the number injected have reached the surface.

Here the outward progress of the electrons is stopped, for the material surrounding the conductor is an insulator not possessing a convenient conduction band.   No charge may remain within the conductor.   If it did, the resulting electric field would force the charges to the surface.

Hence, the final result within a conductor is zero charge density and a surface charge density on the exterior surface.

In order to obtain any quantitative information about the process of charge flow to the surface, we need the ideas of continuity and conservation of charge.   The principle of conservation of charge states simply that charges can be neither created nor destroyed, although equal amounts of positive and negative charge may be simultaneously obtained by separation or lost by combination.

The continuity equation follows from this principle when we consider any region enclosed by a closed surface. The current through the closed surface is

$$I = \oint_s \mathbf{i} \cdot d\mathbf{S}$$

and this *outward* flow of positive charge must be balanced by a decrease of positive charge (or perhaps an increase of negative charge) within the closed surface. If the charge inside the closed surface is denoted by Q_i, then the decrease is $-dQ_i/dt$ and the principle of conservation of charge requires

$$I = \oint_s \mathbf{i} \cdot d\mathbf{S} = -\frac{dQ_i}{dt} \tag{1}$$

It might be well to answer here an often-asked question, "Isn't there a sign error? I thought $I = dQ/dt$." The presence or absence of the negative sign depends on what current and charge we consider. In circuit theory we usually associate the current flow *into* one terminal of a capacitor with the time rate of increase of charge on that plate. The current of (1) is an *outward-flowing* current. Our definition of current itself as the movement of charge involves counting elements of charge flowing from, say, left to right past some reference point. The increment of charge ΔQ represents an increase in the amount of charge to the right of the reference point, and again the current *into* that right-hand region is given by $+dQ/dt$.

Equation (1) is the integral form of the continuity equation, and the differential, or point, form is obtained by changing the surface integral to a volume integral by the divergence theorem:

$$\oint_s \mathbf{i} \cdot d\mathbf{S} = \int_{\text{vol}} (\boldsymbol{\nabla} \cdot \mathbf{i}) \, dv$$

and representing the enclosed charge Q_i by the volume integral of the charge density:

$$\int_{\text{vol}} (\boldsymbol{\nabla} \cdot \mathbf{i}) \, dv = -\frac{d}{dt} \int_{\text{vol}} \rho \, dv$$

If we agree to keep the surface constant, the derivative becomes a partial derivative and may appear within the integral:

$$\int_{\text{vol}} (\boldsymbol{\nabla} \cdot \mathbf{i}) \, dv = \int_{\text{vol}} -\frac{\partial \rho}{\partial t} \, dv$$

Since the expression is true for any volume, however small, it is true for an incremental volume:

$$(\boldsymbol{\nabla} \cdot \mathbf{i}) \, \Delta v = -\frac{\partial \rho}{\partial t} \, \Delta v$$

from which we have our point form of the continuity equation:

$$\nabla \cdot \mathbf{i} = -\frac{\partial \rho}{\partial t} \tag{2}$$

Remembering the physical interpretation of divergence, this equation indicates that the current, or charge per second, diverging from a small volume per unit volume is equal to the time rate of decrease of charge per unit volume at every point.

Returning now to the charge we placed in the interior of the conductor, we can see how fast it disappears by using Ohm's law:

$$\mathbf{i} = \sigma \mathbf{E}$$

in the continuity equation (2):

$$\nabla \cdot \sigma \mathbf{E} = -\frac{\partial \rho}{\partial t}$$

replacing $\mathbf{E}$ by $\mathbf{D}/\epsilon$:

$$\nabla \cdot \frac{\sigma}{\epsilon} \mathbf{D} = -\frac{\partial \rho}{\partial t}$$

removing the constant σ/ϵ from the divergence expression:

$$\nabla \cdot \mathbf{D} = -\frac{\epsilon}{\sigma} \frac{\partial \rho}{\partial t}$$

and using Maxwell's first equation, $\nabla \cdot \mathbf{D} = \rho$:

$$\rho = -\frac{\epsilon}{\sigma} \frac{\partial \rho}{\partial t}$$

The solution of this equation may be obtained by rearranging and integrating:

$$\rho = \rho_0 e^{-(\sigma/\epsilon)t}$$

where ρ_0 = charge density at $t = 0$. This shows an exponential decay of charge density at every point with a time constant of ϵ/σ. This time constant, often called the *relaxation time*, may be approximated for copper by using the free-space value of ϵ, giving

$$\frac{\epsilon_0}{\sigma} = 8.854 \times \frac{10^{-12}}{5.8 \times 10^7} = 1.5 \times 10^{-19} \text{ sec}$$

In less than $\frac{1}{6}$ $\mu\mu\mu$sec, any charge we place in the interior of a piece of copper has dropped to about 37 per cent of its initial value. This rapid decay is characteristic of good conductors and shows that, except for an extremely short transient period, we may safely consider the charge density is always zero within a good conductor. This is one of the two characteristics of a good conductor.

The other characteristic, stated for static conditions in which no current may flow and following directly from Ohm's law, is that the electric field intensity within a conductor is zero. Physically, we see that if an electric field were present, the conduction electrons would move and produce a current, thus leading to a nonstatic condition.

Summarizing for electrostatics, no charge and no electric field may exist within a conducting material. Charge may, however, appear on the surface as a surface charge density, and our next investigation concerns the fields *external* to the conductor.

D5.3. Use the continuity equation to find the current in amperes crossing (outward) the surface of a small 1-mm³ cube centered at the origin at $t = 0$ if:

(a) $\rho = -10^6 \sin (10^3 t - 10^{-3} x)$.

(b) $\rho = 10^{-6} e^{-(10^{16} t + 10^{-3} x)}$.

(c) $i = -10^{10} \sin (10^3 t - 0.5x) \, \mathbf{a}_x$.

Ans. 16 amp.

D5.4. Determine the relaxation time in seconds for:

(a) Silver, $\sigma = 6.1 \times 10^7$ mhos/m; assume $\epsilon = \epsilon_0$.

(b) Distilled water, $\sigma = 2 \times 10^{-4}$ mho/m, $\epsilon_R = 80$.

(c) Fused quartz, $\sigma = 10^{-17}$ mho/m, $\epsilon_R = 3.8$.

Ans. (Product of three parts) 1.73×10^{-18} sec³.

5.3. Conductor Boundaries. Our object now is to relate the fields external to a conductor to the charge on the surface of the conductor. The problem is a simple one, and we may first talk our way to the solution with little mathematics.

If the external electric field intensity is decomposed into two components, one tangential and one normal to the conductor surface, the tangential component is seen to be zero. If it were not zero, a tangential force would be applied to the elements of the surface charge, resulting in their motion and nonstatic conditions. Since static conditions are assumed, the tangential electric field intensity and electric flux density are zero.

Gauss's law answers our questions concerning the normal component. The electric flux leaving a small increment of surface must be equal to the charge residing on that incremental surface. The flux cannot leave the charge in the tangential direction, for this component is zero, and it cannot penetrate into the conductor, for the total field there is zero. It must then leave the surface normally. Quantitatively, we may say that the electric flux density in coulombs per square meter leaving the surface normally is equal to the surface charge density in coulombs per square meter, or $D_n = \rho_s$.

If we use some of our previously derived results in making a more careful analysis (and incidentally introducing a general method which we must use later), we should set up the conductor-insulator boundary

(Fig. 5.2) showing tangential and normal components of **D** and **E** on the insulator side of the boundary. Both fields are zero in the conductor. The tangential field may be determined by applying Sec. 4.5, Eq. (5):

$$\oint \mathbf{E} \cdot d\mathbf{L} = 0$$

around the small closed path $abcda$. The integral must be broken up into four parts:

$$\int_a^b + \int_b^c + \int_c^d + \int_d^a = 0$$

and if the length from a to b or c to d is Δw and from b to c or d to a is Δh, then

$$E_t \, \Delta w - E_{n_{\text{at } b}} \tfrac{1}{2} \, \Delta h + E_{n_{\text{at } a}} \tfrac{1}{2} \, \Delta h = 0$$

As we allow Δh to approach zero, keeping Δw small but finite, it makes no difference whether or not the normal fields are equal at a

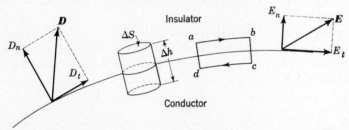

FIG. 5.2. Appropriate closed path and Gaussian surface used to determine boundary conditions at a conductor-insulator boundary.

and b, for Δh causes these terms to become negligibly small. Hence

$$E_t \, \Delta w = 0$$

and therefore

$$E_t = 0$$

The condition on the normal field is found most readily by considering D_n rather than E_n and choosing a small cylinder as the Gaussian surface. Let the height be Δh and the area of the circular top and bottom faces be ΔS. Again we shall let Δh approach zero. Using Gauss's law,

$$\oint_s \mathbf{D} \cdot d\mathbf{S} = Q$$

we integrate over the three distinct surfaces:

$$\int_{\text{top}} + \int_{\text{bottom}} + \int_{\text{sides}} = Q$$

and find the last two are zero.   Then,

$$D_n \, \Delta S = Q = \rho_s \, \Delta S$$

or
$$D_n = \rho_s$$

These are the desired *boundary conditions* for the conductor-insulator boundary in electrostatics:

$$D_t = E_t = 0 \qquad (1)$$
$$D_n = \epsilon E_n = \rho_s \qquad (2)$$

The electric flux leaves the conductor in a direction normal to the surface, and the value of the electric flux density is numerically equal to the surface charge density.   The normal electric field intensity may then be found when the permittivity of the insulating material is specified.

The discussion of the concentric-spheres experiment and of the coaxial capacitor in Chap. 3 both led to results which may be seen to obey (1) and (2).

An immediate and important consequence of a zero tangential electric field intensity is the fact that a conductor surface is an equipotential surface.   The evaluation of the potential between any two points on the surface by the line integral leads to a zero result because the path may be chosen on the surface itself where $\mathbf{E} \cdot d\mathbf{L} = 0$.

D5.5. Determine the magnitude of the surface charge density on a conductor if:

(*a*) $\mathbf{D} = (3\mathbf{a}_x + 4\mathbf{a}_y + 12\mathbf{a}_z) \times 10^{-10}$ at the conductor surface.

(*b*) The potential of the conductor is 100 volts, and $V = -144.2 \ln r$ (cylindrical coordinates).   The conductor is in free space.

(*c*) The conductor is a sphere of 1 cm radius and $\mathbf{D} = 10^{-13} r^{-2} \mathbf{a}_r$ (spherical coordinates).

Ans. 4.85×10^{-9} coulomb/m².

5.4. Capacitance.   Now let us consider two conductors embedded in a homogeneous dielectric (Fig. 5.3).   Conductor M_2 carries a total positive charge of Q coulombs, and M_1 an equal negative charge. There are no other charges present, and the *total* charge of the system is zero.

We now know that the charge is carried on the surface as a surface charge density and also that the electric field is normal to the conductor surface.   Each conductor is, moreover, an equipotential surface, and since M_2 carries the positive charge, the electric flux is directed from M_2 to M_1, and M_2 is at the more positive potential. In other words, work must be done to carry a positive charge from M_1 to M_2.

Let us call the potential difference between M_2 and M_1, V_0. We now may define the *capacitance* of this two-conductor system as the ratio of the magnitudes of the total charge on either conductor to the potential difference between conductors:

$$C = \frac{Q}{V_0} \tag{1}$$

The capacitance is independent of the potential and total charge, for their ratio is constant. If the charge density is increased by a

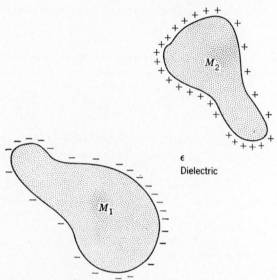

FIG. 5.3. Two oppositely charged conductors M_1 and M_2 surrounded by a uniform dielectric.

factor of N, Gauss's law indicates that the electric flux density or electric field intensity also increases by N, as does the potential difference. The capacitance is a function only of the physical dimensions of the system of conductors and of the permittivity of the homogeneous dielectric.

Capacitance is measured in *farads*, where a farad is defined as one coulomb per volt. Common values of capacitance are apt to be very small fractions of a farad, and consequently more practical units are the microfarad and micromicrofarad.

We can apply the definition of capacitance to a simple two-conductor system in which the conductors are identical, infinite, parallel planes separated d m (Fig. 5.4). Choosing the lower conducting plane at

$z = 0$, the upper at $z = d$, a uniform sheet of surface charge $\pm \rho_s$ on each conductor leads to the uniform field [Sec. 2.6, Eq. (3)]

$$\mathbf{E} = \frac{\rho_s}{\epsilon} \mathbf{a}_z$$

or
$$\mathbf{D} = \rho_s \mathbf{a}_z$$

The charge on the lower plane must then be positive, since $\mathbf{D}$ is directed upward, and the normal value of $\mathbf{D}$,

$$D_n = D_z = \rho_s$$

is equal to the surface charge density there. On the upper plane,

$$D_n = -D_z$$

and the surface charge there is the negative of that on the lower plane.

The potential difference between lower and upper planes is

$$V_0 = -\int_{\text{upper}}^{\text{lower}} \mathbf{E} \cdot d\mathbf{L} = -\int_d^0 \frac{\rho_s}{\epsilon} dz = \frac{\rho_s}{\epsilon} d$$

Since the total charge on either plane is infinite, the capacitance is infinite. A more practical answer is obtained by considering planes,

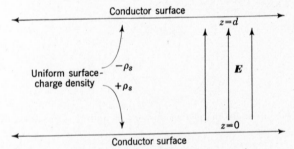

Conductor surface

FIG. 5.4. Problem of the parallel-plate capacitor.

each of area S, whose linear dimensions are much greater than their separation d. The electric field and charge distribution are then almost uniform at all points not adjacent to the edges, and this latter region contributes only a small percentage of the total capacitance, allowing us to write the familiar result:

$$Q = \rho_s S$$

$$V_0 = \frac{\rho_s}{\epsilon} d$$

$$C = \frac{Q}{V_0} = \frac{\epsilon S}{d} \tag{2}$$

More rigorously, we might consider (2) as the capacitance of a portion of the infinite-plane arrangement having a surface area S. Methods of calculating the effect of the unknown and nonuniform distribution near the edges must wait until we are able to solve more complicated potential problems.

As an example, consider a capacitor having a mica dielectric, $\epsilon_R = 6$, a plate area of 10 in.[2], and a separation of 0.01 in. The capacitance is 1,350 $\mu\mu$f. The large plate area is obtained in capacitors of small physical dimensions by stacking smaller plates in 50- or 100-decker sandwiches, or by rolling up foil plates separated by a flexible dielectric.

If more than two conductors are involved, *partial capacitances* between each pair of conductors must be defined. This is interestingly discussed in Maxwell's works.[1]

Finally, the total energy stored in the capacitor is

$$W_E = \frac{1}{2} \int_{\text{vol}} \epsilon E^2 \, dv = \frac{1}{2} \int_0^S \int_0^d \frac{\epsilon \rho_s^2}{\epsilon^2} \, dz \, dS$$
$$= \frac{1}{2} \frac{\rho_s^2}{\epsilon} Sd = \frac{1}{2} \frac{\epsilon S}{d} \frac{\rho_s^2 d^2}{\epsilon^2} = \frac{1}{2} C V_0^2$$

which again is a familiar expression.

D5.6. Find the capacitance of a parallel-plate capacitor if:

(a) $\epsilon_R = 300\pi$, $S = 600$ cm^2, $d = 1$ mm.

(b) $\epsilon_R = \pi$, $V_0 = 150$ volts, $S = 1.8$ m^2, and the energy density is 1.25 joules/m^3.

(c) Using the same dielectric and the same thickness of foil plates as in (a), the metal weight and the dielectric weight are both doubled.

Ans. 1.6 μf.

5.5. Several Capacitance Examples. As our first example, we choose a spherical capacitor, formed by two concentric conducting spherical shells of radius a and b, $b > a$, and use the expression for the electric field obtained previously by Gauss's law,

$$E_r = \frac{Q}{4\pi\epsilon r^2}$$

and the expression for potential difference found from this by the line integral,

$$V_{ab} = \frac{Q}{4\pi\epsilon} \left(\frac{1}{a} - \frac{1}{b} \right)$$

[1] James Clerk Maxwell, "A Treatise on Electricity and Magnetism," 3d ed., Oxford University Press, New York, 1904.

Here Q represents the total charge on the inner sphere, and the capacitance becomes

$$C = \frac{Q}{V_{ab}} = \frac{4\pi\epsilon}{\dfrac{1}{a} - \dfrac{1}{b}} \tag{1}$$

If we allow the outer sphere to become infinitely large, we obtain the capacitance of an isolated spherical conductor:

$$C = 4\pi\epsilon a \tag{2}$$

For a diameter of 1 cm, or a sphere about the size of a marble,

$$C = 0.556 \ \mu\mu f$$

in free space.

Coating this sphere with a different dielectric layer, for which $\epsilon = \epsilon_1$, extending from $r = a$ to $r = r_1$:

$$D_r = \frac{Q}{4\pi r^2}$$

$$E_r = \frac{Q}{4\pi\epsilon_1 r^2} \qquad a < r < r_1$$

$$= \frac{Q}{4\pi\epsilon_0 r^2} \qquad r_1 < r$$

and the potential difference is

$$V_a - V_\infty = -\int_{r_1}^{a} \frac{Q \, dr}{4\pi\epsilon_1 r^2} - \int_{\infty}^{r_1} \frac{Q \, dr}{4\pi\epsilon_0 r^2}$$

$$= \frac{Q}{4\pi} \left[\left(\frac{1}{a} - \frac{1}{r_1} \right) \frac{1}{\epsilon_1} + \frac{1}{r_1} \frac{1}{\epsilon_0} \right]$$

Therefore

$$C = \frac{4\pi}{\left(\dfrac{1}{a} - \dfrac{1}{r_1} \right) \dfrac{1}{\epsilon_1} + \dfrac{1}{r_1} \dfrac{1}{\epsilon_0}}$$

A more difficult, but more practical, example might be obtained by investigating the potential field of two infinite line charges. Following the configuration shown in Fig. 5.5, a positive line charge in the xz plane at $x = a$ and a negative line charge at $x = -a$, we start from the potential of a single line charge, zero reference at r_0:

$$V = \frac{\rho_L}{2\pi\epsilon} \ln \frac{r_0}{r}$$

and write the expression for the combined potential field in terms of the radial distance from the positive and negative line, R_1 and R_2,

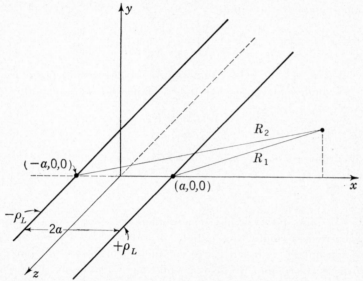

FIG. 5.5. Two parallel infinite line charges carrying opposite charge. The positive line is at $x = a$, $y = 0$, and the negative is at $x = -a$, $y = 0$. A general point in the xy plane is radially distant R_1 and R_2 m from the positive and negative lines, respectively.

respectively:

$$V = \frac{\rho_L}{2\pi\epsilon}\left(\ln\frac{R_{10}}{R_1} - \ln\frac{R_{20}}{R_2}\right) = \frac{\rho_L}{2\pi\epsilon}\ln\frac{R_{10}R_2}{R_{20}R_1}$$

We choose $R_{10} = R_{20}$, thus placing the zero reference at equal distances from each line. This surface is the $x = 0$ plane. Expressing R_1 and R_2 in terms of x and y,

$$V = \frac{\rho_L}{2\pi\epsilon}\ln\sqrt{\frac{(x+a)^2+y^2}{(x-a)^2+y^2}} = \frac{\rho_L}{4\pi\epsilon}\ln\frac{(x+a)^2+y^2}{(x-a)^2+y^2}$$

In order to recognize the equipotential surfaces and adequately understand the problem we are going to solve, some algebraic manipulations are necessary. Choosing an equipotential surface $V = V_1$, let

$$K_1 = e^{4\pi\epsilon V_1/\rho_L}$$

and then

$$K_1 = \frac{(x+a)^2+y^2}{(x-a)^2+y^2}$$

After multiplying and collecting like powers, we obtain

$$x^2 - 2ax\frac{K_1+1}{K_1-1} + y^2 + a^2 = 0$$

We may complete the square:

$$\left(x - a\,\frac{K_1 + 1}{K_1 - 1}\right)^2 + y^2 = \left(\frac{2a\,\sqrt{K_1}}{K_1 - 1}\right)^2$$

showing that the $V = V_1$ equipotential surface is independent of z (or is a cylinder) and intersects the xy plane in a circle of radius b:

$$b = \frac{2a\,\sqrt{K_1}}{K_1 - 1}$$

which is centered at $x = h$, $y = 0$, where

$$h = a\,\frac{K_1 + 1}{K_1 - 1}$$

We can now specify a physical problem by asking for the capacitance between a conducting cylinder of radius b and a plane at a distance h from the cylinder.   The conductors may serve as our equipotential surfaces, and we fit our conditions by choosing the circle of radius b and center at $x = h$, $y = 0$, as given in the two equations above, and solving for a, the location of the equivalent line charge, and K_1, a simplifying parameter which is a function of the potential V_1:

$$a = \sqrt{h^2 - b^2}$$

$$\sqrt{K_1} = e^{2\pi\epsilon V_1/\rho_L} = \frac{h + \sqrt{h^2 - b^2}}{b}$$

Since the plane is at zero potential and the circular cylinder is at potential V_1, the potential difference is V_1, or

$$V_1 = \frac{\rho_L}{2\pi\epsilon}\ln\frac{h + \sqrt{h^2 - b^2}}{b}$$

The magnitude of the charge on the cylinder, on the plane, or on the equivalent line charge is ρ_L coulombs/m by Gauss's law, and the capacitance of a section L m long is therefore

$$C = \frac{\rho_L L}{V_1} = \frac{2\pi\epsilon L}{\ln\left[(h + \sqrt{h^2 - b^2})/b\right]} = \frac{2\pi\epsilon L}{\cosh^{-1}(h/b)} \tag{3}$$

Figure 5.6 shows a cylinder of 5 m radius at a potential of 100 volts separated 13 m from a plane at zero potential.   Numerical values are obtained for the total charge per unit length on the cylinder, the capacitance between cylinder and plane, the position of the 50-volt equipotential surface, and the position of the filamentary line charge which could produce identical equipotential surfaces.

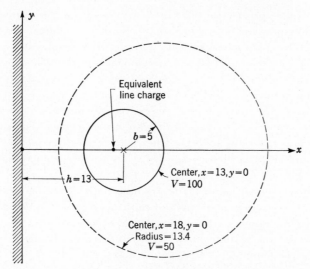

$h=13, b=5, \therefore K_1=25, \therefore \rho_L=3.45 \times 10^{-9}$ coul/m, $\therefore a=12$

If $V_1=50, K_1=5, h=18, b=13.4, \rho_L$ unchanged

$$C=\frac{2\pi\epsilon_0 L}{\ln 5}=34.5\,\mu\mu\text{fd/m}$$

FIG. 5.6. A numerical example determining the capacitance, linear charge density, position of an equivalent line charge, and the characteristics of the mid-equipotential surface for a cylindrical conductor of 5 m radius at a potential of 100 volts parallel to and 13 m from a conducting plane at zero potential.

For a conductor of small radius located far from the plane, we find

$$C \doteq \frac{2\pi\epsilon L}{\ln{(2h/b)}} \tag{4}$$

The capacitance between two circular conductors separated $2h$ m is one-half the capacitance given by (3) or (4). These latter answers are of interest because they allow us to compute the capacitance of a section of two-wire transmission line.

D5.7. Find the capacitance of:

(a) An air-filled spherical capacitor, inner and outer radius of 9 and 10 cm, respectively.

(b) An air-filled coaxial capacitor 1 m long, inner and outer radius of 1 and 2.718 cm.

(c) Two parallel conductors of circular cross section in air, center-to-center spacing of 1 cm, radius 0.5 mm, 1 m long.

Ans. 164.8 $\mu\mu$f.

5.6. The Nature of Dielectric Materials. Starting with Coulomb's law, we have seen the permittivity or dielectric constant appear in every formula for electric field intensity, potential, or stored energy when the expression was given in terms of the charge distribution. This constant also appears in every capacitance formula, and we should feel justified in spending a few minutes learning the physical basis for its different values.

The characteristic which all dielectric materials have in common, whether they are solid, liquid, or gas, and whether or not they are crystalline in nature, is their ability to store electrical energy. This storage takes place by a shift in the relative positions of the internal positive and negative charges against the normal molecular and atomic forces.

This displacement against a restraining force is analogous to lifting a weight or stretching a spring and represents potential energy. The source of the energy is the external field, the motion of the shifting charges resulting perhaps in a transient current through a battery producing the field.

The actual mechanism of the charge displacement differs in the various dielectric materials. Some molecules, termed *polar* molecules, have a permanent displacement existing between the centers of "gravity" of the positive and negative charges, and each pair of charges acts as a dipole. Normally the dipoles are oriented in a random way throughout the interior of the material, and the action of the external field is to align these molecules to some extent in the same direction. A sufficiently strong field may even produce an additional displacement between the positive and negative charges.

A *nonpolar* molecule does not have this dipole arrangement until after a field is applied. The negative and positive charges shift in opposite directions against their mutual attraction and produce a dipole which is aligned with the electric field.

Hence, if we visualize a parallel-plate capacitor with a fixed potential difference across it and, therefore, a fixed electric field intensity between the plates, the additional stored energy must show up as an increase in the permittivity. This is seen from an inspection of the energy stored:

$$W_E = \frac{1}{2} \int_{\text{vol}} \epsilon E^2 \, dv$$

for $\int E^2 \, dv$ is unchanged.

The action of the external field on the dielectric also produces a *bound surface charge* on the surface of the dielectric. This may be explained by reference to Fig. 5.7, in which a polar dielectric is shown. Before the application of the external field, the orientation of the dipoles is random and any region of the dielectric (at least several molecules in dimension) shows a net zero charge. After the field is applied and the dipoles are aligned, certainly not as neatly as the simple sketch shows, any interior region again shows zero charge, but a layer near the surface having a thickness about equal to the dipole length has a net positive or negative charge. The positive charge shows up at the surface nearer the negative capacitor plate, and vice versa. It might seem at first thought that the thickness of the layer should be about *one-half* of the dipole length, but this is untrue because the alignment process shifts charge of one polarity nearer to the surface and charge of the opposite polarity farther from the surface, each shift being about the half-dipole length.

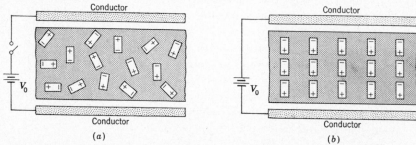

FIG. 5.7. A polar dielectric in a parallel-plate capacitor with a constant potential difference applied. Random orientation is suggested in (a) and alignment in (b).

This surface charge is not the same as the surface charge on a conductor, for the latter consists of the presence or absence of *free* electrons. A portion of a conductor, many molecules in every dimension, which includes a portion of the surface shows a net charge unbalance. An inspection of Fig. 5.7b shows that this is not true in the case of bound surface charge.

The effect of this bound surface charge is, however, just the same as that of free surface charge, and this effect may be used to show again the increase in stored energy resulting from the addition of a dielectric in a capacitor with a constant voltage across it. If the potential difference is V_0, the electric field intensity is V_0/d for a plate separation d. Since we are now considering little dipoles in free space (and are trying to show that the result is *equivalent* to an increase in the permittivity over ϵ_0), the electric flux density is $\epsilon_0 V_0/d$. This value is not changed by the addition of the dielectric, for the effect of the positive and negative charges in the internal region is one of cancellation. This flux must terminate on charge, and we now find that there must be a greater surface charge on the negative capacitor plate than there was without the dielectric because some electric flux arriving at that plate must have originated on the adjacent positive bound surface charge. This increase in surface charge on the conductor plate had to flow through the external source and represents an increase in stored energy.

We simplify the physical conditions by ignoring the bound surface charge (but never the surface charge on the conductor) and by ascribing a permittivity to the dipole assemblage which is greater than that of free space. Strictly, we should always let $\epsilon = \epsilon_0$ and then include the effects of bound surface charge, but this would become very tiresome. In our capacitor above we now say that the addition of the dielectric having a permittivity $\epsilon = \epsilon_R\epsilon_0$ does not change the potential difference or electric field intensity; increases the electric flux density by a factor of ϵ_R; increases the surface charge on the capacitor plates and the stored energy by a factor of ϵ_R; and "there is no such thing as 'bound surface charge'!"

We shall conclude this section with the introduction of several new quantities which become useful in more advanced treatment of dielectric materials. They are more closely allied with the approach of the physicist than that of the engineer, and we shall not have any occasion to refer to them again in this introductory treatment.

We define the polarization $\mathbf{P}$ by

$$\mathbf{D} = \epsilon_0\mathbf{E} + \mathbf{P}$$

or

$$\mathbf{P} = \mathbf{D} - \epsilon_0\mathbf{E}$$

and note that the dimensions of $\mathbf{P}$ must be in coulombs per square meter. Restricting our attention to a homogeneous (the same throughout), isotropic (behaves the same in every direction—which actually rules out crystalline materials), linear (fields directly proportional to strength of source) dielectric material, one which might be termed an *ideal* dielectric, and letting $\mathbf{D} = \epsilon\mathbf{E}$, we have

$$\mathbf{P} = (\epsilon - \epsilon_0)\mathbf{E} = (\epsilon_R - 1)\epsilon_0\mathbf{E}$$

Previously, we found that the insertion of the dielectric into the capacitor without a change in potential led to an increase in the surface charge on the capacitor plates, the new surface charge being greater than the old by the magnitude of the bound charge at the dielectric surface. The ratio of the surface charge with and without the dielectric is the factor by which the energy increased or the dielectric constant increased:

$$\epsilon_R = \frac{|\rho_s| + |\rho_{sb}|}{|\rho_s|} = 1 + \left|\frac{\rho_{sb}}{\rho_s}\right|$$

where ρ_s = surface charge without the dielectric, and ρ_{sb} = bound surface charge on the dielectric. The polarization may then be written:

$$|\mathbf{P}| = \left| \frac{\rho_{sb}}{\rho_s} \right| \epsilon_0|\mathbf{E}| = |\rho_{sb}|$$

since $\qquad\qquad |\rho_s| = \epsilon_0|\mathbf{E}|$

We thus find in this simple case that the polarization is numerically equal to the bound-surface-charge density. In general we cannot expect such a simple uniform field and must expect that the polarization will change in magnitude and direction from point to point within the dielectric, equaling the bound-surface-charge density only at the dielectric surface.

If we assume the small dipoles consist of the two charges $+q$ and $-q$, displaced a distance d_q, and that there are n such dipoles per cubic meter, the bound-surface-charge density may then be found by dividing the total charge found in a layer of thickness d_q and area S by the area S:

$$\rho_{sb} = \frac{nqd_qS}{S} = nqd_q = P$$

The product qd_q is known as the dipole moment, and nqd_q is therefore the total dipole moment per unit volume.

This interpretation of polarization as dipole moment per unit volume is more general than the bound-surface-charge-density picture, for it applies throughout the dielectric material when a nonuniform field is present.

5.7. Boundary Conditions between Perfect Dielectrics. How do we attack a problem in which two different dielectrics are present? This is another example of a *boundary condition* such as we investigated at the surface of a conductor, discovering then that the tangential fields are zero and the normal electric flux density is equal to the surface charge density. Now we take the first step in solving a two-dielectric problem by determining the behavior of the fields at the boundary between the two dielectrics, or at the dielectric interface.

Let us provide ourselves with a general boundary, as shown in Fig. 5.8, containing regions 1 and 2, with .dielectrics having permittivities ϵ_1 and ϵ_2, respectively. We look first at the tangential components by using

$$\oint \mathbf{E} \cdot d\mathbf{L} = 0$$

around the small closed path indicated, obtaining

$$E_{\tan 1}\,\Delta w - E_{\tan 2}\,\Delta w = 0$$

The small contribution to the line integral by the normal component of **E** along the lengths Δh becomes negligible as Δh decreases and the closed path crowds the surface. Immediately, then,

$$E_{\text{tan }1} = E_{\text{tan }2} \tag{1}$$

and we might feel that Kirchhoff's voltage law is still applicable to this case. Certainly we have shown that the potential difference between two points on the boundary separated a distance Δw is the same immediately above or below the boundary.

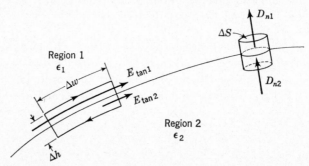

Fig. 5.8. The boundary between perfect dielectrics of permittivity ϵ_1 and ϵ_2. The continuity of D_n is shown by the Gaussian surface, and the continuity of E_{tan} by the line integral about the closed path.

If the tangential electric field intensity is continuous across the boundary, then tangential **D** is discontinuous, for

$$\frac{D_{\text{tan }1}}{\epsilon_1} = E_{\text{tan }1} = E_{\text{tan }2} = \frac{D_{\text{tan }2}}{\epsilon_2}$$

or
$$\frac{D_{\text{tan }1}}{D_{\text{tan }2}} = \frac{\epsilon_1}{\epsilon_2} \tag{2}$$

The boundary conditions on the normal components are found by applying Gauss's law to the small "pillbox" shown in Fig. 5.8. The sides again are very short, and the flux leaving the top and bottom surfaces is

$$D_{n1}\,\Delta S - D_{n2}\,\Delta S = \Delta Q = \rho_s\,\Delta S$$

from which
$$D_{n1} - D_{n2} = \rho_s$$

What is ρ_s? It cannot be the *bound*-surface-charge density, because we agreed to treat the effect of the bound charge as an increase in the permittivity. It is extremely unlikely that any *free* charge is on the interface, for no free charge is available in this perfect dielectric and this charge must then be placed there deliberately, thus unbalancing the total charge in and on this dielectric body. Except for this special case, then, we may assume ρ_s is zero on the interface and

$$D_{n1} = D_{n2} \tag{3}$$

or the normal component of $\mathbf{D}$ is continuous. It follows that

$$\epsilon_1 E_{n1} = \epsilon_2 E_{n2} \tag{4}$$

and normal $\mathbf{E}$ is discontinuous.

These conditions may be combined to show the change in the vectors $\mathbf{D}$ and $\mathbf{E}$ at the surface. Let $\mathbf{D}_1$ (and $\mathbf{E}_1$) make an angle α_1 with the

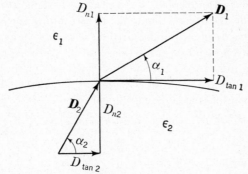

FIG. 5.9. The refraction of $\mathbf{D}$ at a dielectric interface. For the case shown, $\epsilon_1 > \epsilon_2$. $\mathbf{E}_1$ and $\mathbf{E}_2$ are directed along $\mathbf{D}_1$ and $\mathbf{D}_2$. $D_1 > D_2$, and $E_1 < E_2$.

surface (Fig. 5.9). Since the normal components of $\mathbf{D}$ are continuous,

$$D_1 \sin \alpha_1 = D_2 \sin \alpha_2 \tag{5}$$

The ratio of the tangential components is given by (2) as

$$\frac{D_1 \cos \alpha_1}{D_2 \cos \alpha_2} = \frac{\epsilon_1}{\epsilon_2}$$

or

$$\frac{\epsilon_2}{\epsilon_1} D_1 \cos \alpha_1 = D_2 \cos \alpha_2 \tag{6}$$

and division of these two equalities gives

$$\tan \alpha_2 = \frac{\epsilon_1}{\epsilon_2} \tan \alpha_1 \tag{7}$$

In Fig. 5.9 we have assumed that $\epsilon_1 > \epsilon_2$ and therefore $\alpha_2 > \alpha_1$.

The direction of $\mathbf{E}$ on each side of the boundary is identical with the direction of $\mathbf{D}$, because $\mathbf{D} = \epsilon\mathbf{E}$.

The magnitude of **D** in region 2 may be found from (5) and (6):

$$D_2 = D_1 \sqrt{\sin^2 \alpha_1 + \left(\frac{\epsilon_2}{\epsilon_1}\right)^2 \cos^2 \alpha_1} \tag{8}$$

and the magnitude of **E**$_2$ is, then,

$$E_2 = E_1 \sqrt{\cos^2 \alpha_1 + \left(\frac{\epsilon_1}{\epsilon_2}\right)^2 \sin^2 \alpha_1} \tag{9}$$

An inspection of these equations shows that D is larger in the region of larger permittivity (unless $\alpha_1 = \alpha_2 = 90°$, where the magnitude is unchanged) and that E is larger in the region of smaller permittivity (unless $\alpha_1 = \alpha_2 = 0°$, where its magnitude is unchanged).

These boundary conditions, (1) to (4), or the magnitude and direction relations derived from them, (7) to (9), allow us to find quickly the field on one side of a boundary *if we know the field on the other side*. A practical problem most often does not fit these conditions. We usually know a little about the fields on each side of the interface and must use the boundary conditions to determine both fields completely. A simple problem of this type will be considered next.

D5.8. The region $z > 0$ consists of a dielectric for which $\epsilon_{R1} = 4$, and the region $z < 0$ is free space, $\epsilon_{R2} = 1$.
(a) If $\mathbf{D}_1 = 12\mathbf{a}_x - 16\mathbf{a}_y + 12\mathbf{a}_z$, find $|\mathbf{D}_2|$.
(b) If $D_1 = 5$ and $\alpha_1 = 36.8°$, find D_2.
(c) If $D_2 = 5$ and $\alpha_2 = 36.8°$, find D_1.

Ans. 32.4 coulombs/m².

5.8. Multiple Dielectric Capacitors. Suppose we are given a parallel-plate capacitor of area S and spacing d, with the usual assumption that d is small compared to the linear dimensions of the plates.

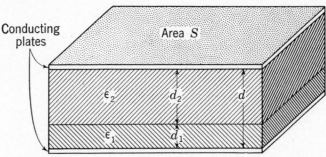

FIG. 5.10. A parallel-plate capacitor containing two dielectrics. The dielectric interface is parallel to the conducting plates.

The capacitance is $\epsilon_1 S/d$, using a dielectric of permittivity ϵ_1. Now let us replace a part of this dielectric by another of permittivity ϵ_2, placing the boundary between the two dielectrics parallel to the plates (Fig. 5.10).

Immediately, some of us may suspect that this combination is effectively two capacitors in series, yielding a total capacitance of

$$C = \frac{1}{\dfrac{1}{C_1} + \dfrac{1}{C_2}}$$

where $C_1 = \epsilon_1 S/d_1$ and $C_2 = \epsilon_2 S/d_2$. This is the correct result, but we can obtain it using less intuition and a more basic approach.

Since our capacitance definition, $C = Q/V$, involves a charge and a voltage, we may assume either and then find the other in terms of it. The capacitance is not a function of either, but only of the dielectrics and the geometry. Suppose we assume a potential difference V_0 between the plates. The electric field intensities in the two regions, E_2 and E_1, are both uniform, and $V_0 = E_1 d_1 + E_2 d_2$. At the dielectric interface E is normal and $D_{n1} = D_{n2}$, or $\epsilon_1 E_1 = \epsilon_2 E_2$. Using our V_0 relation,

$$E_1 = \frac{V_0}{d_1 + (\epsilon_1/\epsilon_2)d_2}$$

and the surface charge therefore has the magnitude

$$\rho_{s1} = D_1 = \epsilon_1 E_1 = \frac{V_0}{d_1/\epsilon_1 + d_2/\epsilon_2}$$

Since $D_1 = D_2$, the magnitude of the surface charge is the same on each plate. The capacitance is, then,

$$C = \frac{Q}{V_0} = \frac{\rho_s S}{V_0} = \frac{1}{d_1/\epsilon_1 S + d_2/\epsilon_2 S} = \frac{1}{1/C_1 + 1/C_2}$$

We might have assumed the charge Q on one plate, leading to a surface charge Q/S and a value of D that is also Q/S. This is true in both regions as $D_{n1} = D_{n2}$ and D is normal. Then $E_1 = D/\epsilon_1 = Q/\epsilon_1 S$, $E_2 = D/\epsilon_2 = Q/\epsilon_2 S$, and the potential difference across each region is $V_1 = E_1 d_1 = Qd_1/\epsilon_1 S$, $V_2 = E_2 d_2 = Qd_2/\epsilon_2 S$. The capacitance is

$$C = \frac{Q}{V} = \frac{Q}{V_1 + V_2} = \frac{1}{\dfrac{d_1}{\epsilon_1 S} + \dfrac{d_2}{\epsilon_2 S}}$$

How would the method of solution or the answer change if there were a third conducting plane along the interface? We would now expect to find surface charge on each side of this conductor, and the magnitudes of these charges should be equal. In other words, we do not think of the electric lines as passing directly from one outer plate to the other, but as terminating on one side of this interior plane and then continuing on the other side. The capacitance is unchanged, provided of course that the added conductor is of negligible thickness. The addition of a thick conducting plate will increase the capacitance if the separation of the outer plates is kept constant, and this is an example of a more general theorem which states that the replacement of any portion of the dielectric by a conducting body will cause an increase in the capacitance.

If the dielectric boundary were placed *normal* to the two conducting plates and the dielectrics occupied areas of S_1 and S_2, then an assumed potential difference V_0 would produce field strengths $E_1 = E_2 = V_0/d$. These are tangential fields at the interface, and they must be equal. Then we may find in succession D_1, D_2, ρ_{s1}, ρ_{s2}, and Q, obtaining a capacitance

$$C = \frac{\epsilon_1 S_1 + \epsilon_2 S_2}{d} = C_1 + C_2$$

as we should expect.

At this time we can do very little with a capacitor in which two dielectrics are used in such a way that the interface is not everywhere normal or parallel to the fields. Certainly we know the boundary conditions at each conductor and at the dielectric interface; however, we do not know the fields to which to apply the boundary conditions. Such a problem must be put aside until our knowledge of field theory has increased and we are willing and able to use more advanced mathematical techniques.

There are many interesting phenomena in the realm of dielectrics. One is the *electret*, which is formed when certain dielectrics are subjected to an electric field in semiliquid state and then allowed to solidify in the field. The dipoles retain their polarization, and the electret becomes analogous to a permanent magnet. Another is electrostriction, the deformation of the dielectric caused by the action of the external field on its bound charges. We have also noted that the energy stored in a dielectric increases as the permittivity increases, provided a constant electric field intensity is maintained within the dielectric, and a little reflection will show that if a dielectric is inserted between two charged plates (no external source of voltage), the stored energy will *decrease*. Where does it go? Evidently work is done by the fields in the capacitor as the dielectric is being placed in position and shows up as a force trying to pull the dielectric out of one's hand and into the capacitor.   A similar force is noted when an iron object is brought near a magnetic field.

D5.9. Find the capacitance of a parallel-plate capacitor, $S = 36\pi$ cm^2, $d = 2$ mm, containing two dielectrics having $\epsilon_{R1} = 5$, $\epsilon_{R2} = 2$, if:

(a) The dielectric interface is midway between the plates.

(b) The dielectric interface is an equipotential surface and one-sixth of the potential difference between the plates occurs in dielectric 1.

(c) The dielectric interface is tangential to the electric flux lines and 40 per cent of the flux is contained in dielectric 2.

$Ans.$ 424 $\mu\mu$f.

SUGGESTED REFERENCES

1. Attwood, S. S.: (see Suggested References for Chap. 4).
2. Boast, W. B.: (see Suggested References for Chap. 2).
3. Kraus, J. D.: (see Suggested References for Chap. 4).
4. Skilling, H. H.: (see Suggested References for Chap. 3).
5. Winch, R. P.: (see Suggested References for Chap. 3).

PROBLEMS

1. In deriving the point form of Ohm's law, $\mathbf{i} = \sigma\mathbf{E}$, from the experimental law, $V = IR$, the equation $V = E\,\Delta L$ was obtained.   Show that this follows from the definition of potential difference, $V_{AB} = -\int_B^A \mathbf{E} \cdot d\mathbf{L}$.

2. The conductivity of carbon is about 3×10^4 mhos/m.   What size and shape sample of carbon has a conductance of 3×10^4 mhos?   What is the conductance if every dimension of the sample is halved?   When we speak of a uniform linear charge density of ρ_L coulombs/m, we think of a charge of ρ_L coulombs on each meter of length.   The conductivity is expressed in mhos per meter; what "meter" is this?

3. The region between two coaxial perfectly conducting cylinders, 2 and 5 mm in radius and 20 cm long, is filled with a relatively poor conductor for which $\sigma = 10^{-2}$ mho/m.   A conduction current density $\mathbf{i} = 0.1\mathbf{a}_r/r$ amp/m^2 is flowing in the poor conductor.   Find the resistance R existing between the coaxial cylinders and the ohmic power dissipated.

4. A material for which $\sigma = 10^{-6}$ mho/m extends from $r = 3$ to $r = 5$ cm. Within this material $\mathbf{E} = 3\mathbf{a}_r/r^2$ volts/m.   Perfectly conducting spherical surfaces are located at $r = 3$ and $r = 5$ cm.   Find the total conductance between the spheres and the energy lost per second in heating the poor conducting material.

5. Take the divergence of the current density of Prob. 3, and explain the significance of the answer.

6. A current density in the z direction does not vary with x or y.   If this current density is i_0 amp/m^2 at $z = z_0$ and $i_0 + \Delta i_0$ amp/m^2 at $z_0 + \Delta z_0$, describe the time rate of change of volume charge density in the region between z_0 and $z_0 + \Delta z_0$.

7. Write the continuity equation for a perfect gas having a density d kg/m³ and velocity $\mathbf{U}$ m/sec, both of which may vary with space and time. Conditions are such that the principle of conservation of mass applies; i.e., the total number of molecules and the mass of a molecule are constant.

8. Given the potential field, $V = 100xy$: (a) Describe the zero-volt equipotential surface. (b) Describe the 100-volt equipotential surface. (c) Determine the $\mathbf{E}$ and $\mathbf{D}$ fields. (d) Assuming free space between the $V = 0$-volt and $V = 100$-volt surfaces and assuming these equipotential surfaces are the surfaces of perfect conductors, find the minimum surface charge density occurring at any point on the 100-volt conductor.

9. Given $V = 100e^{-x} \sin y$, show that the $y = 0$ plane may be a perfectly conducting surface, and find the total charge on the square meter of this surface between $x = 0$ and 1, $z = 0$ and 1. Justify the sign of your answer.

10. A block of perfectly conducting material is solid except for an evacuated hole which is completely within the conductor. (a) There is no charge within this hole. Show that no arrangement of surface charge on the exterior surface of the conductor can produce any field within this hole. (b) Show that the "converse" is not true; i.e., if there is any net charge within the hole, then an exterior surface charge and external field will exist.

11. Show that the capacitance of a coaxial capacitor of inner radius a and outer radius b and L m in length is $2\pi\epsilon L/\ln (b/a)$.

12. A parallel-plate capacitor has a constant potential difference across it. The homogeneous dielectric between the plates is changed to one having a permittivity five times greater than the original value. Determine the factor by which each of the following quantities changes: (a) C, (b) E, (c) D, (d) ρ_s, (e) W_E, (f) Q, (g) V_0.

13. Solve Prob. 12 if the capacitor is originally charged to V_0 volts and the battery is then removed before the dielectric change is made.

14. Dielectric materials have a maximum value of electric field intensity before voltage breakdown, E_m, which differs from one dielectric to another. Using this additional dielectric characteristic, express the capacitance of a parallel-plate capacitor in terms of its dielectric volume Sd, relative dielectric constant ϵ_R, breakdown field strength E_m, and the maximum voltage which may be applied, V_m.

15. In the example of Fig. 5.6: (a) Determine the maximum and minimum values of surface charge density on the cylinder. (b) Find by what factor the capacitance changes if the cylinder is twice as far from the plane ($h = 26$).

16. Show that Sec. 5.5, Eq. (4), follows from Sec. 5.5, Eq. (3). Show also that the capacitance between two wires is half the capacitance of either wire to a central ground plane.

17. Find the capacitance between two small conducting spheres of radius a, if they are separated by a distance very much greater than a, by considering the capacitance of each to a centrally located infinite-plane conductor.

18. Find the capacitance of a spherical capacitor, inner radius a and outer radius b, if the relative permittivity of the dielectric varies with the radius, $\epsilon_R = b^2/r^2$.

19. A certain dielectric material contains 2×10^{20} polar molecules per cubic meter. Assume each molecule may be represented as a dipole consisting of a positive and negative electronic charge separated 10^{-8} m and that the alignment is uniform and parallel to an applied electric field of 10^4 volts/m. Find the relative dielectric constant of this material.

20. A slab of dielectric material, $\epsilon_R = 2$, lies between $x = 0$ and $x = d$. Call this region 2.   Region 1, $x < 0$, and region 3, $x > d$, are free-space.   If the field strength in region 2 is $\mathbf{E}_2 = 3\mathbf{a}_x + 6\mathbf{a}_y + 4\mathbf{a}_z$: (a) Find the angle $\mathbf{E}_2$ makes with each interface, α_2.   (b) Find $\mathbf{E}_1$ and $\mathbf{E}_3$.   (c) Find the angles $\mathbf{E}_1$ and $\mathbf{E}_3$ make with the appropriate interface, α_1 and α_3.   (d) Make a sketch of the slab and show the streamlines in the three regions.   The sketch should be made in such a way that $\mathbf{E}_1$, $\mathbf{E}_2$, and $\mathbf{E}_3$ all lie in the plane of the paper.

21. Plot a curve of α_2 versus α_1 for an interface between air ($\epsilon_{R1} = 1$) and polystyrene ($\epsilon_{R2} = 2.53$).   Also show the ratio D_2/D_1 as a function of α_1, and explain the physical significance of the values at $\alpha_1 = 0°$ and $90°$.

22. Two conducting plates, each 3 by 6 cm, and three slabs of dielectric, each 1 by 3 by 6 cm and having relative dielectric constants of π, 2π, and 3π, are assembled into a capacitor with $d = 3$ cm.   Compute the two values of capacitance obtained by the two possible methods of assembling the capacitor.

23. A parallel-plate, a coaxial, and a spherical capacitor are constructed, each using two dielectric layers for which $\epsilon_R = 3$ and 6.   In each capacitor the dielectric thicknesses are so arranged that the potential difference across each layer is the same.   Find the capacitance in each case if (a) the parallel-plate capacitor has a plate separation of 1.2 cm and a plate area of 24π cm^2; (b) the coaxial capacitor has an inner radius of 1 mm, an outer radius of 8 mm, and a length of 50 cm; (c) the spherical capacitor has an inner radius of 6 cm and an outer radius of 15 cm.

24. A certain potential field is given as $V = 200(x^2 - y^2)$.   The statement is made that the point (2,1) is on the surface of a conductor.   (a) Can this be true? (b) If it is true, find the surface charge density at the point; if it cannot be true, then find the energy density at the point.

25. Find the capacitance of a coaxial capacitor, inner radius a and outer radius b, where $b/a = 2.718^2$, and length 1 m, if the sector from $\phi = 0°$ to $\phi = 90°$ contains a dielectric for which $\epsilon_R = 4$ and the remaining region is evacuated.

CHAPTER 6

EXPERIMENTAL MAPPING METHODS

We have seen in the last few chapters that the potential is the gateway to any information we desire about the electrostatic field at a point. The path is straight, and travel on it is easy in whichever direction we wish to go. The electric field intensity may be found from the potential by the gradient operation, which is a differentiation, and the electric field intensity may then be used to find the electric flux density by multiplying by the permittivity. The divergence of the flux density, again a differentiation, gives the volume charge density, and the surface charge density on any conductors in the field is quickly found by evaluating the flux density at the surface. Our boundary conditions show that it must be normal to such a surface.

Integration is still required if we need more information than the value of a field or charge density *at a point*. Finding the total charge on a conductor or the total energy stored in an electrostatic field are examples of such problems, each requiring an integration. These integrations cannot in general be avoided, no matter how extensive our knowledge of field theory becomes, and indeed we should find that the greater this knowledge becomes, the more integrals we should wish to evaluate. Potential, then, can do one important thing for us, and that is to furnish us quickly and easily with the quantity we must integrate.

Our goal, then, is to find the potential first. This cannot be done in terms of a charge configuration in a practical problem, because no one is kind enough to tell us exactly how the charges are distributed. Instead we are usually given several conducting objects or conducting boundaries and the potential difference between them. Unless we happen to recognize the boundary surfaces as belonging to a simple problem we have already disposed of, we can do little now and must wait until Laplace's equation is discussed in the following chapter.

Although we thus postpone the mathematical solution to this important type of practical problem, we may acquaint ourselves with several experimental methods of finding the potential field. These methods may involve special equipment such as an electrolytic trough, a fluid-flow device, resistance paper and the associated bridge equipment, or rubber sheets. They may involve only pencil, paper, and a good supply of erasers. The exact potential can never be determined, but sufficient accuracy for engineering purposes can usually be attained. One other method, called the *iteration*, or *relaxation*, method, does allow us to achieve any desired accuracy for the potential, but the labor required increases very rapidly as the desired accuracy increases.

We should note carefully for the experimental methods to be described below that the procedures are most often based on an analogy with the electrostatic field rather than directly on measurements on this field itself.

Finally, we cannot introduce this subject of experimental methods of finding potential fields without emphasizing the fact that many practical problems possess such a complicated geometry that no exact method of finding that field is possible or feasible and experimental techniques are the only ones which can be used.

6.1. Curvilinear Squares. Our first method is a graphical method, requiring only pencil and paper. Besides being economical, it is also capable of yielding good accuracy if used skillfully and patiently. Fair accuracy (5 to 10 per cent on a capacitance determination) may be obtained by a beginner who does no more than follow the few rules and hints of the art.

The method to be described is applicable only to fields in which no variation exists in the direction normal to the plane of our sketch. The procedure is based on several facts we have already demonstrated: (1) a conductor boundary is an equipotential surface; (2) the electric field intensity and electric flux density are both perpendicular to the equipotential surfaces; (3) **E** and **D** are therefore perpendicular to the conductor boundaries and possess zero tangential values; (4) the lines of electric flux or streamlines begin and terminate on charge and, hence, in a charge-free, homogeneous dielectric, begin and terminate only on the conductor boundaries.

Let us consider the implications of these statements by drawing the streamlines on a sketch which already shows the equipotential surfaces. In Fig. 6.1a two conductor boundaries are shown and equipotentials have been drawn with a constant potential difference between lines. We should remember that these lines are only the cross sections of the equipotential surfaces, which are cylinders (although not circular), since no variation in the direction normal to the surface of the paper is permitted. We choose to begin, arbitrarily, a streamline or flux line at A on the surface of the more positive conductor. It leaves the surface normally and must cross at right angles the undrawn but very real equipotential surfaces between the conductor and the first surface shown. The line is continued to the other conductor, obeying the single rule that the intersection with each equipotential must be square. Turning the paper from side to side as the line progresses enables one to maintain perpendicularity more accurately. The line has been completed in Fig. 6.1b.

In a similar manner we may start at B and sketch another streamline ending at B'. Before continuing, let us interpret the meaning of this pair of streamlines. The streamline by definition is everywhere tangent to the electric field intensity or to the electric flux density.

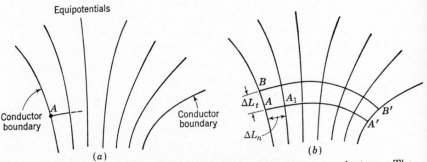

FIG. 6.1. (a) Sketch of the equipotential surfaces between two conductors. The increment of potential between each two adjacent equipotentials is the same. (b) One flux line has been drawn from A to A', and a second from B to B'.

Since it is tangent to the electric flux density, the flux density is tangent to the streamline and no electric flux may cross any streamline. In other words, if there is a charge of 5 μcoulombs on the surface between A and B (and extending 1 m into the paper), then 5 μcoulombs of flux begins in this region and all must terminate between A' and B'. Such a pair of lines is sometimes called a *flux tube* because it physically seems to carry flux from one point to another without losing any.

We now wish to construct a third streamline, and both the mathematical and visual interpretations we may make from the sketch will be greatly simplified if we draw this line starting from some point C chosen so that the same amount of flux is carried in the tube BC as is contained in AB. How do we choose the position of C?

The electric field intensity at the midpoint of the line joining A to B may be found approximately by assuming a value for the flux in the tube AB, say $\Delta\Psi$, which allows us to express the electric flux density by $\Delta\Psi/\Delta L_t$, where ΔL_t is the length of line joining A to B. The magnitude of E is then

$$E = \frac{1}{\epsilon} \frac{\Delta \Psi}{\Delta L_t}$$

However, we may also find the magnitude of the electric field intensity by dividing the potential difference between points A and A_1, lying on two adjacent equipotential surfaces, by the distance from A to A_1. If this distance is designated ΔL_n and an increment of potential between equipotentials of ΔV is assumed, then

$$E = \frac{\Delta V}{\Delta L_n}$$

This value applies most accurately to the point at the middle of the line segment from A to A_1, while the previous value was most accurate at the mid-point of the line segment from A to B. If, however, the equipotentials are close together (ΔV small) and the two streamlines are close together ($\Delta \Psi$ small), the two values found for the electric field intensity must be approximately equal:

$$\frac{1}{\epsilon} \frac{\Delta \Psi}{\Delta L_t} = \frac{\Delta V}{\Delta L_n} \tag{1}$$

Throughout our sketch we have assumed a homogeneous medium (ϵ constant), a constant increment of potential between equipotentials (ΔV constant), and a constant amount of flux per tube ($\Delta \Psi$ constant). In order to satisfy all these conditions, (1) shows that

$$\frac{\Delta L_t}{\Delta L_n} = \text{constant} = \frac{1}{\epsilon} \frac{\Delta \Psi}{\Delta V} \tag{2}$$

A similar argument might be made at any point in our sketch, and we are therefore led to the conclusion that a constant ratio must be maintained between the distance between streamlines, as measured along an equipotential, and the distance between equipotentials, as measured along a streamline. It is this *ratio* which must have the same value at every point, not the individual lengths. Each length must decrease in regions of greater field strength, because ΔV is constant.

The simplest ratio which we can use is unity, and the streamline from B to B' in Fig. 6.1b was started at a point for which $\Delta L_t = \Delta L_n$. Since the ratio of these distances is kept at unity, the streamlines and equipotentials divide the field-containing region into curvilinear squares, a term implying a geometric figure which differs from a true square in having slightly curved and slightly unequal sides, but a figure which approaches a square as its dimensions decrease. The incremental surface elements in our three coordinate systems should be recognized as curvilinear squares.

We may now rapidly sketch in the remainder of the streamlines by keeping each small box as square as possible. The complete sketch is shown in Fig. 6.2.

The only difference between this example and the production of a field map using the method of curvilinear squares is that the intermediate potential surfaces are not given. The streamlines and equipotentials must both be drawn on an original sketch which shows only the conductor boundaries. Only one solution is possible, as we shall prove later by the uniqueness theorem for Laplace's equation, and the rules we have outlined above are sufficient. One streamline is begun, an equipotential line is roughed in, another streamline is added forming a curvilinear square, and the map is gradually extended throughout the desired region. Since none of us can ever expect to be perfect at this, we shall soon find that we can no longer make squares and also maintain right-angle corners. An error is accumulating in the drawing, and our present troubles should indicate the nature of the correction to make on some of the earlier work. It is usually best to start again on a fresh drawing so that the old one is available as a guide.

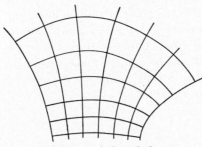

Fig. 6.2. The remainder of the stream-lines have been added to Fig. 6.1b by beginning each new line normally to the conductor and maintaining curvilinear squares throughout the sketch.

The construction of a useful field map is an art; the science merely furnishes the rules. Proficiency in any art requires practice. A good problem for beginners is the coaxial cable or coaxial capacitor, since the equipotentials are circles, and the next sketch attempted should be two parallel circular conductors, where the equipotentials are again circles but with a varying center. Each of these is given as a problem at the end of the chapter, and the accuracy of the sketch may be checked by a capacitance calculation as outlined below.

Figure 6.3 shows a completed map for a cable containing a square inner conductor surrounded by a circular conductor. The capacitance is found from $C = Q/V_0$ by replacing Q by $N_Q \, \Delta Q = N_Q \, \Delta\Psi$, where N_Q is the number of flux tubes joining the two conductors, and letting $V_0 = N_V \, \Delta V$, where N_V is the number of potential increments between conductors:

$$C = \frac{N_Q \, \Delta Q}{N_V \, \Delta V}$$

and then using (2):

$$C = \frac{N_Q}{N_V} \epsilon \frac{\Delta L_t}{\Delta L_n} = \epsilon \frac{N_Q}{N_V} \qquad \text{per meter into paper} \qquad (3)$$

since $\Delta L_t/\Delta L_n = 1$. The determination of the capacitance from a flux plot merely consists of counting squares in two directions, between

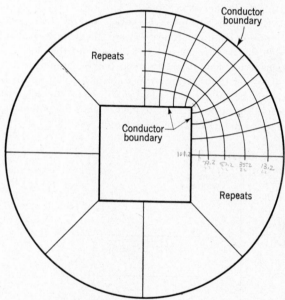

Fig. 6.3. Example of curvilinear-square field map. Side of square is two-thirds radius of circle. $N_Q = 32$, $N_V = 4.6$, and therefore $C = \epsilon_o N_Q/N_V = 61.5 \ \mu\mu\text{f/m}$.

conductors and around either conductor. From Fig. 6.3, we obtain

$$C = \epsilon_0 \frac{32}{4.6} = 61.5 \ \mu\mu\text{f/m}$$

Ramo and Whinnery have an excellent discussion with examples of the construction of field maps by curvilinear squares. They offer the following suggestions:[1]

(1) Plan on making a number of rough sketches, taking only a minute or so apiece, before starting any plot to be made with care.

[1] By permission from S. Ramo and J. R. Whinnery, "Fields and Waves in Modern Radio," 2d ed., pp. 123–124, John Wiley & Sons, Inc., New York, 1953.

(2) Divide the known potential difference between electrodes into an equal number of divisions, say four or eight to begin with.

(3) Begin the sketch of equipotentials in the region where it approaches a uniform field. Extend the equipotentials according to your best guess throughout the plot. Note that they should tend to hug acute angles of the conducting boundary, and be spread out in the vicinity of obtuse angles of the boundary.

(4) Draw in the orthogonal set of field lines. As these are started, they should form curvilinear squares, but, as they are extended, the condition of orthogonality should be kept paramount, even though this will result in some rectangles with ratios other than unity.

(5) Look at the regions with poor side ratios, and try to see what was wrong with the first guess of equipotentials. Correct them and repeat the procedure until reasonable curvilinear squares exist throughout the plot.

(6) In regions of low field intensity, there will be large figures, often of five or six sides. In order to judge the correctness of the plot in this region, these large units should be subdivided. The subdivisions should be started back a way, and, each time a flux tube is divided in half, the potential divisions in this region must be divided by the same factor.

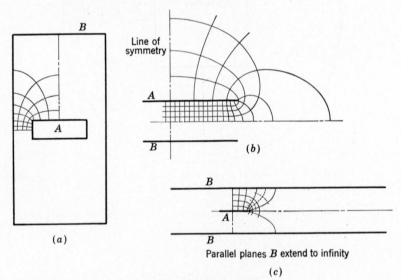

Parallel planes B extend to infinity

(c)

FIG. 6.4. See Prob. D6.1.

D6.1. Find the capacitance between conductors A and B from the rough curvilinear-square maps given in Fig. 6.4a–c.

Ans. 144 $\mu\mu$f/m (approx.).

6.2. Physical Models. The analogy between the electric field and the gravitational field has been mentioned several times previously and may be used to permit the construction of physical models which are capable of yielding solutions to electrostatic problems of complicated geometry. The basis of the analogy is simply this: In the electrostatic field the potential difference between two points is the difference in potential energy of unit positive charges at these points, and in a uniform gravitational field the difference in potential energy of point masses at two points is proportional to their difference in height. In other words,

$$\Delta W_E = Q \, \Delta V \qquad \text{(electrostatic)}$$
$$\Delta W_G = Mg \, \Delta h \qquad \text{(gravitational)}$$

where M = point mass, and g = acceleration due to gravity, essentially constant at the surface of the earth. For the same energy difference, then,

$$\Delta V = \frac{Mg}{Q} \, \Delta h = k \, \Delta h$$

where k = constant of proportionality. This shows the direct analogy between difference in potential and difference in elevation.

This analogy allows us to construct a physical model of a known potential field by fabricating a surface, perhaps from wood, whose elevation h above any point (x,y), located in the zero-elevation, zero-potential plane, is proportional to the potential at that point. Note that fields in which the potential varies in three dimensions,

$$V = V(x,y,z)$$

cannot be handled because we have no method of showing the elevation of a "three-dimensional" point.

The field of an infinite line charge,

$$V = \frac{\rho_L}{2\pi\epsilon} \ln \frac{r_B}{r}$$

is shown on such a model in Fig. 6.5,

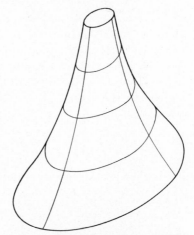

Fig. 6.5. Model of the potential field of an infinite line charge. Difference in potential is proportional to difference in elevation. Contour lines indicate equal potential increments.

which provides an accurate picture of the variation of potential with radius between r_A and r_B. The potential and elevation at r_B are conveniently set equal to zero.

Such a model may be constructed for any two-dimensional potential field and enables us to visualize the field a little better. Besides furnishing us with this three-dimensional picture, the model is capable of providing information on the paths taken by charged particles in the field. From the definition of the gradient, it is apparent that the gradient of the elevation h at any point is a vector whose magnitude is the maximum slope of the surface at that point and whose direction is "upward," or toward increasing elevation. The "point" in question is specified by its x and y coordinate values and lies in the xy plane; the slope is measured on the model surface. Since the potential is proportional to the elevation, the gradient of the potential is proportional to the gradient of the elevation, or the electric field intensity is proportional to the negative gradient of the elevation at any point.

A positively charged particle in this field experiences a force:

$$\mathbf{F}_E = Q\mathbf{E}$$

whereas a small point mass M, such as a steel marble, placed on the surface of the physical model, experiences an accelerating force due to gravity:

$$\mathbf{F}_G = Mg(\sin\theta)\mathbf{a}_F$$

where g = acceleration due to gravity, and θ = angle of inclination, measured with respect to a horizontal surface. The sine of this angle may be expressed in other terms by noting that $\sin\theta \doteq \tan\theta$ for small angles (less than about 18° for less than 5 per cent error), and $\tan\theta$ is given by the magnitude of the gradient of the elevation. For small slopes, then,

$$F_G = Mg|\nabla h|$$
$$\mathbf{F}_G = -Mg\,\nabla h$$

and in view of the elevation-potential analogy,

$$\frac{\mathbf{F}_E}{\mathbf{F}_G} = \frac{-Q\,\nabla V}{-Mg\,\nabla h} = \frac{-Q(Mg/Q)\,\nabla h}{-Mg\,\nabla h} = 1$$

or

$$\mathbf{F}_E = \mathbf{F}_G$$

As long as the model has only gentle slopes, the gravitational and electrical forces are analogous. This allows us to obtain the trajectories of charged particles by releasing frictionless marbles at various points on the surface of the model.

The construction of the models themselves is enormously simplified, both physically and theoretically, by the use of rubber sheets. The sheet is placed under moderate tension and becomes closely the *elastic membrane* of applied mechanics. It can be shown[1] that the vertical displacement h of the membrane satisfies the second-order partial differential equation:

$$\frac{\partial^2 h}{\partial x^2} + \frac{\partial^2 h}{\partial y^2} = 0$$

if the surface slope is small. We shall see in the next chapter that every potential field in a charge-free region also satisfies this equation, Laplace's equation in two dimensions:

$$\frac{\partial^2 V}{\partial x^2} + \frac{\partial^2 V}{\partial y^2} = 0$$

We shall also prove a uniqueness theorem which assures us that if a potential solution in some specified region satisfies the above equation and also gives the correct potential on the boundaries of this region,

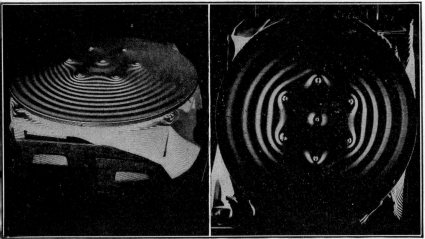

FIG. 6.6. Rubber-sheet model of the electrostatic field of a cylindrical triode with six grid rods and no space charge. (*From W. E. Rogers, "Introduction to Electric Fields," McGraw-Hill Book Company, Inc., New York, 1954. By permission of the publishers.*)

then this solution is the only solution. Hence we need only force the elevation of the sheet to corresponding prescribed potential values on the boundaries, and the elevation at all other points is proportional to the potential.

For instance, the infinite-line-charge field may be displayed by recognizing the circular symmetry and fastening the rubber sheet at zero

[1] See, for instance, K. R. Spangenberg, "Vacuum Tubes," pp. 75–76, McGraw-Hill Book Company, Inc., New York, 1948.

elevation around a circle by the use of a large clamping ring of radius r_B. Since the potential is constant at r_A, we raise that portion of the sheet to a greater elevation by pushing a cylinder of radius r_A up against the rubber sheet. The analogy breaks down for large surface slopes, and only a slight displacement at r_A is possible. The surface then represents the potential field, and marbles may be used to determine particle trajectories, in this case obviously radial lines as viewed from above.

The photograph of Fig. 6.6 shows the surface corresponding to the potential field inside a cylindrical triode vacuum tube (operating without space charge) possessing six grid rods rather than a mesh grid. The theoretical solution of this problem can only be approximated. The map is illuminated by a projector, using a ruled grating in order to show the equipotential contours.

6.3. Current Analogies. Several experimental methods depend upon an analogy between current density in conducting media and electric flux density in dielectric media. The analogy is easily demonstrated, for in a conducting medium Ohm's law and the gradient relationship are, for direct currents only,

$$\mathbf{i} = \sigma \mathbf{E}_\sigma$$
$$\mathbf{E}_\sigma = -\nabla V_\sigma$$

whereas in a homogeneous dielectric,

$$\mathbf{D} = \epsilon \mathbf{E}_\epsilon$$
$$\mathbf{E}_\epsilon = -\nabla V_\epsilon$$

The subscripts serve to identify the analogous problems. It is evident that the potentials V_σ and V_ϵ, the electric field intensities $\mathbf{E}_\sigma$ and $\mathbf{E}_\epsilon$, the conductivity and permittivity σ and ϵ, and the current density and electric flux density $\mathbf{i}$ and $\mathbf{D}$ are analogous in pairs. Referring to a curvilinear square map we should interpret flux tubes as current tubes, each tube now carrying an incremental current which cannot leave the tube.

Finally, we must look at the boundaries. What is analogous to a conducting boundary which terminates electric flux normally and is an equipotential surface? The analogy furnishes the answer, and we see that the surface must terminate current density normally and again be an equipotential surface. This is the surface of a *perfect* conductor, or at least one whose conductivity is many times that of the conducting medium.

Therefore, if we wished to find the field within a coaxial capacitor, which as we have seen several times before is a portion of the field of an infinite line charge, we might take two copper cylinders and fill the region between them with, for convenience, an electrolytic solution. Upon applying a potential difference between the cylinders, a probe may be used to establish the potential at any intermediate point, or to find all those points having the same potential. This is the essence of the electrolytic trough, or tank. The greatest advantage of this method lies in the fact that it is not limited to two-dimensional problems. Practical suggestions for the construction and use of the tank are given in many places; Weber is good.[1]

The determination of capacitance from electrolytic-trough measurements is particularly easy. The total current leaving the more positive conductor is

$$I = \oint_s \mathbf{i} \cdot d\mathbf{S} = \sigma \oint_s \mathbf{E} \cdot d\mathbf{S}$$

where the closed-surface integral is taken over the entire conductor surface. The potential difference is given by the negative line integral from the less to the more positive plate:

$$V_0 = -\int \mathbf{E} \cdot d\mathbf{L}$$

and the total resistance is therefore

$$R = \frac{V_0}{I} = \frac{-\int \mathbf{E} \cdot d\mathbf{L}}{\sigma \oint_s \mathbf{E} \cdot d\mathbf{S}}$$

The capacitance is given by the ratio of the total charge to the potential difference:

$$C = \frac{Q}{V_0} = \frac{\epsilon \oint_s \mathbf{E} \cdot d\mathbf{S}}{-\int \mathbf{E} \cdot d\mathbf{L}}$$

and therefore

$$RC = \frac{\epsilon}{\sigma} \tag{1}$$

Knowing the conductivity of the electrolyte, the capacitance may be determined by a simple resistance measurement.

A simpler technique is available for two-dimensional problems. Conducting paper is available upon which silver paint may be used to draw the conducting boundaries. In the case of the coaxial capacitor, we should draw two circles of radius r_A and r_B, $r_B > r_A$, extending the paint a small distance outward from r_B and inward from r_A to provide sufficient area to make a good contact with wires to an external poten-

---

[1] See bibliography at end of chapter.

tial source.   A probe is again used to establish potential values between the circles (cylinders).   Suggestions for the use of this conducting-paper technique may be found in the Sunshine Scientific Instrument instruction manual.[1]

6.4. Fluid-flow Maps.   An analogy also exists between electrostatics and hydraulics and is particularly useful in obtaining photographs of the streamlines or flux lines.   The proof of the analogy will not be given here,[2] but the assumptions require an incompressible fluid flowing in a thin sheet.   This is satisfied by the flow of water between parallel planes, closely spaced; at least one of the planes should be glass.   Conductor boundaries represent sources and sinks, or

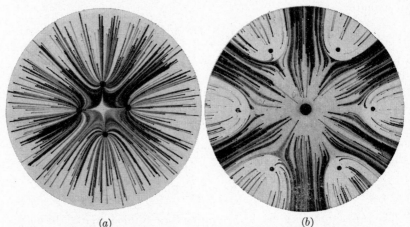

(a)   (b)

FIG. 6.7. Photographs of fluid-flow maps taken by Moore.   (a) The field of four equal line charges.   (b) The field of a triode having six grid rods.   The streamlines from the plate which terminate on the grid rods all lie within the regions having the white background; those which terminate on the cathode pass through the large region with a gray background.   (*Courtesy of A. D. Moore.*)

regions at which the flow of the water originates and terminates.   The flow lines are made visible by placing small crystals of potassium permanganate on the lower plane before the flow begins.   As the crystals dissolve, the flow lines or streamlines become visible.

This process is described completely by Moore in a number of publications[3] which include many excellent photographs.   Figure 6.7 shows several photographs taken by these techniques.

6.5. The Iteration and Relaxation Methods.   In potential problems where the potential is completely specified on the boundaries of a

[1] See bibliography at end of chapter.
[2] See Weber, pp. 76–78.
[3] See bibliography at end of chapter.

given region, particularly including problems in which the potential does not vary in one direction, i.e., two-dimensional potential distributions, there exists a pencil-and-paper repetitive method which is capable of yielding any desired accuracy. Computing machines should be used when the value of the potential is required with high accuracy, for the time required is prohibitive except in the simplest problems. This is not a drawback, however, for the iterative method, to be described below, is well suited for calculation by any automatic, sequentially controlled computer.

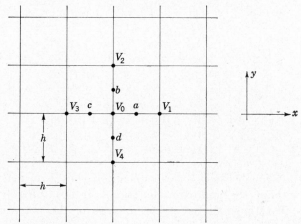

Fig. 6.8. A portion of a region containing a two-dimensional potential field, divided into squares of side h.

Let us assume a two-dimensional problem in which the potential does not vary with the z coordinate and divide the interior of a cross section of the region where the potential is desired into squares of length h on a side. A portion of this region is shown in Fig. 6.8. The unknown values of the potential at five adjacent points are indicated as V_0, V_1, V_2, V_3, and V_4. If the region is charge-free, then $\nabla \cdot \mathbf{D} = 0$ and $\nabla \cdot \mathbf{E} = 0$, from which we have, in two dimensions,

$$\frac{\partial E_x}{\partial x} + \frac{\partial E_y}{\partial y} = 0$$

But the gradient operation gives $E_x = -\partial V/\partial x$ and $E_y = -\partial V/\partial y$, from which we obtain[1]

$$\frac{\partial^2 V}{\partial x^2} + \frac{\partial^2 V}{\partial y^2} = 0$$

[1] This is Laplace's equation in two dimensions. The three-dimensional form will be derived in the following chapter.

Approximate values for these partial derivatives may be obtained in terms of the assumed potentials, for

$$\frac{\partial V}{\partial x}\bigg|_a \doteq \frac{V_1 - V_0}{h}$$

and

$$\frac{\partial V}{\partial x}\bigg|_c \doteq \frac{V_0 - V_3}{h}$$

from which

$$\frac{\partial^2 V}{\partial x^2}\bigg|_0 \doteq \frac{\dfrac{\partial V}{\partial x}\bigg|_a - \dfrac{\partial V}{\partial x}\bigg|_c}{h} \doteq \frac{V_1 - V_0 - V_0 + V_3}{h^2}$$

and, similarly,

$$\frac{\partial^2 V}{\partial y^2}\bigg|_0 \doteq \frac{V_2 - V_0 - V_0 + V_4}{h^2}$$

Combining, we have

$$\frac{\partial^2 V}{\partial x^2} + \frac{\partial^2 V}{\partial y^2} \doteq \frac{V_1 + V_2 + V_3 + V_4 - 4V_0}{h^2} = 0$$

or

$$V_0 \doteq \tfrac{1}{4}(V_1 + V_2 + V_3 + V_4) \tag{1}$$

The expression becomes exact as h approaches zero, and we shall write it without the approximation sign. It is intuitively correct, telling us that the potential is the average of the potential at the four neighboring points. The iterative method merely uses (1) to determine the potential at the corner of every square subdivision in turn, and then the process is repeated over the entire region as many times as is necessary until the values no longer change. The method is best shown in detail by an example.

For simplicity consider a square region with conducting boundaries (Fig. 6.9). The potential of the top is 100 volts, and that of the sides and bottom is zero. The problem is two-dimensional, and the sketch is a cross section of the physical configuration. The region is divided first into 16 squares, and some estimate of the potential must now be made at every corner before applying the iterative method. These values could be obtained from a rough curvilinear-square map, but it is easier here to apply (1) to the large squares. At the center of the figure the potential estimate is then $\tfrac{1}{4}(100 + 0 + 0 + 0) = 25.0$.

The potential may now be estimated at the centers of the four double-sized squares by taking the average of the potentials at the four corners, or applying (1) along a diagonal set of axes. Use of this "diagonal average" is made only in preparing initial estimates. For the two upper double squares, $V = \tfrac{1}{4}(50 + 100 + 25 + 0) = 43.8$

(to the nearest tenth of a volt[1]), and for the lower ones,

$$V = \tfrac{1}{4}(0 + 25 + 0 + 0) = 6.2$$

The potential at the remaining four points may now be obtained by applying (1) directly. The complete set of estimated values is shown in Fig. 6.9.

The initial traverse is now made to obtain a corrected set of potentials, beginning in the upper left corner (with the 43.8 value, not with

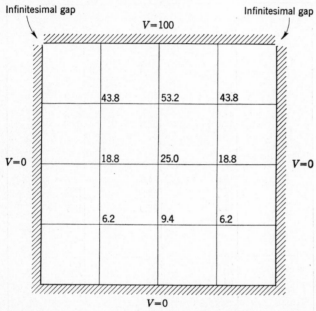

Infinitesimal gap   Infinitesimal gap

$V = 100$

43.8   53.2   43.8

$V = 0$ 18.8   25.0   18.8 $V = 0$

6.2   9.4   6.2

$V = 0$

FIG. 6.9. Cross section of a square trough with sides and bottom at zero potential and top at 100 volts. The cross section has been divided into 16 squares, and the potential estimated at every corner.

the boundary where the potentials are known and fixed), working across the row to the right, and then dropping down to the second row and proceeding from left to right again. Thus the 43.8 value changes to $\tfrac{1}{4}(100 + 53.2 + 18.8 + 0) = 43.0$. The best or newest potentials are always used when applying (1), so both points marked 43.8 are changed to 43.0, because of the evident symmetry, and the 53.2 value becomes $\tfrac{1}{4}(100 + 43.0 + 25.0 + 43.0) = 52.8$.

[1] When rounding off a decimal ending exactly with a 5, the preceding digit should be made *even;* e.g., 42.75 becomes 42.8 and 6.25 becomes 6.2. This generally ensures a random process leading to better accuracy than would be obtained by always increasing the previous digit by 1.

Because of the symmetry, little would be gained by continuing across the top line. Each point of this line has now been improved once. Dropping down to the next line, the 18.8 value becomes

$$\frac{1}{4}(43.0 + 25.0 + 6.2 + 0) = 18.6$$

and the traverse is completed in this manner. The values at the end of this traverse are shown as the top numbers in each column of Fig.

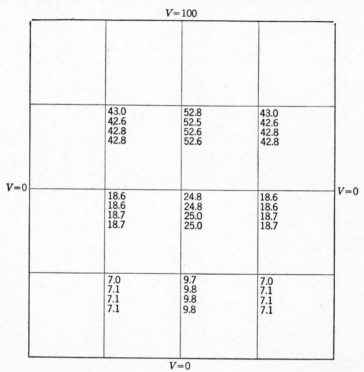

FIG. 6.10. The results of each of the four necessary traverses of the problem of Fig. 6.9 are shown in order in the columns. The final values, unchanged in the last traverse, are at the bottom of each column.

6.10. Additional traverses must now be made until the value at each corner shows no change. The values for the successive traverses are usually entered below each other in column form, as shown in Fig. 6.10, and the final value is shown at the bottom of each column. Only four traverses are required in this example.

Since there is a large difference in potential from square to square, we should not expect our answers to be accurate to the tenth of a volt shown (and perhaps not to the nearest volt). Increased accuracy

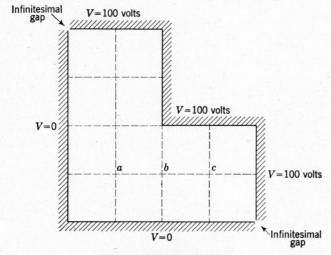

FIG. 6.13. See Prob. D6.2.

D6.3. In Fig. 6.14 the cross section of a rectangular region completely enclosed by conductors is shown. Potential estimates are given at six points of intersection of grid lines. Compute the residual at each point, and use the relaxation method to establish the potential at these points to the nearest volt. What is the final value of potential obtained at:

(a) Point a?

(b) Point b?

(c) Point c?

Ans. 45 volts.

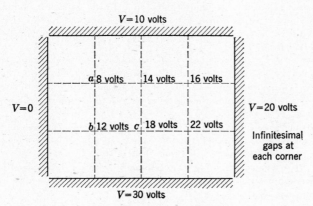

FIG. 6.14. See Prob. D6.3.

SUGGESTED REFERENCES

1. Attwood, S. S.: (see Suggested References for Chap. 4). Chapter 7 is devoted to mapping fields by curvilinear squares.
2. Moore, A. D.: Fields from Fluid Flow Mappers, *J. Appl. Phys.*, vol. 20, pp. 790–804, August, 1949; Soap Film and Sandbed Mapper Techniques, *J. Appl. Mechanics* (bound with *Trans. ASME*), vol. 17, pp. 291–298, September, 1950; Four Electromagnetic Propositions, with Fluid Mapper Verifications, *Elec. Eng.*, vol. 69, pp. 607–610, July, 1950; The Further Development of Fluid Mappers, *Trans. AIEE*, vol. 69, pt. II, pp. 1615–1624, 1950; Mapping Techniques Applied to Fluid Mapper Patterns, *Trans. AIEE*, vol. 71, 1952.
3. Ramo, S., and J. R. Whinnery: "Fields and Waves in Modern Radio," 2d ed., John Wiley & Sons, Inc., New York, 1953. Suggestions for improving curvilinear maps are given on pages 122–127.
4. Rogers, W. E.: (see Suggested References for Chap. 2). Discussion of fluid mapper techniques (following A. D. Moore).
5. Scarborough, J. B.: "Numerical Mathematical Analysis," 3d ed., Johns Hopkins Press, Baltimore, 1955. Describes iteration and relaxation methods and gives several complete examples. Inherent errors are discussed.
6. Spangenberg, K. R.: "Vacuum Tubes," McGraw-Hill Book Company, Inc., New York, 1948. Experimental mapping methods are discussed on pages 75–82.
7. Sunshine Scientific Instrument Company: "Instruction Manual IM24," Philadelphia, 1950.
8. Weber, E.: "Electromagnetic Fields," vol. I, John Wiley & Sons, Inc., New York, 1950. Experimental mapping methods are discussed in chap. 5.

PROBLEMS

1. Construct a curvilinear-square map for a coaxial capacitor of inner radius 1.25 in. and outer radius 5 in. These dimensions are suitable for the drawing. As a check on the accuracy, compute the capacitance both from your sketch and from the exact formula.

2. Construct a curvilinear-square map of the potential field about two parallel circular cylinders, each of 1 in. radius, separated a center-to-center distance of 12 in. These dimensions are suitable for the actual sketch if symmetry is considered. As a check, compute the capacitance both from your sketch and from the exact formula.

3. Construct a curvilinear-square map of the problem sketched in Fig. 6.13. Estimate the value of the potential from your map at the points marked *a*, *b*, *c*, and compare with your answers to Prob. D6.2.

4. In the potential map of Fig. 6.3, assume a potential difference of 100 volts between conductors with the inner conductor positive. If the square conductor is 1 cm on a side, find:

   (*a*) The charge per meter length on the inner conductor.
   (*b*) The minimum value of the surface charge density on the inner conductor.
   (*c*) The approximate value of the maximum electric field intensity occurring at any point on the 87.5-volt equipotential surface.

5. A square sheet of Teledeltos type L resistance paper, 10 cm on a side, has contact made all along each of two opposite edges. An ohmmeter shows a resistance between edges of 4,000 ohms. If the measurement is repeated with a square sheet 5 cm on a side, what resistance would be measured? If a capacitor cross section is now drawn on the paper, find the theoretical relationship existing between the capacitance C, the resistance per square R_s of the paper itself, and the resistance R measured between the painted boundaries representing the capacitor plates. The cross section of a coaxial capacitor, inner radius 1.5 cm and outer radius 4 cm, is now placed on a suitably large sheet of this paper. What resistance should be measured between the inner and outer circles?

6. Two parallel conducting planes extend from $x = 0$ to $x = \infty$ and from $z = -\infty$ to $z = \infty$ and are located at $y = 0$ and $y = 1$. Each is at zero potential. A third plane at $x = 0$, extending from $y = 0$ to $y = 1$ and from $z = -\infty$ to $z = \infty$, is at 100 volts. Infinitesimal insulating gaps are located at $(x = 0,\ y = 0)$ and $(x = 0,\ y = 1)$. Use the iteration or relaxation method to find the potential field near $x = 0$. A grid of squares 0.25 on a side is suggested. Potentials should be found to the nearest volt.

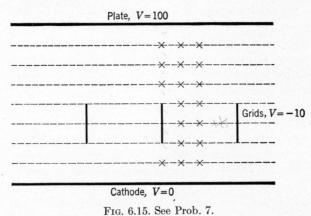

Fig. 6.15. See Prob. 7.

7. A planar triode vacuum tube without space charge is shown in Fig. 6.15. The grid of the triode consists of strips, placed edgewise to the plate and cathode, and it may be assumed that the structure repeats itself indefinitely to the right and left. Use the iteration or relaxation method to find the potential field at the set of marked points. Is this tube cut off or not?

CHAPTER 7

POISSON'S AND LAPLACE'S EQUATIONS

A study of the previous chapter shows that several of the analogies used to obtain experimental field maps involved demonstrating that the analogous quantity satisfies Laplace's equation. This is true for small deflections of an elastic membrane, the flow of a fluid in a thin layer, and we might have proved the current analogy by showing that the d-c density in a conducting medium also satisfies Laplace's equation. It appears that this is a fundamental equation in more than one field of science, and it also is apparent that without our knowledge we have spent this last chapter in obtaining solutions for it by experimental, graphical, and numerical methods. This is quite true. Now we are ready to obtain this equation formally and discuss several methods by which it may be solved rigorously.

It may seem that this material properly belongs before that of the previous chapter; as long as we are solving one equation by so many methods, would it not be fitting to see the equation first? The disadvantage of this more logical order lies in the fact that solving Laplace's equation is an exercise in mathematics, and unless we have the physical problem well in mind, we may easily miss completely the physical significance of what we are doing. A rough curvilinear map can tell us much about a field and then may be used later to check our mathematical solutions for gross errors or to indicate certain peculiar regions in the field which require special treatment.

With this explanation let us finally obtain the equations of Laplace and Poisson.

7.1. Poisson's and Laplace's Equations. Obtaining Poisson's equation is exceedingly simple, for from the point form of Gauss's law,

$$\nabla \cdot \mathbf{D} = \rho \tag{1}$$

the definition of $\mathbf{D}$,

$$\mathbf{D} = \epsilon \mathbf{E} \tag{2}$$

and the gradient relationship,

$$\mathbf{E} = -\nabla V \tag{3}$$

156

by substitution we have

$$\nabla \cdot \mathbf{D} = \nabla \cdot (\epsilon \mathbf{E}) = -\nabla \cdot (\epsilon \, \nabla V) = \rho$$

or $\qquad \nabla \cdot \nabla V = -\dfrac{\rho}{\epsilon}$ $\qquad\qquad\qquad$ (4)

for ϵ constant.

Equation (4) is *Poisson's equation*, but the "double ∇" operation must be interpreted and expanded, at least in cartesian coordinates, before the equation can be useful. In cartesian coordinates,

$$\nabla \cdot \mathbf{A} = \frac{\partial A_x}{\partial x} + \frac{\partial A_y}{\partial y} + \frac{\partial A_z}{\partial z}$$

$$\nabla V = \frac{\partial V}{\partial x} \, \mathbf{a}_x + \frac{\partial V}{\partial y} \, \mathbf{a}_y + \frac{\partial V}{\partial z} \, \mathbf{a}_z$$

and therefore

$$\nabla \cdot \nabla V = \frac{\partial}{\partial x} \left(\frac{\partial V}{\partial x} \right) + \frac{\partial}{\partial y} \left(\frac{\partial V}{\partial y} \right) + \frac{\partial}{\partial z} \left(\frac{\partial V}{\partial z} \right)$$

$$= \frac{\partial^2 V}{\partial x^2} + \frac{\partial^2 V}{\partial y^2} + \frac{\partial^2 V}{\partial z^2} \qquad\qquad (5)$$

Usually the operation $\nabla \cdot \nabla$ is abbreviated ∇^2 (and pronounced "del squared"), a good reminder of the second-order partial derivatives appearing in (5), and we have

$$\nabla^2 V = \frac{\partial^2 V}{\partial x^2} + \frac{\partial^2 V}{\partial y^2} + \frac{\partial^2 V}{\partial z^2} = -\frac{\rho}{\epsilon} \qquad\qquad (6)$$

in cartesian coordinates.

If $\rho = 0$, indicating zero *volume* charge density, but allowing point charges, line charge, and surface charge density to exist on the boundaries as sources of the field, then

$$\nabla^2 V = 0 \qquad\qquad\qquad (7)$$

which is *Laplace's equation*. The ∇^2 operation is called the *Laplacian of V*.

In cartesian coordinates Laplace's equation is

$$\nabla^2 V = \frac{\partial^2 V}{\partial x^2} + \frac{\partial^2 V}{\partial y^2} + \frac{\partial^2 V}{\partial z^2} = 0 \qquad\qquad (8)$$

and the form of $\nabla^2 V$ in cylindrical and spherical coordinates may be obtained by using the expressions for the divergence and gradient already obtained in those coordinate systems. For reference, the

Laplacian in cylindrical coordinates is

$$\nabla^2 V = \frac{1}{r} \frac{\partial}{\partial r} \left(r \frac{\partial V}{\partial r} \right) + \frac{1}{r^2} \left(\frac{\partial^2 V}{\partial \phi^2} \right) + \frac{\partial^2 V}{\partial z^2} \qquad \text{(cylindrical)} \qquad (9)$$

and in spherical coordinates is

$$\nabla^2 V = \frac{1}{r^2} \frac{\partial}{\partial r} \left(r^2 \frac{\partial V}{\partial r} \right) + \frac{1}{r^2 \sin \theta} \frac{\partial}{\partial \theta} \left(\sin \theta \frac{\partial V}{\partial \theta} \right)$$
$$+ \frac{1}{r^2 \sin^2 \theta} \frac{\partial^2 V}{\partial \phi^2} \qquad \text{(spherical)} \qquad (10)$$

These equations may be expanded by taking the indicated partial derivatives, but it is usually more helpful to have them in the forms given above. Furthermore, it is much easier to expand them later if necessary than it is to put the broken pieces back together again.

Laplace's equation is all-embracing, for, applying as it does wherever volume charge density is zero, it states that every conceivable configuration of electrodes or conductors produces a field for which $\nabla^2 V = 0$. Of course, all these fields are different, having different potential values and different spatial rates of change, yet for each $\nabla^2 V = 0$. Since *every* field (if $\rho = 0$) satisfies Laplace's equation, how can we expect to reverse the procedure and use Laplace's equation to find one specific field in which we happen to have an interest? Obviously, more information is required, and we shall find that we must solve Laplace's equation subject to certain *boundary conditions*.

Every physical problem must contain at least one conducting boundary and usually contains two or more. The potentials on these boundaries are assigned values, perhaps V_0, V_1, etc., or perhaps numerical values. These definite equipotential surfaces will provide the boundary conditions for the type of problem to be solved in this chapter.

Before using Laplace's equation or Poisson's equation in several examples, we must first pause to show that if our answer satisfies Laplace's equation and also satisfies the boundary conditions, then it is the only possible answer. It would be very distressing to work a problem by solving Laplace's equation using two different approved methods and then to obtain two different answers. We shall show that the two answers must be identical.

D7.1. Show that the following potential fields satisfy Laplace's equation in the appropriate coordinate system:

(a) The field of a parallel plate capacitor, $V = Ax + B$.

(b) The field of a coaxial capacitor, $V = A \ln r + B$.

(c) The field of a dipole, $V = A \dfrac{\cos \theta}{r^2}$.

Ans. $\nabla^2 V = 0$.

D7.2. Find the volume charge density necessary for the potential fields:
(a) $V = Ax^2$.
(b) $V = A(\cos ax)e^{ay}$.
(c) $V = Ae^{ax}e^{by} \cos (\sqrt{a^2 + b^2}\, z)$.

Ans. $\rho = -2A\epsilon$.

7.2. Uniqueness Theorem.

Let us assume that we have two solutions of Laplace's equation, V_1 and V_2, both general functions of the coordinates used. Therefore

$$\nabla^2 V_1 = 0$$

and
$$\nabla^2 V_2 = 0$$

from which
$$\nabla^2(V_1 - V_2) = 0$$

Each solution must also satisfy the boundary conditions, and if we represent the given potential values on the boundaries by V_b, then the value of V_1 on the boundary V_{1b} and the value of V_2 on the boundary V_{2b} must both be identical to V_b:

$$V_{1b} = V_{2b} = V_b$$

or
$$V_{1b} - V_{2b} = 0$$

In Sec. 4.8, Eq. (5), we made use of a vector identity:

$$\nabla \cdot (V\mathbf{D}) \equiv V(\nabla \cdot \mathbf{D}) + \mathbf{D} \cdot (\nabla V)$$

which holds for any scalar V and any vector $\mathbf{D}$. For the present application we shall select $(V_1 - V_2)$ as the scalar and $\nabla(V_1 - V_2)$ as the vector, giving

$$\nabla \cdot [(V_1 - V_2)\nabla(V_1 - V_2)]$$
$$\equiv (V_1 - V_2)[\nabla \cdot \nabla(V_1 - V_2)] + \nabla(V_1 - V_2) \cdot \nabla(V_1 - V_2)$$

which we shall integrate throughout the volume enclosed by the boundary surfaces specified:

$$\int_{\text{vol}} \nabla \cdot [(V_1 - V_2)\nabla(V_1 - V_2)]\, dv$$
$$\equiv \int_{\text{vol}} (V_1 - V_2)[\nabla \cdot \nabla(V_1 - V_2)]\, dv + \int_{\text{vol}} [\nabla(V_1 - V_2)]^2\, dv \quad (1)$$

The divergence theorem allows us to replace the volume integral on the left side of the equation by the closed surface integral over the surface surrounding the volume. This surface consists of the boundaries already specified on which $V_{1b} = V_{2b}$, and therefore

$$\int_{\text{vol}} \nabla \cdot [(V_1 - V_2)\nabla(V_1 - V_2)]\, dv$$
$$= \oint_s [(V_{1b} - V_{2b})\nabla(V_{1b} - V_{2b})] \cdot d\mathbf{S} = 0$$

One of the factors of the first integral on the right side of (1) is $\nabla \cdot \nabla(V_1 - V_2)$, or $\nabla^2(V_1 - V_2)$, which is zero by hypothesis, and therefore that integral is zero. Hence, the remaining volume integral must be zero:

$$\int_{\text{vol}} [\nabla(V_1 - V_2)]^2 \, dv = 0$$

There are in general two reasons why an integral may be zero; either the integrand (the quantity under the integral sign) is everywhere zero, or the integrand is positive in some regions, negative in others, and the contributions cancel algebraically. In this case the first reason must hold because $[\nabla(V_1 - V_2)]^2$ cannot be negative. Therefore

$$[\nabla(V_1 - V_2)]^2 = 0$$
and $$\nabla(V_1 - V_2) = 0$$

Finally, if the gradient of $V_1 - V_2$ is everywhere zero, then $V_1 - V_2$ cannot change with any coordinates and

$$V_1 - V_2 = \text{constant}$$

If we can show that this constant is zero, we shall have accomplished our proof. The constant is easily evaluated by considering a point on the boundary. Here $V_1 - V_2 = V_{1b} - V_{2b} = 0$, and we see that the constant is indeed zero, and therefore

$$V_1 = V_2$$

giving two identical solutions.

The uniqueness theorem also applies to Poisson's equation, for if $\nabla^2 V_1 = -\rho/\epsilon$ and $\nabla^2 V_2 = -\rho/\epsilon$, then $\nabla^2(V_1 - V_2) = 0$ as before. Boundary conditions still require that $V_{1b} - V_{2b} = 0$, and the proof is identical from this point.

This constitutes the proof of the uniqueness theorem. Viewed as the answer to a question, "How do two solutions of Laplace's or Poisson's equation compare if they both satisfy the same boundary conditions?" the uniqueness theorem should please us by its assurance that the answers are identical. Once we can find any method of solving Laplace's or Poisson's equation subject to given boundary conditions, we have solved our problem once and for all. No other method can ever give a different answer.

D7.3. The following alternative potential solutions have been found for the boundary conditions specified. Show that each pair of solutions satisfies the boundary conditions and Laplace's or Poisson's equation. Show also that the uniqueness theorem is satisfied.

(a) $V = 0$ at $x = -1$, $V = \frac{1}{2}$ at $x = 0$; $V_1 = \dfrac{1}{1 + 1/(1 + x)}$, $V_2 = 1 - \dfrac{1}{x + 2}$.

(b) $V = 0$ at $r = 2$, $V = 100$ at $r = 1$ (cylindrical); $V_1 = 100 \dfrac{\ln (r/2)}{\ln \frac{1}{2}}$, $V_2 =$ $100 + 144.3 \ln \dfrac{1}{r}$.

(c) $V = 0$ at $\theta = \dfrac{\pi}{2}$, $V = 100$ at $\theta = \dfrac{\pi}{4}$; $V_1 = 100 \dfrac{\ln [\tan (\theta/2)]}{\ln [\tan (\pi/8)]}$, $V_2 =$ $113.5 [\ln (1 + \cos \theta) - \ln \sin \theta]$.

Ans. All satisfy boundary conditions and either Laplace's or Poisson's equation.

7.3. Example of the Solution of Laplace's Equation. There have been developed several methods for solving the second-order partial differential equation known as Laplace's equation. The first and simplest method is that of direct integration, and we shall use this technique to work several examples in various coordinate systems in this section. In the last section of the chapter one other method will be used on a more difficult problem. Other methods, requiring a more advanced mathematical knowledge, are described in the references given at the end of the chapter.

The method of direct integration is applicable only to problems which are "one-dimensional," or in which the potential field is a function of only one of the three coordinates. Since we are working with only three coordinate systems, it might seem, then, that there are nine problems to be solved, but a little reflection will show that a field which varies only with x is fundamentally the same as a field which varies only with y. Rotating the physical problem a quarter turn is no change. Actually, there are only five problems to be solved, one in cartesian coordinates, two in cylindrical, and two in spherical. We shall solve them all.

Example 1. Let us assume that V is a function only of x and worry later about which physical problem we are solving when we have a need for boundary conditions. Laplace's equation reduces to

$$\frac{\partial^2 V}{\partial x^2} = 0$$

and the partial derivative may be replaced by an ordinary derivative since y and z are not involved:

$$\frac{d^2 V}{dx^2} = 0$$

We integrate twice, obtaining

$$\frac{dV}{dx} = A$$

and
$$V = Ax + B \tag{1}$$

where A and B = constants of integration. Equation (1) contains two such constants, as we should expect for a second-order differential equation. These constants can be determined only from the boundary conditions.

What boundary conditions should we supply? They are our choice since no physical problem has yet been specified, with the exception of the original hypothesis that the potential varied only with x. We should now attempt to visualize such a field. Most of us probably already have the answer, but it may be obtained by exact methods.

Since the field varies only with x and is not a function of y and z, if x is a constant, then V is a constant, or in other words, the equipotential surfaces are described by setting x = constant. These surfaces are parallel planes normal to the x axis. The field is thus that of a parallel-plate capacitor, and as soon as we specify the potential on any two planes we may evaluate our constants of integration.

To be very general, let $V = V_1$ at $x = x_1$, and $V = V_2$ at $x = x_2$. These values are then substituted into (1), giving

$$V_1 = Ax_1 + B \qquad V_2 = Ax_2 + B$$

$$A = \frac{V_1 - V_2}{x_1 - x_2} \qquad B = \frac{V_2 x_1 - V_1 x_2}{x_1 - x_2}$$

and
$$V = \frac{V_1(x - x_2) - V_2(x - x_1)}{x_1 - x_2} \tag{2}$$

A simpler answer would have been obtained by choosing simpler boundary conditions. If we had fixed $V = 0$ at $x = 0$ and $V = V_0$ at $x = d$, then

$$A = \frac{V_0}{d} \qquad B = 0$$

and
$$V = \frac{V_0 x}{d} \tag{3}$$

Suppose our primary aim is to find the capacitance of a parallel-plate capacitor. We have solved Laplace's equation, obtaining (1) with the two constants A and B. Should they be evaluated or left alone? Presumably we are not interested in the potential field itself, but only in the capacitance, and we may continue successfully with A and B or we may simplify the algebra by a little foresight. Capacitance is given by the ratio of charge to potential difference, so we may choose now the potential *difference* as V_0, which is equivalent to one boundary condition, and then choose whatever second boundary condition seems to help the form of the equation the most. This is the essence of the second set of boundary conditions which produced (3).

The potential difference was fixed as V_0 by choosing the potential of one plate zero and the other V_0; the location of these plates was made as simple as possible by letting $V = 0$ at $x = 0$.

Using (3), then, we still need the total charge on either plate before the capacitance can be found. We should remember that when we first solved this capacitor problem in Chap. 5 the sheet of charge provided our starting point. We did not have to work very hard to find the charge, for all the fields were expressed in terms of it. The work then was spent in finding potential difference. Now the problem is reversed (and simplified).

The necessary steps are these after the choice of boundary conditions has been made:

1. Given V, use $\mathbf{E} = -\nabla V$ to find $\mathbf{E}$.
2. Use $\mathbf{D} = \epsilon \mathbf{E}$ to find $\mathbf{D}$.
3. Evaluate $\mathbf{D}$ at either capacitor plate, $\mathbf{D} = \mathbf{D}_s = D_n \mathbf{a}_n$.
4. Recognize that $\rho_s = D_n$.
5. Find Q by a surface integration over the capacitor plate:

$$Q = \int_s \rho_s \, dS$$

Here we have

$$V = V_0 \frac{x}{d}$$

$$\mathbf{E} = -\frac{V_0}{d} \mathbf{a}_x$$

$$\mathbf{D} = -\epsilon \frac{V_0}{d} \mathbf{a}_x$$

$$\mathbf{D}_s = \mathbf{D} \Big|_{x=0} = -\epsilon \frac{V_0}{d} \mathbf{a}_x$$

$$\mathbf{a}_n = \mathbf{a}_x$$

$$D_n = -\epsilon \frac{V_0}{d} = \rho_s$$

$$Q = \int_s \frac{-\epsilon V_0}{d} \, dS = -\epsilon \frac{V_0 S}{d}$$

and the capacitance is

$$C = \frac{|Q|}{V_0} = \frac{\epsilon S}{d}$$

We shall use this procedure several times in the examples to follow.

Example 2. Since no new problems are solved by choosing fields which vary only with y or with z in cartesian coordinates, we pass on to cylindrical coordinates for our next example. Variations with respect to z are again nothing new, and we finally assume variation with respect to r only.   Laplace's equation becomes

$$\frac{1}{r}\frac{\partial}{\partial r}\left(r\frac{\partial V}{\partial r}\right) = 0$$

or

$$\frac{1}{r}\frac{d}{dr}\left(r\frac{dV}{dr}\right) = 0$$

We may multiply by r and then integrate:

$$r\frac{dV}{dr} = A$$

rearrange and integrate again:

$$V = A \ln r + B \tag{4}$$

The equipotential surfaces are given by $r =$ constant and are cylinders, and the problem is that of the coaxial capacitor or coaxial transmission line.   We choose a potential difference of V_0 volts by letting $V = V_0$ at $r = a$, $V = 0$ at $r = b$, $b > a$, and obtain

$$V = V_0 \frac{\ln (b/r)}{\ln (b/a)}$$

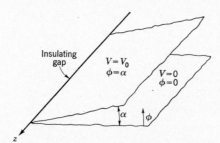

from which

$$E = \frac{V_0}{r}\frac{1}{\ln (b/a)}\mathbf{a}_r$$

$$D_{n(r=a)} = \frac{\epsilon V_0}{a \ln (b/a)}$$

$$Q = \frac{\epsilon V_0 2\pi a L}{a \ln (b/a)}$$

$$C = \frac{2\pi \epsilon L}{\ln (b/a)}$$

FIG. 7.1. Two infinite radial planes with an interior angle α.   An infinitesimal insulating gap exists at $r = 0$.

Example 3.   Now let us assume that V is a function only of ϕ in cylindrical coordinates.   We might look at the physical problem first for a change and see that equipotential surfaces are given by $\phi =$ constant.   These are radial planes.   Boundary conditions might be $V = 0$ at $\phi = 0$ and $V = V_0$ at $\phi = \alpha$, leading to the physical problem detailed in Fig. 7.1.

Laplace's equation is now

$$\frac{1}{r^2}\frac{\partial^2 V}{\partial \phi^2} = 0$$

or

$$\frac{d^2 V}{d\phi^2} = 0$$

from which we have

$$V = A\phi + B$$

The boundary conditions determine A and B, and

$$V = V_0 \frac{\phi}{\alpha} \qquad (5)$$

Taking the gradient of (5) produces the electric field intensity:

$$\mathbf{E} = -\frac{V_0 \mathbf{a}_\phi}{\alpha r}$$

and it is interesting to note that E is a function of r and not of ϕ. This does not contradict our original assumptions, however, which were restrictions only on the potential field.

A problem involving the capacitance of these two radial planes is included at the end of the chapter.

Example 4. We now turn to spherical coordinates, dispose immediately of variations with respect to ϕ only as having just been solved, and treat first $V = V(r)$.

The details are left for a problem later, but the final potential field is given by

$$V = V_0 \frac{1/r - 1/b}{1/a - 1/b} \qquad (6)$$

where the boundary conditions are evidently $V = 0$ at $r = b$ and $V = V_0$ at $r = a$, $b > a$. The problem is that of concentric spheres. The capacitance has been found previously (by a somewhat different method) and is

$$C = \frac{4\pi\epsilon}{1/a - 1/b}$$

Example 5. In spherical coordinates we now restrict the potential function to $V = V(\theta)$, obtaining

$$\frac{1}{r^2 \sin\theta} \frac{d}{d\theta}\left(\sin\theta \frac{dV}{d\theta}\right) = 0$$

from which

$$\sin\theta \frac{dV}{d\theta} = A$$

The second integral is, then,

$$V = \int \frac{A\, d\theta}{\sin\theta} + B$$

which is not as obvious as the previous ones. From integral tables (or a good memory), we have

$$V = A \ln (\tan \tfrac{1}{2}\theta) + B$$

The equipotential surfaces are cones, and if $V = 0$ at $\theta = \pi/2$ and $V = V_0$ at $\theta = \alpha$, $\alpha < \pi/2$, then

$$V = V_0 \frac{\ln (\tan \tfrac{1}{2}\theta)}{\ln (\tan \tfrac{1}{2}\alpha)} \tag{7}$$

In order to find the capacitance between a conducting cone with its vertex separated from a conducting plane by an infinitesimal insulating gap, and its axis normal to the plane, we need the field strength:

$$\mathbf{E} = -\nabla V = -\frac{1}{r} \frac{\partial V}{\partial \theta} \mathbf{a}_\theta = -\frac{V_0}{r \sin \theta \ln (\tan \tfrac{1}{2}\alpha)} \mathbf{a}_\theta$$

The surface charge density on the cone is, then,

$$\rho_s = \frac{\epsilon V_0}{r \sin \alpha \ln (\tan \tfrac{1}{2}\alpha)}$$

producing a total charge Q:

$$Q = \frac{\epsilon V_0}{\sin \alpha \ln (\tan \tfrac{1}{2}\alpha)} \int_0^\infty \int_0^{2\pi} \frac{r \sin \alpha \, d\phi \, dr}{r}$$

This leads to an infinite value of charge and capacitance, and it becomes necessary to consider a cone of finite size. Our answer will now be only an approximation because the theoretical equipotential surface is $\theta = \alpha$, a conical surface extending from $r = 0$ to $r = \infty$, whereas our physical conical surface extends only from $r = 0$ to, say, $r = r_1$. The approximate capacitance is

$$C \doteq \frac{2\pi\epsilon r_1}{\ln (\tan \tfrac{1}{2}\alpha)}$$

If we desire a more accurate answer we may make an estimate of the capacitance of the base of the cone, a circular plate of radius r_1, to the zero potential plane and add this amount to our answer above. Fringing, or nonuniform, fields in this region have been neglected and introduce an additional source of error.

D7.4. Determine the surface charge density (including sign) at a point:
    (a) On the inner of two conducting coaxial cylinders of radius 0.5 m and 4.0 m if the inner cylinder is at $V = 60$ volts and the outer at $V = 120$ volts.
    (b) On the inner of two concentric conducting spheres of radius 0.5 m and 4.0 m if the inner sphere is at $V = 60$ volts and the outer at $V = 120$ volts.

(c) On the inner of two conducting coaxial cones, 1 m from the common vertex, if the generating angles are $\theta = 30°$ and $\theta = 60°$, and the inner cone is at $V = 60$ volts and the outer at $V = 120$ volts.

$Ans. -3.1 \times 10^{-9}$ coulomb/m².

D7.5. Find the potential at a point located an equal distance (as measured along a streamline) from the two conducting surfaces described in each part of Prob. D7.4.

$Ans.$ 311 volts.

7.4. Example of the Solution of Poisson's Equation. As a very simple example of the solution of Poisson's equation let us assume a parallel-plane diode with a uniform volume charge density of $-\rho_0$. For boundary conditions we may take $V = 0$ at $x = 0$ (cathode) and $V = V_0$ at $x = d$ (plate). Poisson's equation,

$$\nabla^2 V = \frac{-\rho}{\epsilon_0}$$

then becomes

$$\frac{\partial^2 V}{\partial x^2} = \frac{\rho_0}{\epsilon_0}$$

or

$$\frac{d^2 V}{dx^2} = \frac{\rho_0}{\epsilon_0}$$

Here again the solution may be obtained by integrating twice:

$$\frac{dV}{dx} = \frac{\rho_0}{\epsilon_0} x + A$$

and

$$V = \frac{\rho_0}{2\epsilon_0} x^2 + Ax + B$$

The boundary conditions require

$$B = 0$$
$$A = \frac{V_0 - \frac{1}{2}\rho_0 d^2/\epsilon_0}{d}$$

and hence

$$V = \frac{V_0}{d} x - \frac{1}{2} \frac{\rho_0}{\epsilon_0} x(d - x) \tag{1}$$

We might plot V as a function of x for various values of ρ_0, and we also might obtain the electric field intensity and show its variation with distance. We should not be accomplishing much, however, for we have no assurance that our assumption of a uniform charge density agrees with the actual charge density present in a diode under any condition of operation. In order to determine the volume charge distribution, we need to include consideration of the forces on the electrons making up the volume charge (or "space charge") and we also need to obey the principle of continuity of current.   These additional relationships, considered in the final chapter, complicate most practical problems immensely.

7.5. Product Solution of Laplace's Equation.   In this section we are confronted with the class of potential fields which vary with more than one of the three coordinates, and in particular the three cartesian coordinates.   Although our examples are taken in this simplest coordinate system, the general method is applicable to the other coordinate systems.   We shall avoid these applications because the potential fields are given in terms of more advanced mathematical functions, such as Bessel functions and spherical and cylindrical harmonics, and our interest now does not lie with new mathematical functions but with the techniques and methods of solving electrostatic-field problems.

We may provide ourselves with a general class of problems by specifying merely that the potential is a function of x and y alone, so that

$$\frac{\partial^2 V}{\partial x^2} + \frac{\partial^2 V}{\partial y^2} = 0 \tag{1}$$

We now assume that the potential is expressible as the *product* of a function of x alone and a function of y alone.   It might seem that this prohibits too many solutions, such as $V = x + y$, or any *sum* of a function of x and a function of y, but we should realize that Laplace's equation is linear and the sum of any two solutions is also a solution.[1] We could treat $V = x + y$ as the sum of $V_1 = x$ and $V_2 = y$, where each of these latter potentials is now a (trivial) product solution.

Representing the function of x by X and the function of y by Y, we have

$$V = XY \tag{2}$$

which is substituted into (1):

$$Y \frac{\partial^2 X}{\partial x^2} + X \frac{\partial^2 Y}{\partial y^2} = 0$$

Since X does not involve y and Y does not involve x, ordinary derivatives may be used:

$$Y \frac{d^2 X}{dx^2} + X \frac{d^2 Y}{dy^2} = 0 \tag{3}$$

---

[1] If $\partial^2 V_1/\partial x^2 + \partial^2 V_1/\partial y^2 + \partial^2 V_1/\partial z^2 = 0$ and also $\partial^2 V_2/\partial x^2 + \partial^2 V_2/\partial y^2 + \partial^2 V_2/\partial z^2 = 0$, then addition produces $\partial^2(V_1 + V_2)/\partial x^2 + \partial^2(V_1 + V_2)/\partial y^2 + \partial^2(V_1 + V_2)/\partial z^2 = 0$, showing that the sum $V = V_1 + V_2$ is also a solution. Would this hold for $(\partial^2/\partial x^2)(V^2) + (\partial^2/\partial y^2)(V^2) + (\partial^2/\partial z^2)(V^2) = 0$?

Equation (3) may be solved by separating the variables through division by XY, giving

$$\frac{1}{X}\frac{d^2X}{dx^2} + \frac{1}{Y}\frac{d^2Y}{dy^2} = 0$$

or

$$\frac{1}{X}\frac{d^2X}{dx^2} = -\frac{1}{Y}\frac{d^2Y}{dy^2}$$

Now we need one of the cleverest arguments of mathematics: since $(1/X)d^2X/dx^2$ involves no y and $-(1/Y)d^2Y/dy^2$ involves no x, and since the two quantities are equal, then $(1/X)d^2X/dx^2$ cannot be a function of x either and $-(1/Y)d^2Y/dy^2$ similarly cannot be a function of y! In other words, we have shown that each of these terms must be a constant. For convenience, let us call this constant α^2:

$$\frac{1}{X}\frac{d^2X}{dx^2} = \alpha^2 \tag{4}$$

$$-\frac{1}{Y}\frac{d^2Y}{dy^2} = \alpha^2 \tag{5}$$

The constant α^2 is called the *separation constant* because its use results in separating one equation into two simpler equations.

Equation (4) may be written

$$\frac{d^2X}{dx^2} = \alpha^2X \tag{6}$$

and must now be solved. There are several methods by which a solution may be obtained. The first method is experience, or recognition, which becomes more powerful with practice. We are just beginning and can barely recognize Laplace's equation itself. The second method might be that of direct integration, when applicable of course. Applying it here, we should write

$$d\left(\frac{dX}{dx}\right) = \alpha^2X\,dx$$

$$\frac{dX}{dx} = \alpha^2 \int X\,dx$$

and then pass on to the next method, for X is some unknown function of x, and the method of integration is not applicable here. The third method we might describe as intuition, common sense, or inspection. It involves taking a good look at the equation, perhaps putting the operation into words. This method will work on (6) for some of us if we ask ourselves the question, "What function has a second derivative which has the same form as the function itself, except for multiplication by a constant?" The answer is the exponential function, of course, and we could go on from here to construct the solution. Instead, let us work with those of us whose intuition is suffering from exposure and apply a very powerful but longer method, the infinite-power-series substitution.

We assume hopefully that X may be represented by

$$X = \sum_{n=0}^{\infty} a_n x^n$$

and substitute into (6), giving

$$\frac{d^2X}{dx^2} = \sum_{0}^{\infty} n(n-1)a_n x^{n-2} = \alpha^2 \sum_{0}^{\infty} a_n x^n$$

If these two different infinite series are to be equal for all x, they must be identical, and the coefficients of like powers of x equated term by term. Thus,

$$(2)(1)a_2 = \alpha^2 a_0$$
$$(3)(2)a_3 = \alpha^2 a_1$$

and, in general,

$$(n+2)(n+1)a_{n+2} = \alpha^2 a_n$$

The even coefficients may be expressed in terms of a_0:

$$a_2 = \frac{\alpha^2}{(1)(2)} a_0$$
$$a_4 = \frac{\alpha^2}{(3)(4)} a_2 = \frac{\alpha^4}{4!} a_0$$
$$a_6 = \frac{\alpha^6}{6!} a_0$$

and, in general, for n even:

$$a_n = \frac{\alpha^n}{n!} a_0 \qquad (n \text{ even})$$

For odd values of n, we have

$$a_3 = \frac{\alpha^2}{(2)(3)} a_1 = \frac{\alpha^3}{3!} \left(\frac{a_1}{\alpha} \right)$$
$$a_5 = \frac{\alpha^5}{5!} \left(\frac{a_1}{\alpha} \right)$$

and, in general, for n odd,

$$a_n = \frac{\alpha^n}{n!}\left(\frac{a_1}{\alpha}\right) \qquad (n \text{ odd})$$

Substituting back into the original power series for X, we obtain

$$X = a_0 \sum_{0,\text{ even}}^{\infty} \frac{\alpha^n}{n!} x^n + \frac{a_1}{\alpha} \sum_{1,\text{ odd}}^{\infty} \frac{\alpha^n}{n!} x^n$$

or

$$X = a_0 \sum_{0,\text{ even}}^{\infty} \frac{(\alpha x)^n}{n!} + \frac{a_1}{\alpha} \sum_{1,\text{ odd}}^{\infty} \frac{(\alpha x)^n}{n!}$$

The sum of these two infinite series is the solution of the differential equation in x, although the form of the solution may be improved immeasurably by recognizing the first series as the hyperbolic cosine:

$$\cosh \alpha x = \sum_{0,\text{ even}}^{\infty} \frac{(\alpha x)^n}{n!} = 1 + \frac{(\alpha x)^2}{2!} + \frac{(\alpha x)^4}{4!} + \cdots$$

and the second series as the hyperbolic sine:

$$\sinh \alpha x = \sum_{1,\text{ odd}}^{\infty} \frac{(\alpha x)^n}{n!} = \alpha x + \frac{(\alpha x)^3}{3!} + \frac{(\alpha x)^5}{5!} + \cdots$$

The solution may therefore be written

$$X = a_0 \cosh \alpha x + \frac{a_1}{\alpha} \sinh \alpha x$$

or

$$X = A \cosh \alpha x + B \sinh \alpha x$$

where the slightly simpler terms A and B have replaced a_0 and a_1/α and are the two constants which must be evaluated in terms of the boundary conditions. The separation constant is not an arbitrary constant as far as the solution of (6) is concerned, for it appears in that equation.

The solution of (5) proceeds along similar lines, leading to two power series representing the sine and cosine, and we have

$$Y = C \cos \alpha y + D \sin \alpha y$$

from which the potential is

$$V = XY = (A \cosh \alpha x + B \sinh \alpha x)(C \cos \alpha y + D \sin \alpha y) \qquad (7)$$

Before describing a physical problem and forcing the constants appearing in (7) to fit the boundary conditions prescribed, let us consider the physical nature of the potential field given by a simple choice of these constants. Letting $A = 0$, $C = 0$, $BD = V_1$, we have

$$V = V_1 \sinh \alpha x \sin \alpha y \tag{8}$$

The $\sinh \alpha x$ factor is zero at $x = 0$ and increases smoothly with x, soon becoming nearly exponential in form, since

$$\sinh \alpha x = \tfrac{1}{2}(e^{\alpha x} - e^{-\alpha x})$$

The $\sin \alpha y$ term causes the potential to be zero at $y = 0$, $y = \pi/\alpha$, $y = 2\pi/\alpha$, and so forth. We therefore may place zero-potential conducting planes at $x = 0$, $y = 0$, and $y = \pi/\alpha$. Finally, we can describe the V_1 equipotential surface by setting $V = V_1$ in (8), obtaining

$$\sinh \alpha x \sin \alpha y = 1$$

or
$$\alpha y = \sin^{-1} \frac{1}{\sinh \alpha x}$$

This is not a familiar equation, but a slide rule or a set of tables can furnish enough numerical values to allow us to plot αy as a function of αx. Such a curve is shown in Fig. 7.2. Note that the curve is double-valued and symmetrical about the line $\alpha y = \tfrac{1}{2}\pi$. The information of Fig. 7.2 is transferred directly to the sketch of the $V = 0$ and $V = V_1$ equipotential conducting surfaces in Fig. 7.3. The surfaces are shown in cross section since the potential is not a function of z.

It is very unlikely that we shall ever be asked to find the potential field of these peculiarly shaped electrodes, but we should bear in mind the possibility of combining a number of the fields having the form given by (7) or (8) and thus satisfying the boundary conditions of a more practical problem. One example of such a combination will be our final example.

The problem to be solved is that shown in Fig. 7.4. The boundary conditions shown by this sketch are $V = 0$ at $x = 0$, $y = 0$, and $y = b$, and $V = V_0$ at $x = d$ for all y between 0 and b. It is immediately apparent that the potential field given by (8) and outlined in Fig. 7.3 satisfies two of the four boundary conditions. A third condition, $V = 0$ at $y = b$, may be satisfied by the choice of α, for the substitution of these values into (8) leads to an equation:

$$0 = V_1 \sinh \alpha x \sin \alpha b$$

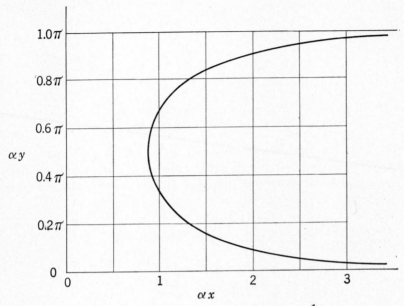

FIG. 7.2. A graph of the function $\alpha y = \sin^{-1} \dfrac{1}{\sinh \alpha x}$.

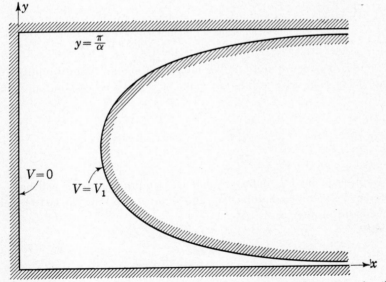

FIG. 7.3. Cross section of the $V = 0$ and $V = V_1$ equipotential surfaces for the potential field $V = V_1 \sinh \alpha x \sin \alpha y$.

which may be satisfied by setting

$$\alpha b = m\pi \qquad m = 1, 2, 3, \ldots$$

or

$$\alpha = \frac{m\pi}{b}$$

The potential function

$$V = V_1 \sinh \frac{m\pi x}{b} \sin \frac{m\pi y}{b}$$

thus produces the correct potential at $x = 0$, $y = 0$, and $y = b$, regardless of the choice of m or the value of V_1. It is impossible to choose m or V_1 in such a way that $V = V_0$ at $x = d$ for each and every

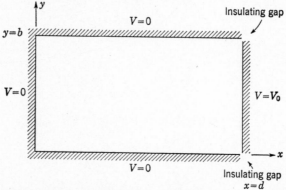

FIG. 7.4. Potential problem requiring an infinite summation of fields of the form $V = V_1 \sinh \alpha x \sin \alpha y$.

value of y between 0 and b. We must combine an infinite number of these fields, each with a different value of m and a corresponding value of V_1:

$$V = \sum_{m=0}^{\infty} V_{1m} \sinh \frac{m\pi x}{b} \sin \frac{m\pi y}{b} \qquad (9)$$

The subscript on V_{1m} indicates that this amplitude factor will have a different value for each different value of m. Applying the last boundary condition now,

$$V_0 = \sum_{m=0}^{\infty} V_{1m} \sinh \frac{m\pi d}{b} \sin \frac{m\pi y}{b} \qquad 0 < y < b, \, m = 1, 2, \ldots$$

Since $V_{1m} \sinh (m\pi d/b)$ is only a function of m, we may simplify the expression by replacing this factor by c_m:

$$V_0 = \sum_{m=0}^{\infty} c_m \sin \frac{m\pi y}{b} \qquad 0 < y < b, \, m = 1, 2, \ldots$$

This is a Fourier sine series, and the c_m coefficients may be determined by the standard Fourier-series methods[1] if we can interpret V_0 as a periodic function of y. Since our physical problem is bounded by conducting planes at $y = 0$ and $y = b$, and our interest in the potential does not extend outside of this region, we may *define* the potential at $x = d$ for y *outside* of the range 0 to b in any manner we choose. Probably the simplest periodic expression is obtained by selecting the interval $0 < y < b$ as the half period and choosing $V = -V_0$ in the adjacent half period, or

$$V = V_0 \qquad 0 < y < b$$
$$V = -V_0 \qquad b < y < 2b$$

The c_m coefficients are, then,

$$c_m = \frac{1}{b} \left[\int_0^b V_0 \sin \frac{m\pi y}{b} \, dy + \int_b^{2b} (-V_0) \sin \frac{m\pi y}{b} \, dy \right]$$

leading to

$$c_m = \frac{4V_0}{m\pi} \qquad (m \text{ odd})$$
$$= 0 \qquad (m \text{ even})$$

However, $c_m = V_{1m} \sinh (m\pi d/b)$, and therefore

$$V_{1m} = \frac{4V_0}{m\pi \sinh (m\pi d/b)} \qquad (m \text{ odd only})$$

which may be substituted into (9) to give the desired potential function:

$$V = \frac{4V_0}{\pi} \sum_{1,\text{odd}}^{\infty} \frac{1}{m} \frac{\sinh (m\pi x/b)}{\sinh (m\pi d/b)} \sin \frac{m\pi y}{b} \qquad (10)$$

The map of this field may be obtained by evaluating (10) at a number of points and drawing equipotentials by interpolation between these points. If we let $b = d$ and $V_0 = 100$, the problem is identical with that used as the example in the discussion of the iteration and relaxation methods. Checking one of the grid points in that problem,

---

[1] Fourier series are discussed in almost every electrical-engineering text on circuit theory. See, for example, the Rideout reference given in the bibliography.

we let $x = \frac{1}{4}d = \frac{1}{4}b$, $y = \frac{1}{2}b = \frac{1}{2}d$, $V_0 = 100$, and obtain

$$V = \frac{400}{\pi} \sum_{1,\text{odd}}^{\infty} \frac{1}{m} \frac{\sinh \frac{1}{4}m\pi}{\sinh m\pi} \sin \frac{1}{2}m\pi$$

$$= \frac{400}{\pi} \left(\frac{\sinh \frac{1}{4}\pi}{\sinh \pi} - \frac{1}{3} \frac{\sinh \frac{1}{4}3\pi}{\sinh 3\pi} + \frac{1}{5} \frac{\sinh \frac{1}{4}5\pi}{\sinh 5\pi} - \cdots \right)$$

$$= \frac{400}{\pi} \left[\frac{0.8687}{11.549} - \frac{5.228}{(3)(6{,}197.2)} + \cdots \right]$$

$$= \frac{400}{\pi} (0.07522 - 0.00028 + \cdots)$$

$$= 9.542 \text{ volts}$$

The equipotentials are drawn for increments of 10 volts in Fig. 7.5, and flux lines have been added graphically to produce a curvilinear map..

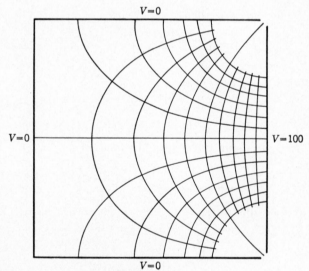

FIG. 7.5. The field map corresponding to

$$V = \frac{4V_0}{\pi} \sum_{1,\text{odd}}^{\infty} \frac{1}{m} \frac{\sinh (m\pi x/b)}{\sinh (m\pi d/b)} \sin \frac{m\pi y}{b} \qquad \text{with } b = d,\ V_0 = 100$$

The material covered in this discussion of the product solution has been more difficult than much of the preceding work, and it has, moreover, presented three new ideas. The first new technique was the assumption that the potential might be expressed as the product of a function of x and a function of y, and the resultant separation of Laplace's equation into two simpler ordinary differential equations. The second new approach was employed when an infinite-power-series solution was assumed as the solution for one of the ordinary differential equations. Finally, we considered an example which required the combination of an infinite number of simpler product solutions, each having a different amplitude and a different variation in one of the coordinate directions. All these techniques are very powerful. They are useful in all coordinate systems, and they can be used in problems in which the potential varies with all three coordinates.

We have merely introduced the subject here, and more information can be obtained from the references listed below, several of which devote hundreds of pages to the solution of Laplace's equation.

D7.6. Using (10) with $V_0 = 100$ volts, $b = d = 1$, use the gradient to obtain an expression for **E**, and then evaluate **E** at:

(a) $x = 0$, $y = 0$.

(b) $x = 0$, $y = \frac{1}{2}b$.

(c) $x = \frac{1}{2}d$, $y = 0$ [note the magnitude of this answer as compared with that of (b)].

Ans. $-34.6a_x - 83.5a_y$ volts/m.

SUGGESTED REFERENCES

1. Ramo, S., and J. R. Whinnery: (see Suggested References for Chap. 6). A more complete and advanced discussion of methods of solving Laplace's equation is given in chap. 3.

2. Rideout, V. C.: "Active Networks," Prentice-Hall, Inc., Englewood Cliffs, N.J., 1954.

3. Smythe, W. R.: "Static and Dynamic Electricity," 2d ed., McGraw-Hill Book Company, Inc., New York, 1950. An advanced treatment of potential theory is given in chap. 4.

4. Weber, E.: (see Suggested References for Chap. 6). There are a tremendous number of potential solutions given with the original references.

PROBLEMS

1. For a homogeneous medium containing no volume charge density, show that $\nabla^2 i_u$, $\nabla^2 E_u$, and $\nabla^2 D_u = 0$, where the u subscript represents either x, y, or z. In other words, show that every cartesian component of **i**, **E**, and **D** satisfies Laplace's equation. The only currents present are direct.

2. If $\nabla^2 V_1 = 0$ and $\nabla^2 V_2 = 0$, is (a) $\nabla^2 (V_1 - V_2) = 0$? (b) $\nabla^2 (V_1 V_2) = 0$?

3. Show that Sec. 7.1, Eqs. (9) and (10), follow from the expression for gradient and divergence in the appropriate coordinate systems.

4. Show that $V = (V_0 r/d) \cos \phi$ satisfies Laplace's equation in cylindrical coordinates. What is the physical nature of the equipotential surfaces? Specifically describe the equipotential surfaces $V = 0$ and $V = V_0$. Write the potential expression in cartesian coordinates.

5. Show that the potential function $V = E_0(r - a^2/r) \cos \phi$ satisfies Laplace's equation in cylindrical coordinates. Determine the asymptotic form of the equipotential surfaces for $r \gg a$. (Hint: See Prob. 4.) Describe the $V = 0$ surface. What physical problem may then possess this potential field? Find $\mathbf{E}$, and show that $\mathbf{E}$ is normal to the conductor boundaries of the physical problem.

6. Without evaluating the constants A and B in terms of boundary conditions, use Sec. 7.3, Eq. (4), to find the capacitance between two coaxial cylinders of radius r_1 and r_2. The expressions for total charge and potential difference will now be given in terms of A and B.

7. Two radial conducting planes, located in free space at $\phi^\circ = 0$ and $\phi = 90^\circ$, are finite in area, extending from $r = 1$ mm to $r = 10$ cm, and from $z = 0$ to $z = 1$ m.

(a) Neglecting any charge on the outside of the plates (by "outside" we refer to the range $90^\circ < \phi < 360^\circ$), find the capacitance between the plates. Fringing flux is to be neglected.

(b) What percentage increase in capacitance results from including the charges on the outside?

8. Solve Laplace's equation for the region between two concentric conducting spheres of radius a and b, $b > a$. Let $V = 0$ at $r = b$ and $V = V_0$ at $r = a$. From the resultant potential function [given in Sec. 7.3, Eq. (6)], find the capacitance between the spheres.

9. In spherical coordinates the cones $\theta = \theta_1$ and $\theta = \theta_2$ are conductors. Region 1, extending from θ_1 to θ_a, and region 2, extending from θ_a to θ_2, have permittivities of ϵ_1 and ϵ_2, respectively, where $\theta_1 < \theta_a < \theta_2$. Write the general solution of Laplace's equation for each region, and evaluate the four constants of integration by choosing $V = 0$ at $\theta = \theta_1$, $V = V_0$ at $\theta = \theta_2$, and by using the relationship between the values of V immediately on either side of the dielectric interface at $\theta = \theta_a$ and the relationship between the values of $\mathbf{E}$ or $\mathbf{D}$ in the two regions at the interface.

10. Using cylindrical coordinates, find the potential within a uniform volume charge density of $-\rho_0$ coulombs/m^3, extending from $r = 0$ to $r = 1$. The charge density does not vary with ϕ or z. Evaluate the constants by choosing $V = 0$ at $r = 1$ and $V = 100$ at $r = 0.1$.

11. A parallel-plane diode operates with *space-charge-limited* emission (space-charge-limited emission is emission which is limited by the field produced at the cathode due to the space charge and the externally applied potential; the cathode temperature is not a limiting factor). If the cathode is described by $x = 0$, $V = 0$, and the plate by $x = d$, $V = V_0$, the potential is given as $V = V_0(x/d)^{4/3}$. Find the volume charge density and electric field intensity as functions of x. How do the maximum and minimum values of $\mathbf{E}$ compare with the uniform $\mathbf{E}$ present with no space charge? What percentage of the total energy acquired by an electron in passing from the cathode to the plate is attained at the halfway point, $x = \frac{1}{2}d$?

12. Given Laplace's equation in cylindrical coordinates, assume no variation of potential with ϕ. Assume also that V may be expressed as the product of a function of r and a function of z, $V = RZ$. Substitute this product into Laplace's equation, and show that the separated equations are $d^2R/dr^2 + (1/r) \, dR/dr + \alpha^2R = 0$ and $d^2Z/dz^2 = \alpha^2Z$, where α^2 is the separation constant.

13. Solve the differential equation $(1/Y)\ d^2Y/dy^2 = -\alpha^2$ by assuming Y is expressible by an infinite power series in y. Show that the resultant series is a combination of the power series for the trigonometric sine and cosine.

14. Given Laplace's equation in cylindrical coordinates, assume no variation of potential with z. Assume also that V may be expressed as the product of a function of r and a function of ϕ, $V = R\Phi$. Substitute this product into Laplace's equation, and show that the separated equations are $d^2R/dr^2 + (1/r)\ dR/dr - n^2R/r^2 = 0$ and $d^2\Phi/d\phi^2 = -n^2\Phi$, where n^2 is the separation constant. Assume a power series including both positive and negative powers for R, $R = \sum_{-\infty}^{\infty} a_m r^m$, and show that $R = Ar^n + Br^{-n}$, where n may be any positive integer.

15. With reference to Fig. 7.4, change the potential of the side at $y = b$ to $V = 50$ volts and let $V_0 = 100$, $b = d = 1$. Show that the potential at the center is 37.5 volts.

CHAPTER 8

THE STEADY MAGNETIC FIELD

At this point the concept of the "field" should be a familiar one. Since we first accepted the experimental law of forces existing between two point charges and defined the electric field intensity as the force per unit charge on a test charge in the presence of a second charge, we have met numerous fields. These fields possess no real physical basis, for physical measurements must always be in terms of the forces on the charges in the detection equipment. Those charges which are the source cause measurable forces to be exerted on other charges which we may think of as detector charges. The fact that we attribute a field to the source charges and then determine the effect of this field on the detector charges amounts merely to a division of the basic problem into two parts for our own convenience.

We shall begin our study of the magnetic field with a definition of the magnetic field itself and show how it arises from a current distribution. The effect of this field on other currents, or the second half of the physical problem, will be discussed in the following chapter.

The relation of the steady magnetic field to its source is more complicated than is the relation of the electrostatic field to its source. We shall find it necessary to accept several laws temporarily on faith alone, relegating their proof to the (rather difficult) final section in this chapter. The author's feeling is that this section may well be omitted when meeting magnetic fields for the first time. It is included to make acceptance of the laws a little easier; the proof of the laws does exist and is available for the disbelievers or the more advanced student.

8.1. Biot-Savart Law. The source of the steady magnetic field may be a permanent magnet, an electric field changing linearly with time, or a direct current. We shall largely ignore the permanent magnet and save the time-varying electric field for a later discussion. Our present relationships will concern the magnetic field produced by a differential current element.

We may think of this differential current element as a vanishingly small section of a current-carrying filamentary conductor, where a

180

filamentary conductor is the limiting case of a cylindrical conductor of circular cross section as the radius approaches zero. We assume a current of I amp flowing in a differential vector length of the filament $d\mathbf{L}$. The experimental law of Biot-Savart[1] then states that at any point P the magnitude of the magnetic field intensity produced by the differential element is proportional to the product of the current, the magnitude of the differential length, and the sine of the angle lying between the filament and a line connecting the filament to the point P at which the field is desired. The magnitude of the magnetic field intensity is inversely proportional to the square of the distance from the differential element to the point P. The direction of the magnetic field intensity is normal to the plane containing the differential filament and the line drawn from the filament to the point P. Of the two possible normals, that one is to be chosen which is in the direction of progress of a right-handed screw turned from $d\mathbf{L}$ through the smaller angle to the line from the filament to P. Using rationalized mks units, the constant of proportionality is $1/4\pi$.

The *Biot-Savart law*, described above in some 150 words, may be written concisely using vector notation:

$$d\mathbf{H} = \frac{I\,d\mathbf{L} \times \mathbf{a}_R}{4\pi R^2} \qquad (1)$$

The units of the *magnetic field intensity* $\mathbf{H}$ are evidently amperes per meter. The geometry is illustrated in Fig. 8.1. Subscripts may be used to indicate the point to which each of the quantities in (1) refers. If we locate the current element at point 1 and describe the point P at which the field is to be determined as point 2, then

$$d\mathbf{H}_2 = \frac{I_1\,d\mathbf{L}_1 \times \mathbf{a}_{R12}}{4\pi R_{12}^2} \qquad (2)$$

The law of Biot-Savart is sometimes called *Ampère's law for the current element*, but we shall retain the former name because of possible confusion with Ampère's circuital law, to be met later.

It is impossible to check experimentally the law of Biot-Savart as expressed by (1) or (2) because the differential current element cannot be isolated. We have restricted our attention to direct currents only, for which the charge density is not a function of time. The continuity equation in Sec. 5.2, Eq. (2),

$$\nabla \cdot \mathbf{i} = -\frac{\partial \rho}{\partial t}$$

[1] Biot and Savart were colleagues of Ampère, and all three were Professors of Physics at the Collège de France at one time or another. The Biot-Savart law was proposed in 1820.

therefore shows that

$$\nabla \cdot \mathbf{i} = 0$$

or upon applying the divergence theorem,

$$\oint_s \mathbf{i} \cdot d\mathbf{S} = 0$$

The total current crossing any closed surface is zero, and this condition may be satisfied only by assuming a current flow around a closed path.

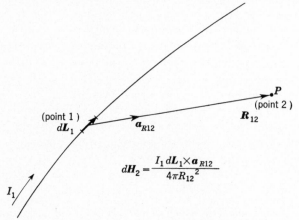

FIG. 8.1. The law of Biot-Savart expresses the magnetic field intensity $d\mathbf{H}_2$ produced by a differential current element $I_1\,d\mathbf{L}_1$. The direction of $d\mathbf{H}_2$ in this sketch is into the page.

It is this current flowing in a closed circuit which must be our experimental source, not the differential element.

It follows that only the integral form of the Biot-Savart law can be verified experimentally,

$$\mathbf{H} = \oint \frac{I\,d\mathbf{L} \times \mathbf{a}_R}{4\pi R^2} \qquad (3)$$

Equation (1) or (2) of course leads directly to the integral form (3), but other differential expressions also yield the same integral formulation. Any term may be added to (1) whose integral around a closed path is zero. We have seen that the electric field intensity is such an expression, and although we might feel somewhat foolish doing so, we could add the term $\mathbf{E} \cdot d\mathbf{L}$ to (1) without changing (3) in the slightest. This qualification on (1) or (2) is mentioned to show that if we later ask some foolish questions, not subject to any experimental check, concerning the force exerted by one *differential* current element on another, we should expect foolish answers.

We may illustrate the application of the Biot-Savart law by considering an infinitely long straight filament. We shall apply (2) first and then integrate. This of course is the same as using the integral form (3) in the first place.[1]

Referring to Fig. 8.2, we should recognize the symmetry of this field. No variation with z or with ϕ can exist. Point 2, at which we shall determine the field, is therefore chosen in the $z = 0$ plane, and the unit vector $\mathbf{a}_{R12}$ is found from

$$\mathbf{R}_{12} = r\mathbf{a}_r - z\mathbf{a}_z$$

by

$$\mathbf{a}_{R12} = \frac{r\mathbf{a}_r - z\mathbf{a}_z}{\sqrt{r^2 + z^2}}$$

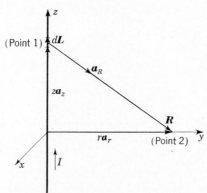

FIG. 8.2. An infinitely long straight filament carrying a direct current of I amp.

The direction of $d\mathbf{L}$ is in the direction in which I flows, or

$$d\mathbf{L} = dz\,\mathbf{a}_z$$

and (2) becomes

$$d\mathbf{H}_2 = \frac{I\,dz\,\mathbf{a}_z \times (r\mathbf{a}_r - z\mathbf{a}_z)}{4\pi(r^2 + z^2)^{3/2}}$$

The integral becomes

$$\mathbf{H}_2 = \int_{-\infty}^{\infty} \frac{I\,dz\,\mathbf{a}_z \times (r\mathbf{a}_r - z\mathbf{a}_z)}{4\pi(r^2 + z^2)^{3/2}}$$

$$= \frac{I}{4\pi} \int_{-\infty}^{\infty} \frac{r\,dz\,\mathbf{a}_\phi}{(r^2 + z^2)^{3/2}}$$

At this point the unit vector $\mathbf{a}_\phi$ under the integral sign should be investigated, for it is not always a constant, as are the unit vectors of the cartesian coordinate system. A vector is constant when its magnitude and direction are both constant. The unit vector certainly has constant magnitude, but its direction may change. Here, $\mathbf{a}_\phi$ changes with the coordinate ϕ but not with r or z. Fortunately, the integration is with respect to z, and $\mathbf{a}_\phi$ is a constant in this case and may be

---

[1] The closed path for the current may be considered to include a return filament parallel to the first filament and infinitely far removed. Practically, the problem is an impossible one, but we should realize that our answer will be quite accurate near a very long straight wire having a distant return path for the current.

removed from under the integral sign:

$$\mathbf{H}_2 = \frac{Ir\mathbf{a}_\phi}{4\pi} \int_{-\infty}^{\infty} \frac{dz}{(r^2 + z^2)^{3/2}}$$

$$= \frac{Ir\mathbf{a}_\phi}{4\pi} \frac{z}{r^2 \sqrt{r^2 + z^2}}\Big|_{-\infty}^{\infty}$$

and $\qquad \mathbf{H}_2 = \dfrac{I}{2\pi r} \mathbf{a}_\phi \qquad\qquad\qquad (4)$

The magnitude of the field is not a function of ϕ or z and varies inversely as the distance from the filament.   The direction of the magnetic field intensity vector is circumferential.   The streamlines are therefore circles about the filament, and the field may be mapped in cross section as in Fig. 8.3.

The separation of the streamlines is proportional to the radius or inversely proportional to the magnitude of $\mathbf{H}$.   More generally, the streamlines have been drawn with curvilinear squares in mind.   As yet we have no name for the family of lines which are perpendicular to these circular streamlines, but the spacing of the streamlines has been adjusted so that the addition of this second set of lines will produce an array of curvilinear squares.

A comparison of Fig. 8.3 with the map of the *electric* field about an infinite line *charge* shows that the streamlines of the magnetic field correspond exactly to the equipotentials of the electric field, and the unnamed (and undrawn) perpendicular family of lines in the magnetic field corresponds to the streamlines of the electric field.

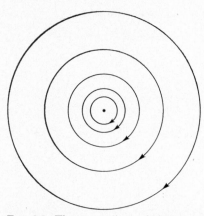

FIG. 8.3. The streamlines of the magnetic field intensity about an infinitely long straight filament carrying a direct current of I amp.   The direction of I is into the page.

This correspondence is not an accident, but there are several other concepts which must be mastered before the analogy between electric and magnetic fields can be explored more thoroughly.

Using the Biot-Savart law to find $\mathbf{H}$ is in many respects similar to the use of Coulomb's law to find $\mathbf{E}$.   Each requires the determination of a moderately complicated integrand containing vector quantities, followed by an integration.   When we were concerned with Coulomb's law we solved a number of examples, including the field of the point charge, line charge, and sheet of charge. The law of Biot-Savart can be used to solve analogous problems in magnetic fields, and these problems now appear as exercises at the end of the chapter rather than as examples here.

D8.1. Find the magnetic field intensity at point P due to a current of 144π ma flowing in a differential length $d\mathbf{L}$ at the origin, where P and $d\mathbf{L}$ are given by:

(a) $P(2,0,0)$, $d\mathbf{L} = 3 \times 10^{-3}\mathbf{a}_y$.

(b) $P(0,2,2)$, $d\mathbf{L} = 3 \times 10^{-3}(\mathbf{a}_y - \mathbf{a}_z)/\sqrt{2}$.

(c) $P(1,2,2)$, $d\mathbf{L} = 3 \times 10^{-3}\mathbf{a}_x$.

Ans. $(13.5\mathbf{a}_x - 8\mathbf{a}_y - 19\mathbf{a}_z)10^{-6}$ amp/m.

D8.2. A current of 1 amp is flowing in a filament forming a closed circular path in the $z = 0$ plane, centered at the origin, radius 60 cm. The direction of flow is given by $\mathbf{a}_\phi$. Find the contribution $d\mathbf{H}$ to the magnetic field intensity at $(0,0,0.8)$ in cartesian coordinates caused by the current in a 1-mm length of arc located at:

(a) $\phi = 0°$.

(b) $\phi = 180°$.

(c) $\phi = 45°$.

Ans. $(45.1\mathbf{a}_x + 45.1\mathbf{a}_y + 143.4\mathbf{a}_z)10^{-6}$ amp/m.

8.2. Ampère's Circuital Law. After solving a number of simple problems with Coulomb's law, the same problems were solved much more easily by using Gauss's law, which required a careful consideration of the symmetry and a determination of which variables and components were involved. Again, an analogous procedure exists in magnetic fields. The law we shall use is known as *Ampère's circuital law*, sometimes called Ampère's work law. This law may be derived from the Biot-Savart law, and the derivation is indicated in Sec. 8.7 below. For the present we might agree to accept Ampère's circuital law temporarily as another law which is capable of experimental proof.

Ampère's circuital law states that the line integral of $\mathbf{H}$ about any *closed* path is exactly equal to the current enclosed by that path:

$$\oint \mathbf{H} \cdot d\mathbf{L} = I \tag{1}$$

We define positive current as flowing in the direction of advance of a right-handed screw turned in the direction in which the closed path is traversed.

Referring to Fig. 8.4, which shows a circular wire carrying a direct current I, the line integral of $\mathbf{H}$ about the closed paths lettered a and b results in an answer of I amp; the integral about the closed path c which passes through the conductor gives an answer less than I amp and is exactly that portion of the total current which is enclosed by the path c. Although paths a and b give the same answer, the integrands are of course different. The line integral directs us to multiply the component of **H** in the direction of the path by a small increment of path length at one point of the path, move along the path to the next incremental length and repeat the process, continuing until the path is completely traversed.   Since **H** will in general vary from point to point and since paths a and b are not alike, the contributions to the integral made by, say, each millimeter of path length are quite different.   Only the final answer is the same.

We should also consider exactly what is meant by the expression "current enclosed by the path."   Suppose we solder a circuit together after passing the conductor once through a rubber band which we shall use to represent the closed path.   Some strange and formidable paths

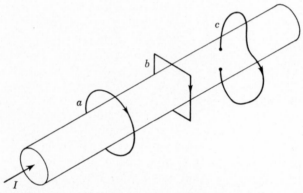

FIG. 8.4. A conductor has a total current of I amp.   The line integral of **H** about the closed paths a and b is equal to I, and the integral around path c is less than I since the entire current is not enclosed by the path.

can be constructed by twisting and knotting the rubber band, but if neither the rubber band nor the conducting circuit is broken, the current enclosed by the path is that carried by the conductor.   Now let us replace the rubber band by a circular ring of spring steel across which is stretched a rubber sheet.   The steel loop forms the closed path, and the current-carrying conductor must pierce the rubber sheet if the current is to be enclosed by the path.   Again we may twist the steel loop, and we may also deform the rubber sheet by pushing our fist into it or folding it in any way we wish.   A single current-carrying conductor still pierces the sheet once, and this is the true measure of the current enclosed by the path.   If we should thread the conductor once through the sheet from front to back and once from back to front, the total current enclosed by the path is the algebraic sum, which is zero.

In more general language, given a closed path, we recognize this path as the perimeter of an infinite number of surfaces (not closed surfaces). Any current-carrying conductor enclosed by the path must pass through every one of these surfaces once. Certainly some of the surfaces may be chosen in such a way that the conductor pierces them twice in one direction and once in the other direction, but the algebraic total current is still the same.

We shall find that the closed path is usually of an extremely simple nature and can be drawn on a plane. The simplest surface is, then, that portion of the plane enclosed by the path. We need merely find the total current passing through this plane.

The application of Gauss's law involves finding the total charge enclosed by a closed surface; the application of Ampère's circuital law involves finding the total current enclosed by a closed path.

Let us again find the magnetic field intensity produced by an infinitely long filament carrying a current of I amp. The filament lies on the z axis, and the current flows in the direction given by $\mathbf{a}_z$. Symmetry inspection comes first, showing that there is no variation with z or ϕ. Next we consider the components of $\mathbf{H}$ which are present by using the Biot-Savart law. Without specifically using the cross product we may say that the direction of $d\mathbf{H}$ is perpendicular to the plane containing $d\mathbf{L}$ and $\mathbf{R}$ and therefore is in the direction of $\mathbf{a}_\phi$. Hence, the only component of $\mathbf{H}$ is H_ϕ, and it is a function only of r.

We therefore choose a path to which $\mathbf{H}$ is either perpendicular or tangential and along which H is constant. The first requirement allows us to replace the dot product of Ampère's circuital law with the product of the scalar magnitudes, except along that portion of the path where $\mathbf{H}$ is normal to the path and the dot product is zero; the second requirement then permits us to remove the magnetic field intensity from the integral sign. The integration required is usually trivial and consists of finding the length of that portion of the path to which $\mathbf{H}$ is parallel.

In our example, the path is a circle of radius r, and Ampère's circuital law becomes

$$\oint \mathbf{H} \cdot d\mathbf{L} = \int_0^{2\pi} H_\phi r \, d\phi = H_\phi r \int_0^{2\pi} d\phi = H_\phi 2\pi r = I$$

or

$$H_\phi = \frac{I}{2\pi r}$$

as before.

As a second example of the application of Ampère's circuital law, consider a coaxial transmission line carrying a uniformly distributed total current of I amp in the center conductor and $-I$ amp in the outer conductor.   The line is sketched in Fig. 8.5.   Symmetry shows that H is not a function of ϕ or z.   In order to determine the components

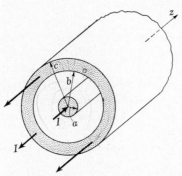

present, we may use the results of the previous example by considering the solid conductors as being composed of a large number of filaments. No filament has a z component. Furthermore, the H_r component at $\phi = 0°$ produced by one filament located at $r = r_1$, $\phi = \phi_1$, is canceled by the H_r component produced by a symmetrically located filament at $r = r_1$, $\phi = -\phi_1$. Again we find only an H_ϕ component which varies with r.

FIG. 8.5. Cross section of a coaxial cable carrying a uniformly distributed current of I amp in the inner conductor and $-I$ amp in the outer conductor.

A circular path of radius r, where r is larger than the radius of the inner conductor but less than the inner radius of the outer conductor, then leads immediately to

$$H_\phi = \frac{I}{2\pi r} \qquad b > r > a$$

If we choose r smaller than the radius of the inner conductor, the current enclosed is

$$I_{encl} = I \frac{r^2}{a^2}$$

and
$$H_\phi = \frac{Ir}{2\pi a^2} \qquad a > r$$

If the radius r is larger than the outer radius of the outer conductor, no current is enclosed and

$$H_\phi = 0 \qquad r > c$$

Finally, if the path lies within the outer conductor, we have

$$H_\phi = \frac{I}{2\pi r} \frac{c^2 - r^2}{c^2 - b^2} \qquad c > r > b$$

The magnetic-field-strength variation with radius is shown in Fig. 8.6 for a coaxial cable in which $b = 3a$, $c = 4a$.   It should be noted that the magnetic field intensity $\mathbf{H}$ is continuous at all the conductor boundaries.   In other words, a slight increase in the radius of the closed path does not result in the enclosure of a tremendously different current.   The value of H_ϕ shows no sudden jumps.

The external field is zero.   This, we see, results from equal positive
and negative currents enclosed by the path.   Each produces an external field of magnitude $I/2\pi r$, but complete cancellation occurs.   This
is another example of "shielding."

As a final example, let us consider a sheet of current flowing in the
positive z direction and located in the $x = 0$ plane.   We shall assume
that the sheet has zero thickness in the x direction.   The current density is therefore infinite.   A surface current density may be defined
to take care of a case such as this where current flow takes place in a

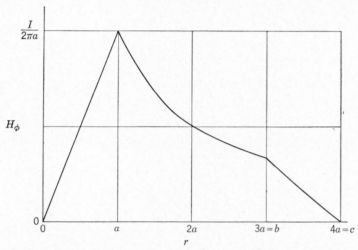

FIG. 8.6. The magnetic field intensity as a function of radius in a coaxial transmission line with an inner radius of the outer conductor and an outer radius of the
outer conductor three and four times the radius of the inner conductor, respectively.

sheet or on a surface.   Surface current density is measured in amperes
per meter width and is designated by $\mathbf{J}_s$.   If the surface current density is uniform, the total current I in any width b is

$$I = J_s b$$

where we have assumed that the width b is measured perpendicularly
to the direction of the current flow.   In the general case, integration
is necessary:

$$I = \int J_s \, dL$$

The sheet of current of uniform surface current density $\mathbf{J}_s = J_{sz}\mathbf{a}_z$
is shown in Fig. 8.7. $\mathbf{H}$ cannot vary with y or z, and subdivision of the
sheet into a number of filaments and application of the Biot-Savart
law show that only H_y is present.   We therefore choose the path

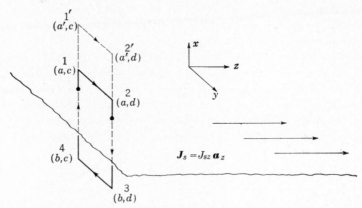

FIG. 8.7. A uniform sheet of surface current, $\mathbf{J}_z = J_{sz}\mathbf{a}_z$, in the $x = 0$ plane.

1-2-3-4-1 composed of straight line segments and have

$$(H_{y \text{ at } x=a})(d - c) + (H_{y \text{ at } x=b})(c - d) = J_{sz}(d - c)$$

or $$H_{y \text{ at } x=a} - H_{y \text{ at } x=b} = J_{sz}$$

If the path $1'$-$2'$-3-4-$1'$ is now chosen, the same current is enclosed and

$$H_{y \text{ at } x=a'} - H_{y \text{ at } x=b} = J_{sz}$$

and therefore

$$H_{y \text{ at } x=a'} = H_{y \text{ at } x=a}$$

It follows that H_y is the same for all positive x. Similarly, H_y is the same for all negative x. Because of the symmetry, then,

$$H_{y \text{ for } x>0} = -H_{y \text{ for } x<0}$$

and therefore

$$H_{y \text{ for } x>0} = \tfrac{1}{2}J_{sz}$$

and $$H_{y \text{ for } x<0} = -\tfrac{1}{2}J_{sz}$$

Letting $\mathbf{a}_n$ be a unit vector normal to the current sheet, the result may be written in a form correct for all x:

$$\mathbf{H} = \tfrac{1}{2}\mathbf{J}_s \times \mathbf{a}_n \qquad (2)$$

If a second sheet of current flowing in the opposite direction, $\mathbf{J}_s = -J_{sz}\mathbf{a}_z$, is placed at $x = h$, (2) shows that the field in the region between the current sheets is

$$\mathbf{H} = \mathbf{J}_s \times \mathbf{a}_n \qquad 0 < x < h \qquad (3)$$

and is zero elsewhere:

$$\mathbf{H} = 0 \qquad x < 0 \text{ and } x > h \qquad (4)$$

The most difficult part of the application of Ampère's circuital law is the determination of the components of the field which are present. The surest method is the logical application of the Biot-Savart law and a knowledge of the magnetic fields of simple form.

D8.3. A direct current of 3 amp is flowing in a filamentary conductor of helical shape. The helix lies along the z axis with a 1-m radius and a separation between turns of 0.1 m. The helix passes through the point $(1,0,0)$. Find the magnitude of the current enclosed by the path:

(a) Circle in $z = 0$ plane, radius 2 m, center at origin.

(b) Square in plane $y = 0$, sides of length 1.3 m and parallel to coordinate axes, center at $(0.5,0,0)$.

(c) Path consisting of straight line segments connecting, in order, $(0,1,0)$, $(0,0,0)$, $(0,0,2)$, $(0.5,0,2)$, $(0.5,0,-2)$, $(0.5,0.5,-2)$, $(0,1,0)$.

                                                                Ans. 42 amp.

D8.4. A sheet of surface current $J_s = 6a_x$ is located at $z = 0$, and a filamentary current of 12π amp, flowing in the positive x direction, is at $y = 0$, $z = 1$. Find **H** at:

(a) $(0,0,0.5)$.

(b) $(0,0,1.5)$.

(c) $(0,1,1)$.

                                                    Ans. $-9a_y + 6a_z$ amp/m.

8.3. Curl. We completed our study of Gauss's law by applying this law to a differential volume element and were led to the concept of

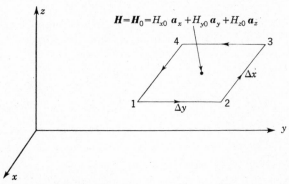

FIG. 8.8. An incremental closed path in cartesian coordinates is selected for the application of Ampère's circuital law.

divergence. We shall now apply Ampère's circuital law to a differential closed path and meet the third and last of the special derivatives of vector analysis, the curl. Our immediate object is to obtain the point form of Ampère's circuital law.

Again we shall choose cartesian coordinates, and an incremental closed path of sides Δx and Δy is selected (Fig. 8.8). We shall assume a reference value for $\mathbf{H}$ at the center of this small rectangle as

$$\mathbf{H}_0 = H_{x0}\mathbf{a}_x + H_{y0}\mathbf{a}_y + H_{z0}\mathbf{a}_z$$

The closed line integral of $\mathbf{H}$ about this path is then approximately the sum of the four values of $\mathbf{H} \cdot \Delta\mathbf{L}$ on each side. Choosing the direction of traverse as 1-2-3-4-1, the first contribution is therefore

$$(\mathbf{H} \cdot \Delta\mathbf{L})_{1\text{-}2} = H_{y,1\text{-}2}\,\Delta y$$

where the value of H_y on this section of the path may be given in terms of the reference value H_{y0} and the rate of change of H_y with x:

$$H_{y,1\text{-}2} \doteq H_{y0} + \frac{\partial H_y}{\partial x}\left(\frac{1}{2}\,\Delta x\right)$$

Thus

$$(\mathbf{H} \cdot \Delta\mathbf{L})_{1\text{-}2} \doteq \left(H_{y0} + \frac{1}{2}\frac{\partial H_y}{\partial x}\,\Delta x\right)\Delta y$$

Along the next section of the path, we have

$$(\mathbf{H} \cdot \Delta\mathbf{L})_{2\text{-}3} \doteq H_{x,2\text{-}3}(-\Delta x) \doteq -\left(H_{x0} + \frac{1}{2}\frac{\partial H_x}{\partial y}\,\Delta y\right)\Delta x$$

Continuing for the remaining two segments and adding the results,

$$\oint \mathbf{H} \cdot d\mathbf{L} \doteq \left(\frac{\partial H_y}{\partial x} - \frac{\partial H_x}{\partial y}\right)\Delta x\,\Delta y$$

By Ampère's circuital law, this result must be equal to the current enclosed by the path, or the current crossing the surface bounded by the path. If we assume a general current density of $\mathbf{i}$ amp/m^2, the enclosed current is then $\Delta I \doteq i_z\,\Delta x\,\Delta y$ and

$$\oint \mathbf{H} \cdot d\mathbf{L} \doteq \left(\frac{\partial H_y}{\partial x} - \frac{\partial H_x}{\partial y}\right)\Delta x\,\Delta y \doteq i_z\,\Delta x\,\Delta y$$

or

$$\frac{\oint \mathbf{H} \cdot d\mathbf{L}}{\Delta x\,\Delta y} \doteq \frac{\partial H_y}{\partial x} - \frac{\partial H_x}{\partial y} \doteq i_z$$

As we cause the closed path to shrink, the above expression becomes more nearly exact, and in the limit we have an equality:

$$\lim_{\Delta x,\Delta y \to 0} \frac{\oint \mathbf{H} \cdot d\mathbf{L}}{\Delta x\,\Delta y} = \frac{\partial H_y}{\partial x} - \frac{\partial H_x}{\partial y} = i_z \qquad (1)$$

After beginning with Ampère's circuital law equating the closed line integral of $\mathbf{H}$ to the current enclosed, we have now arrived at a relationship involving the closed line integral of $\mathbf{H}$ *per unit area* enclosed and the current *per unit area* enclosed, or current density. We performed a similar analysis in passing from the integral form of Gauss's law, involving flux through a closed surface and charge enclosed, to the point form, relating flux through a closed surface *per unit volume* enclosed and charge *per unit volume* enclosed, or volume charge density. In each case a limit is necessary to produce an equality.

If we choose closed paths which are oriented perpendicularly to each of the remaining two coordinate axes, analogous processes lead to expressions for the y and z components of the current density:

$$\lim_{\Delta y, \Delta z \to 0} \frac{\oint \mathbf{H} \cdot d\mathbf{L}}{\Delta y \, \Delta z} = \frac{\partial H_z}{\partial y} - \frac{\partial H_y}{\partial z} = i_x \tag{2}$$

and

$$\lim_{\Delta z, \Delta x \to 0} \frac{\oint \mathbf{H} \cdot d\mathbf{L}}{\Delta z \, \Delta x} = \frac{\partial H_x}{\partial z} - \frac{\partial H_z}{\partial x} = i_y \tag{3}$$

Comparing (1), (2), and (3) we see that a component of the current density is given by the limit of the quotient of the closed line integral of $\mathbf{H}$ about a small path in a plane normal to that component and of the area enclosed as the path shrinks to zero. This limit has its counterpart in other fields of science and long ago received the name of *curl*. The curl of any vector is a vector, and any component of the curl is given by the limit of the quotient of the closed line integral of the vector about a small path in a plane normal to that component desired and the area enclosed, as the path shrinks to zero. It should be noted that the above definition of curl does not refer specifically to a particular coordinate system. The mathematical form of the definition is

$$(\text{curl } \mathbf{H})_n = \lim_{\Delta S_n \to 0} \frac{\oint \mathbf{H} \cdot d\mathbf{L}}{\Delta S_n} \tag{4}$$

where ΔS_n is the area enclosed by the closed line integral, and n represents any component in any coordinate system. This subscript also indicates that the component of the curl is that component which is *normal* to the surface enclosed by the closed path.

In cartesian coordinates the definition (4) shows that the x, y, and z components of the curl of $\mathbf{H}$ are given by (1), (2), and (3), and therefore

$$\text{curl } \mathbf{H} = \left(\frac{\partial H_z}{\partial y} - \frac{\partial H_y}{\partial z} \right) \mathbf{a}_x + \left(\frac{\partial H_x}{\partial z} - \frac{\partial H_z}{\partial x} \right) \mathbf{a}_y + \left(\frac{\partial H_y}{\partial x} - \frac{\partial H_x}{\partial y} \right) \mathbf{a}_z \tag{5}$$

This result may be written in the form of a determinant:

$$\text{curl } \mathbf{H} = \begin{vmatrix} \mathbf{a}_x & \mathbf{a}_y & \mathbf{a}_z \\ \dfrac{\partial}{\partial x} & \dfrac{\partial}{\partial y} & \dfrac{\partial}{\partial z} \\ H_x & H_y & H_z \end{vmatrix} \tag{6}$$

and may also be written in terms of the vector operator:

$$\text{curl } \mathbf{H} = \boldsymbol{\nabla} \times \mathbf{H} \tag{7}$$

Equation (5) is the result of applying the definition (4) to the cartesian coordinate system. We obtained the z component of this expression by evaluating Ampère's circuital law about an incremental path of sides Δx and Δy, and we could have obtained the other two components just as easily by choosing the appropriate paths. Equation (6) is a neat method of storing the cartesian coordinate expression for curl; the form is symmetrical and easily remembered. Equation (7) is even more concise and leads to (5) upon applying the definitions of the cross product and vector operator.

The expressions for curl $\mathbf{H}$ in cylindrical and spherical coordinates are derived in the Appendix by applying the definition (4):

$$\boldsymbol{\nabla} \times \mathbf{H} = \left(\frac{1}{r} \frac{\partial H_z}{\partial \phi} - \frac{\partial H_\phi}{\partial z} \right) \mathbf{a}_r + \left(\frac{\partial H_r}{\partial z} - \frac{\partial H_z}{\partial r} \right) \mathbf{a}_\phi$$

$$+ \left[\frac{1}{r} \frac{\partial (r H_\phi)}{\partial r} - \frac{1}{r} \frac{\partial H_r}{\partial \phi} \right] \mathbf{a}_z \qquad \text{(cylindrical)} \tag{8}$$

$$= \frac{1}{r \sin \theta} \left[\frac{\partial (H_\phi \sin \theta)}{\partial \theta} - \frac{\partial H_\theta}{\partial \phi} \right] \mathbf{a}_r + \frac{1}{r} \left[\frac{1}{\sin \theta} \frac{\partial H_r}{\partial \phi} - \frac{\partial (r H_\phi)}{\partial r} \right] \mathbf{a}_\theta$$

$$+ \frac{1}{r} \left[\frac{\partial (r H_\theta)}{\partial r} - \frac{\partial H_r}{\partial \theta} \right] \mathbf{a}_\phi \qquad \text{(spherical)} \tag{9}$$

Although we have described curl as a line integral per unit area, this does not provide everyone with a satisfactory physical picture of the nature of the curl operation, for the closed line integral itself requires physical interpretation. The closed line integral was first met in the electrostatic field, where we saw that $\oint \mathbf{E} \cdot d\mathbf{L} = 0$. Inasmuch as the integral was zero we did not belabor the physical picture. Since then we have discussed recently the closed line integral of $\mathbf{H}$, $\oint \mathbf{H} \cdot d\mathbf{L} = I$. Either of these closed line integrals is also known by the name of "circulation," a term obviously borrowed from the field of hydraulics.

The circulation of $\mathbf{H}$, or $\oint \mathbf{H} \cdot d\mathbf{L}$, is obtained by multiplying the component of $\mathbf{H}$ parallel to the specified path at each point along the path by the differential path lengths and summing the results as the differential lengths approach zero and as their number becomes infinite. We do not require a vanishingly small path. Ampère's circuital law tells us that if $\mathbf{H}$ does possess circulation about a given path, then current passes through this path. In electrostatics we see that the circulation of $\mathbf{E}$ is zero about every path, a direct consequence of the fact that zero work is required to carry a charge around a closed path.

We may now describe curl as *circulation per unit area*.   The closed path is now vanishingly small, and curl is defined at a point.   The curl of **E** must be zero, for the circulation is zero.   The curl of **H** is not zero, however; the circulation of **H** per unit area is the current density by Ampère's circuital law [or (1), (2), and (3)].

Skilling[1] suggests the use of a very small paddle wheel as a "curl meter."   Our vector quantity, then, must be thought of as capable of applying a force to each blade of the paddle wheel, the force being proportional to the component of the field normal to the surface of that blade.   In order to test a field for curl, we therefore dip our paddle wheel into the field, with the axis of the paddle wheel lined up

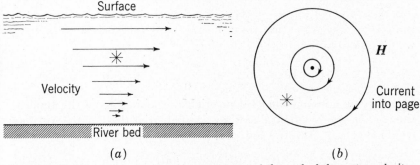

(a)   (b)

FIG. 8.9. (a) The curl meter shows a component of the curl of the water velocity into the page.   (b) The curl of the magnetic field about an infinitely long filament is zero.

with the direction of the component of curl desired, and note the action of the field on the paddle.   No rotation means no curl; larger angular velocities mean greater values of the curl; a reversal in the direction of spin means a reversal in the sign of the curl.   In order to find the direction of the vector curl and not merely to establish the presence of any particular component, we should place our paddle wheel in the field and hunt around for the orientation which produces the greatest velocity.   The direction of the curl is then along the axis of the paddle wheel, as given by the right-hand rule.

As an example, consider the flow of water in a river.   Figure 8.9a shows the longitudinal section of a wide river taken near the middle of the river.   The water velocity is zero at the bottom and increases linearly as the surface is approached.   A paddle wheel placed in the position shown, with its axis perpendicular to the paper, will turn in a

[1] See references at end of chapter.

clockwise direction, showing the presence of a component of curl in the direction of an inward normal to the surface of the page. If the velocity of the water does not change as we go up- or downstream and also shows no variation as we go across the river (or even if it decreases in the same fashion toward either bank), then this component is the only component present and the curl of the water velocity has a direction into the page.

In Fig. 8.9b the streamlines of the magnetic field intensity about an infinitely long filamentary conductor are shown. The curl meter placed in this field of curved lines shows that a larger number of blades have a clockwise force exerted on them but that this force is in general smaller than the counterclockwise force exerted on the smaller number of blades closer to the wire. It seems possible that if the curvature of the streamlines is correct and also if the variation of the field strength is just right, the net torque on the paddle wheel may be zero. Actually, the paddle wheel does not rotate in this case, for since $\mathbf{H} = I\mathbf{a}_\phi/2\pi r$, we may substitute into (8), obtaining

$$\text{curl } \mathbf{H} = -\frac{\partial H_\phi}{\partial z}\,\mathbf{a}_r + \frac{1}{r}\frac{\partial(rH_\phi)}{\partial r}\,\mathbf{a}_z = 0$$

Returning now to complete our original examination of the application of Ampère's circuital law to a differential-sized path, we may combine (1), (2), (3), (5), and (7):

$$\text{curl } \mathbf{H} = \nabla \times \mathbf{H} = \left(\frac{\partial H_z}{\partial y} - \frac{\partial H_y}{\partial z}\right)\mathbf{a}_x + \left(\frac{\partial H_x}{\partial z} - \frac{\partial H_z}{\partial x}\right)\mathbf{a}_y$$
$$+ \left(\frac{\partial H_y}{\partial x} - \frac{\partial H_x}{\partial y}\right)\mathbf{a}_z = \mathbf{i} \quad (10)$$

and write the *point form of Ampère's circuital law:*

$$\nabla \times \mathbf{H} = \mathbf{i} \tag{11}$$

This is the second of Maxwell's four equations as they apply to non-time-varying conditions. We may write the third of these equations at this time; it is the point form of $\oint \mathbf{E} \cdot d\mathbf{L} = 0$, or

$$\nabla \times \mathbf{E} = 0$$

The fourth equation appears below in Sec. 8.5.

D8.5. Ampère's circuital law is applied to a small closed path in the $z = 0$ plane enclosing the origin. The direction of traversal is such that $\mathbf{a}_z \times d\mathbf{L}$ always points toward the enclosed region. Find the approximate value of the vector current density at the origin for each path and field specified:

(a) Triangle, 1-2-3-1, sides each 1 mm in length; value of $\mathbf{H} \cdot d\mathbf{L}$ along side 1-2 is 1 amp; along 2-3, 4 amp; and along 3-1, -2 amp.

(b) Circle, radius 1 mm; **H** is everywhere in $d\mathbf{L}$ direction and has a uniform value of 10^3 amp/m^2.

(c) Regular dodecagon inscribed in circle of (b); same **H** as (b).

Ans. i $= 10.9 \times 10^6 \mathbf{a}_z$ amp/m.

D8.6. Show that $\nabla \times \mathbf{E} = 0$ for the field of a:

(a) Point charge in spherical coordinates.

(b) Line charge in cylindrical coordinates.

(c) Sheet of charge in cartesian coordinates.

Ans. $\nabla \times \mathbf{E} = 0$.

8.4. Stokes' Theorem. Although the last section was devoted primarily to a discussion of the curl operation, the contribution to the

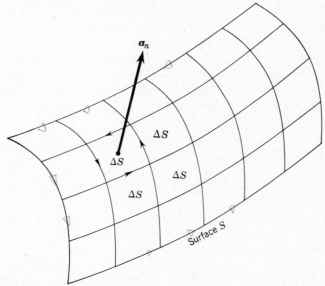

FIG. 8.10. The sum of the closed line integrals about the perimeter of every ΔS is the same as the closed line integral about the perimeter of S because of cancellation on every interior path.

subject of magnetic fields should not be overlooked. From Ampère's circuital law we derived one of Maxwell's equations, $\nabla \times \mathbf{H} = \mathbf{i}$. This latter equation should be considered the point form of Ampère's circuital law and applies on a "per-unit-area" basis. In this section we shall again devote a major share of the material to the mathematical theorem known as Stokes' theorem, but in the process we shall show that we may obtain Ampère's circuital law from $\nabla \times \mathbf{H} = \mathbf{i}$. In other words, we are then prepared to obtain the integral form from the point form or to obtain the point form from the integral form. Either form leads directly to the other.

Consider the surface S of Fig. 8.10, which is broken up into incremental surfaces of area ΔS.   If we apply the definition of the curl to one of these incremental surfaces, then

$$\frac{\oint \mathbf{H} \cdot d\mathbf{L}_{\Delta S}}{\Delta S} \doteq (\nabla \times \mathbf{H})_n$$

where the n subscript again indicates the right-hand normal to the surface.   The subscript on $d\mathbf{L}_{\Delta S}$ indicates the closed path is the perimeter of an incremental area ΔS.   This result may also be written

$$\frac{\oint \mathbf{H} \cdot d\mathbf{L}_{\Delta S}}{\Delta S} \doteq (\nabla \times \mathbf{H}) \cdot \mathbf{a}_n$$

or $\oint \mathbf{H} \cdot d\mathbf{L}_{\Delta S} \doteq (\nabla \times \mathbf{H}) \cdot \mathbf{a}_n \, \Delta S = (\nabla \times \mathbf{H}) \cdot \Delta \mathbf{S}$

where $\mathbf{a}_n$ = a unit vector in direction of right-hand normal to $\Delta \mathbf{S}$.

Now let us determine this circulation for every ΔS comprising S and sum the results.   As we evaluate the closed line integral for each ΔS, some cancellation will occur because every *interior* wall is covered once in each direction.   The only boundaries on which cancellation cannot occur form the outside boundary, the path enclosing S.   Therefore we have

$$\oint \mathbf{H} \cdot d\mathbf{L} \equiv \int_s (\nabla \times \mathbf{H}) \cdot d\mathbf{S} \tag{1}$$

where $d\mathbf{L}$ is taken only on the perimeter of S.

Equation (1) is an identity, holding for any vector field, and is known as *Stokes' theorem*.

It is now very easy to obtain Ampère's circuital law from $\nabla \times \mathbf{H} = \mathbf{i}$, for we merely have to dot each side by $d\mathbf{S}$, integrate each side over the same (open) surface S, and apply Stokes' theorem:

$$\int_s (\nabla \times \mathbf{H}) \cdot d\mathbf{S} = \int_s \mathbf{i} \cdot d\mathbf{S} = \oint \mathbf{H} \cdot d\mathbf{L}$$

The integral of the current density over the surface S is the total current I passing through the surface, and therefore

$$\oint \mathbf{H} \cdot d\mathbf{L} = I$$

This short derivation shows clearly that the current I, described as being "enclosed by the closed path," is also the current passing through any of the infinite number of surfaces which have the closed path as a perimeter.

Stokes' theorem relates a surface integral to a closed line integral. It should be recalled that the divergence theorem relates a volume integral to a closed surface integral.   Both theorems find their greatest use in general vector proofs.   As an example, let us find another expression for $\nabla \cdot \nabla \times \mathbf{A}$, where $\mathbf{A}$ represents any vector field.   The result must be a scalar (why?), and we may let this scalar be T, or

$$\nabla \cdot \nabla \times \mathbf{A} = T$$

Multiplying by dv and integrating throughout any volume v,

$$\int_{\mathrm{vol}} (\nabla \cdot \nabla \times \mathbf{A})\, dv = \int_{\mathrm{vol}} T\, dv$$

we first apply the divergence theorem to the left side, obtaining

$$\oint_{s} (\nabla \times \mathbf{A}) \cdot d\mathbf{S} = \int_{\mathrm{vol}} T\, dv$$

The left side is the surface integral of the curl of $\mathbf{A}$ over the *closed* surface surrounding the volume v. Stokes' theorem relates the surface integral of the curl of $\mathbf{A}$ over the *open* surface enclosed by a given closed path. If we think of the path as the opening of a laundry bag and the open surface as the surface of the bag itself, we see that as we gradually approach a closed surface by pulling on the drawstrings, the closed path becomes smaller and smaller and finally disappears as the surface becomes closed. Hence, the application of Stokes' theorem to a *closed* surface produces a zero result, and we have

$$\int_{\mathrm{vol}} T\, dv = 0$$

Since this is true for any volume, it is true for the differential volume dv:

$$T\, dv = 0$$

and therefore

$$T = 0$$

or

$$\nabla \cdot \nabla \times \mathbf{A} \equiv 0 \qquad (2)$$

Equation (2) is a useful identity of vector calculus. We may apply it immediately to the non-time-varying magnetic field for which

$$\nabla \times \mathbf{H} = \mathbf{i}$$

and show, then, that

$$\nabla \cdot \mathbf{i} = 0$$

which is the same result we obtained earlier in the chapter by using the continuity equation.

Before introducing several new magnetic field quantities in the following section, we may review our accomplishments at this point. We initially accepted the Biot-Savart law as an experimental result:

$$d\mathbf{H} = \frac{I\, d\mathbf{L} \times \mathbf{a}_R}{4\pi R^2}$$

and tentatively accepted Ampère's circuital law, subject to later proof:

$$\oint \mathbf{H} \cdot d\mathbf{L} = I$$

From Ampère's circuital law the definition of curl led to the point form of this same law:

$$\nabla \times \mathbf{H} = \mathbf{i}$$

We now see that Stokes' theorem enables us to obtain the integral form of Ampère's circuital law from the point form. It therefore makes no difference whether we later prove this law in its point or integral form, for either form may be obtained in terms of the other.

D8.7. Evaluate both sides of Stokes' theorem for the indicated surface and $\mathbf{H}$ field. In each case the positive normal to the surface is in the direction (or at least the general direction) of the positive z axis:

(a) Surface: portion of $z = 0$ plane bounded by $x = 0$, $x = 1$, $y = 0$, $y = 1$; $\mathbf{H} = 10x\mathbf{a}_y$.

(b) Surface: portion of $z = 0$ plane bounded by $r = 1$; $\mathbf{H} = 5r\mathbf{a}_\phi$.

(c) Surface: hemisphere, $r = 1$, $0 \le \theta \le \frac{1}{2}\pi$; $\mathbf{H} = 2r\mathbf{a}_\phi$.

Ans. 54.0 amp.

8.5. Magnetic Flux and Magnetic Flux Density. The laws of Biot-Savart and Ampère are not restricted in their application to any particular type of medium. They apply equally well to free space, dielectric materials, conducting materials, or to the magnetic materials to be discussed in the following chapter. Any combination of these materials is also satisfactory, for homogeneity is not required.

Now we shall restrict our discussion to nonmagnetic materials, and this is most easily accomplished at this stage by considering magnetic fields only in free space. We are not then forced to distinguish between magnetic and nonmagnetic materials at this time.

In free space, let us define the *magnetic flux density* $\mathbf{B}$:

$$\mathbf{B} = \mu_0 \mathbf{H} \qquad \text{webers/m}^2 \tag{1}$$

where, in the rationalized mks system of units, the constant μ_0 is not dimensionless and has the defined value for free space:

$$\mu_0 = 4\pi \times 10^{-7} \qquad \text{henry/m} \tag{2}$$

The name given to μ_0 is the *permeability* of free space.

We should note that since $\mathbf{H}$ is measured in amperes per meter, the weber is dimensionally equal to the product of henrys and amperes. Considering the "henry" as a new unit, the weber is merely a convenient abbreviation for the product of henrys and amperes. When time-varying fields are introduced, it will be shown that a weber is also equivalent to the product of volts and seconds.

The magnetic flux density vector **B**, as the name implies, is a member of the flux density family of vector fields. One of the possible analogies between electric and magnetic fields compares the laws of Biot-Savart and Coulomb, thus establishing an analogy between **H** and **E**. The relations $\mathbf{B} = \mu_0\mathbf{H}$ and $\mathbf{D} = \epsilon_0\mathbf{E}$ then serve to relate **B** and **D**. If **B** is measured in webers per square meter, then magnetic flux should be measured in webers. Let us represent magnetic flux by Φ and define Φ as the flux passing through any designated area:

$$\Phi = \int_s \mathbf{B} \cdot d\mathbf{S} \qquad \text{webers} \tag{3}$$

Our analogy should now remind us of the electric flux Ψ, measured in coulombs, and of Gauss's law, which states that the total flux passing through any *closed* surface is equal to the charge enclosed:

$$\Psi = \oint_s \mathbf{D} \cdot d\mathbf{S} = Q$$

The charge Q is the source of the lines of electric flux, and these lines begin and terminate on positive and negative charge, respectively.

No such source has ever been discovered for the lines of magnetic flux. In the example of the infinitely long straight filament carrying a direct current I, the **H** field formed concentric circles about the filament. Since $\mathbf{B} = \mu_0\mathbf{H}$, the **B** field is of the same form. The magnetic flux lines are closed and do not terminate on a "magnetic charge." For this reason, Gauss's law for the magnetic field is

$$\oint_s \mathbf{B} \cdot d\mathbf{S} = 0 \tag{4}$$

and application of the divergence theorem shows us that

$$\nabla \cdot \mathbf{B} = 0 \tag{5}$$

We have not proved (5), but only suggested the truth of the statement by considering the single field of the infinite filament. It is possible to show that (4) or (5) follows from the Biot-Savart law and the definition of **B**, $\mathbf{B} = \mu_0\mathbf{H}$, but this is another proof which we shall postpone to Sec. 8.7.

Equation (5) is the last of Maxwell's four equations as they apply to static electric fields and steady magnetic fields. Collecting these equations, we then have:

$$\nabla \cdot \mathbf{D} = \rho$$
$$\nabla \times \mathbf{E} = 0$$
$$\nabla \times \mathbf{H} = i$$
$$\nabla \cdot \mathbf{B} = 0 \tag{6}$$

Note that the four equations specify the divergence and curl of an electric and a magnetic field. They should be recognized, in the order given above, as the point forms of these integral equations:

$$\oint_s \mathbf{D} \cdot d\mathbf{S} = Q = \int_{\text{vol}} \rho \, dv$$

$$\oint \mathbf{E} \cdot d\mathbf{L} = 0$$

$$\oint \mathbf{H} \cdot d\mathbf{L} = I = \int_s \mathbf{i} \cdot d\mathbf{S} \tag{7}$$

$$\oint_s \mathbf{B} \cdot d\mathbf{S} = 0$$

Our study of electric and magnetic fields would have been much simpler if we could have assumed either set of equations, (6) or (7). With a good knowledge of vector analysis, such as we should now have, either set may be readily obtained from the other by applying the divergence theorem or Stokes' theorem. The various experimental laws could have been obtained readily from these equations.

As an example of the use of flux and flux density in magnetic fields, let us find the flux between the conductors of the coaxial line of Fig. 8.5. The magnetic field intensity was found to be

$$H_\phi = \frac{I}{2\pi r} \qquad a < r < b$$

and therefore

$$\mathbf{B} = \mu_0 \mathbf{H} = \frac{\mu_0 I}{2\pi r} \mathbf{a}_\phi$$

The magnetic flux contained between the conductors in a length L is the flux crossing any radial plane extending from $r = a$ to $r = b$ and from, say, $z = 0$ to $z = L$:

$$\Phi = \int_s \mathbf{B} \cdot d\mathbf{S} = \int_0^L \int_a^b \frac{\mu_0 I}{2\pi r} \mathbf{a}_\phi \cdot dr \, dz \, \mathbf{a}_\phi$$

or

$$= \frac{\mu_0 I L}{2\pi} \ln \frac{b}{a} \tag{8}$$

This expression will be used later to obtain the inductance of the coaxial transmission line.

D8.8. A coaxial transmission line has a copper inner conductor of radius 0.3 cm, a copper outer conductor of inner radius 0.9 cm and outer radius 1.2 cm, and carries a direct current of 2 amp. Assume that copper is a nonmagnetic material ($\mathbf{B} = \mu_0 \mathbf{H}$). Compute the total magnetic flux in a 1-m length of the coaxial line:

    (a) Between the inner and outer conductors.
    (b) Within the inner conductor.
    (c) Within the outer conductor.

Ans. 0.702 μweber.

8.6. Vector Magnetic Potential. The solution of electrostatic field problems is greatly simplified by the use of the scalar electrostatic potential V. Although this potential possesses a very real physical significance for us, it is mathematically no more than a steppingstone which allows us to solve a problem by several smaller steps. Given a charge configuration, we may first find the potential and then later the electric field intensity.

We should question whether or not such assistance is available in magnetic fields. Can we define a potential function which may be found from the current distribution and from which the magnetic fields may be easily determined? Can a scalar magnetic potential be defined, similar to the scalar electrostatic potential? Let us answer this last question by assuming the existence of a scalar magnetic potential which we may designate V_m, whose gradient gives the magnetic field intensity:

$$\mathbf{H} = \nabla V_m$$

This definition must not conflict with our previous results for the magnetic field, and therefore

$$\nabla \times \mathbf{H} = \mathbf{i} = \nabla \times \nabla V_m$$

However, the curl of the gradient of any scalar is identically zero, a vector identity the proof of which is left as a problem. Therefore we see that if $\mathbf{H}$ is to be defined as the gradient of a scalar magnetic potential, then current density must be zero throughout the region in which the scalar magnetic potential is to be defined. With this restriction, then, a scalar magnetic potential may be defined. We shall not consider this scalar potential further, but merely point out that it is very easy to show that it satisfies Laplace's equation and that its equipotential surfaces provide the missing perpendicular family of lines in Fig. 8.3.

Let us now try a vector magnetic potential. Our choice is indicated by noting that

$$\nabla \cdot \mathbf{B} = 0$$

Another vector identity, which we proved in Sec. 8.4, shows that the divergence of the curl of any vector field is zero. Therefore, we select

$$\mathbf{B} = \nabla \times \mathbf{A} \tag{1}$$

where $\mathbf{A}$ signifies a vector magnetic potential, and automatically satisfy the condition that the magnetic flux density shall have zero divergence. The $\mathbf{H}$ field is

$$\mathbf{H} = \frac{1}{\mu_0} \nabla \times \mathbf{A} \tag{2}$$

and
$$\nabla \times \mathbf{H} = \mathbf{i} = \frac{1}{\mu_0} \nabla \times \nabla \times \mathbf{A}$$

The curl of the curl of a vector field is not zero and is given by a fairly complicated expression,[1] which we need not know in general form. In specific cases for which the form of $\mathbf{A}$ is known, the curl operation may be applied twice, with no difficulty, to determine the current density.

Equation (1) serves as a useful definition of the *vector magnetic potential* $\mathbf{A}$. Since the curl operation implies differentiation with respect to a length, the units of $\mathbf{A}$ are webers per meter.

As yet we have seen only that the definition for $\mathbf{A}$ does not conflict with any previous results. It still remains to show that this particular definition can help us to determine magnetic fields more easily.

We shall show in the following section that, given the Biot-Savart law, the definition of $\mathbf{B}$, and the definition of $\mathbf{A}$, then $\mathbf{A}$ may be determined from the differential current elements by

A not unique

$$\mathbf{A} = \oint \frac{\mu_0 I \, d\mathbf{L}}{4\pi R} \tag{3}$$

The significance of the terms in (3) is the same as in the Biot-Savart law; a direct current of I amp flows along a filamentary conductor of which any differential length $d\mathbf{L}$ is R m from the point at which $\mathbf{A}$ is to be found.

The fact that $\mathbf{A}$ is a vector magnetic *potential* is more apparent when (3) is compared with the similar expression for the electrostatic potential:

$$V = \int \frac{\rho_L \, dL}{4\pi \epsilon R}$$

Each expression is the integral along a line source, in one case line charge and in the other line current; each integrand is inversely proportional to the distance from the source to the point of interest; and each involves a characteristic of the medium, the permeability or the permittivity.

Equation (3) may be written in differential form:

$$d\mathbf{A} = \frac{\mu_0 I \, d\mathbf{L}}{4\pi R} \tag{4}$$

if we again agree not to attribute any physical significance to any magnetic fields we obtain from (4) until the *entire closed path in which*

[1] $\nabla \times \nabla \times \mathbf{A} \equiv \nabla(\nabla \cdot \mathbf{A}) - \nabla^2 \mathbf{A}$. In cartesian coordinates,
$$\nabla^2 \mathbf{A} \equiv \nabla^2 A_x \mathbf{a}_x + \nabla^2 A_y \mathbf{a}_y + \nabla^2 A_z \mathbf{a}_z$$

the current flows is considered. With this reservation, let us go right ahead and consider the vector magnetic potential field about a differential filament. Locating the filament at the origin and allowing it to extend in the positive z direction, $d\mathbf{L} = dz\,\mathbf{a}_z$, and we use cylindrical coordinates to determine $d\mathbf{A}$ at the point (r,ϕ,z):

$$d\mathbf{A} = \frac{\mu_0 I\,dz\,\mathbf{a}_z}{4\pi\,\sqrt{r^2+z^2}}$$

or

$$d A_z = \frac{\mu_0 I\,dz}{4\pi\,\sqrt{r^2+z^2}} \tag{5}$$

$$d A_\phi = 0 \qquad d A_r = 0$$

We note first that the direction of $d\mathbf{A}$ is the same as that of $I\,d\mathbf{L}$. Each small section of a current-carrying conductor produces a contribution to the total vector magnetic potential which is in the same direction as the current flow in the conductor. The magnitude of the vector magnetic potential varies inversely as the distance to the current element, being strongest in the neighborhood of the current and gradually falling off to zero at distant points. Skilling[1] describes the vector magnetic potential field as "like the current distribution but fuzzy around the edges, or like a picture of the current out of focus."

In order to find the magnetic field intensity we must take the curl of (5) in cylindrical coordinates, leading to

$$d\mathbf{H} = \frac{1}{\mu_0}\,\boldsymbol{\nabla}\times d\mathbf{A} = \frac{1}{\mu_0}\left(-\frac{\partial A_z}{\partial r}\right)\mathbf{a}_\phi$$

or

$$d\mathbf{H} = \frac{I\,dz}{4\pi}\,\frac{z}{(r^2+z^2)^{3/2}}\,\mathbf{a}_\phi$$

which is easily shown to be the same as the value given by the Biot-Savart law.

Expressions for the vector magnetic potential $\mathbf{A}$ can also be obtained for a current source which is distributed. For a surface current of $\mathbf{J}_s$ amp/m, the differential current element becomes

$$I\,d\mathbf{L} = \mathbf{J}_s\,dS$$

In the case of current flow throughout a volume with a density of $\mathbf{i}$ amp/m^2, we have

$$I\,d\mathbf{L} = \mathbf{i}\,dv$$

In each of these two expressions the vector character has been given to the current; for the filamentary element it is customary, although not necessary, to use $I\,d\mathbf{L}$ instead of $\mathbf{I}\,dL$. Since the magnitude of the filamentary current is constant, we have chosen the form which allows

[1] See references at end of chapter.

us to remove one quantity from the integral.   The alternative expressions for **A** are, then,

$$\mathbf{A} = \int_s \frac{\mu_0 \mathbf{J}_s \, dS}{4\pi R} \tag{6}$$

and

$$= \int_{\text{vol}} \frac{\mu_0 \mathbf{i} \, dv}{4\pi R} \tag{7}$$

D8.9. The direction of current flow at the origin is in the positive z direction. The incremental vector magnetic potential is desired at the point $(1,1,1)$ if the differential current element:

(a) Is an incremental current filament of 1 mm length carrying 5 amp.

(b) Is an incremental area of 1 mm² on a current sheet of surface density 3,000 amp/m.

(c) Is an incremental volume of 1 mm³ in a region of current density 10^6 amp/m².

Ans. 520 $\mu\mu$webers/m.

8.7. Derivation of Steady-magnetic-field Laws. We shall now supply the promised proofs of the several relationships between the magnetic field quantities.   The permeability is taken as μ_0, but the discussion of magnetic materials in the following chapter will show that the proofs are equally valid for a material having a permeability μ.

All the relationships between the several magnetic field quantities may be obtained from the definitions of **H**:

$$\mathbf{H} = \oint \frac{I \, d\mathbf{L} \times \mathbf{a}_R}{4\pi R^2} \tag{1}$$

of **B**:

$$\mathbf{B} = \mu_0 \mathbf{H} \tag{2}$$

and of **A**:

$$\mathbf{B} = \nabla \times \mathbf{A} \tag{3}$$

Let us assume that we may express **A** by

$$\mathbf{A} = \int_{\text{vol}} \frac{\mu_0 \mathbf{i} \, dv}{4\pi R} \tag{4}$$

and show that (1) follows.   First we should add subscripts to indicate the point at which the current element is located, (x_1, y_1, z_1), and the point at which **A** is given, (x_2, y_2, z_2).   The differential volume element dv is then written dv_1 and in cartesian coordinates would be $dx_1 \, dy_1 \, dz_1$. The variables of integration are x_1, y_1, and z_1.   Using these subscripts, then,

$$\mathbf{A}_2 = \int_{\text{vol}} \frac{\mu_0 \mathbf{i}_1 \, dv_1}{4\pi R_{12}} \tag{5}$$

From (2) and (3) we have

$$\mathbf{H} = \frac{\mathbf{B}}{\mu_0} = \frac{\nabla \times \mathbf{A}}{\mu_0} \tag{6}$$

In order to show that (1) follows from (5) it is necessary to substitute (5) into (6). This step involves taking the curl of $\mathbf{A}_2$, a quantity expressed in terms of the variables x_2, y_2, and z_2, and the curl therefore involves partial derivatives with respect to x_2, y_2, and z_2. We do this, placing a subscript on the del operator to remind us of the variables involved in the partial differentiation process:

$$\mathbf{H}_2 = \frac{\nabla_2 \times \mathbf{A}_2}{\mu_0} = \frac{1}{\mu_0} \nabla_2 \times \int_{\text{vol}} \frac{\mu_0 \mathbf{i}_1 \, dv_1}{4\pi R_{12}}$$

The order of partial differentiation and integration is immaterial, and $\mu_0/4\pi$ is assumed constant, allowing us to write

$$\mathbf{H}_2 = \frac{I}{4\pi} \int_{\text{vol}} \nabla_2 \times \frac{\mathbf{i}_1 \, dv_1}{R_{12}}$$

The curl operation within the integrand represents partial differentiation with respect to x_2, y_2, and z_2. The differential volume element dv_1 is a scalar and a function only of x_1, y_1, and z_1. Consequently, it may be factored out of the curl operation as any other constant, leaving

$$\mathbf{H}_2 = \frac{I}{4\pi} \int_{\text{vol}} \left(\nabla_2 \times \frac{\mathbf{i}_1}{R_{12}} \right) dv_1 \tag{7}$$

The curl of the product of a scalar and a vector is given by an identity which may be checked by expansion in cartesian coordinates:

$$\nabla \times (S\mathbf{V}) \equiv (\nabla S) \times \mathbf{V} + S(\nabla \times \mathbf{V})$$

This identity is used to expand the integrand of (7):

$$\mathbf{H}_2 = \frac{I}{4\pi} \int_{\text{vol}} \left[\left(\nabla_2 \frac{1}{R_{12}} \right) \times \mathbf{i}_1 + \frac{1}{R_{12}} (\nabla_2 \times \mathbf{i}_1) \right] dv_1 \tag{8}$$

The second term of this integrand is zero because $\nabla_2 \times \mathbf{i}_1$ indicates partial derivatives of a function of x_1, y_1, and z_1 taken with respect to the variables x_2, y_2, and z_2. The first set of variables is not a function of the second set, and all partial derivatives are zero.

The first term of the integrand may be determined by expressing R_{12} in terms of the coordinate values:

$$R_{12} = \sqrt{(x_2 - x_1)^2 + (y_2 - y_1)^2 + (z_2 - z_1)^2}$$

and taking the gradient.   The x component of the gradient is

$$\frac{\partial}{\partial x_2}\left(\frac{1}{R_{12}}\right) = \frac{-(x_2 - x_1)}{[(x_2 - x_1)^2 + (y_2 - y_1)^2 + (z_2 - z_1)^2]^{3/2}}$$

$$= -\frac{x_2 - x_1}{R_{12}{}^3}$$

and the y and z components are obtained in a similar manner.   Adding vectorially,

$$\nabla_2\left(\frac{1}{R_{12}}\right) = -\frac{(x_2 - x_1)\mathbf{a}_x + (y_2 - y_1)\mathbf{a}_y + (z_2 - z_1)\mathbf{a}_z}{R_{12}{}^3}$$

or

$$= -\frac{\mathbf{R}_{12}}{R_{12}{}^3} = -\frac{\mathbf{a}_{R12}}{R_{12}{}^2}$$

Substituting this result into (8), we have

$$\mathbf{H}_2 = -\frac{I}{4\pi}\int_{\text{vol}} \frac{\mathbf{a}_{R12} \times \mathbf{i}_1}{R_{12}{}^2}\, dv_1$$

or

$$= \int_{\text{vol}} \frac{\mathbf{i}_1 \times \mathbf{a}_{R12}}{4\pi R_{12}{}^2}\, dv_1$$

which is the equivalent of (1) in terms of current density.   Replacing $\mathbf{i}_1\, dv_1$ by $I_1\, d\mathbf{L}_1$, we may rewrite the volume integral as

$$\mathbf{H}_2 = \oint \frac{I_1\, d\mathbf{L}_1 \times \mathbf{a}_{R12}}{4\pi R_{12}{}^2}$$

Equation (4) is therefore correct and agrees with the three definitions (1), (2), and (3).

Now we shall prove Ampère's circuital law in point form:

$$\nabla \times \mathbf{H} = \mathbf{i} \tag{9}$$

Combining (2) and (3), we obtain

$$\nabla \times \mathbf{H} = \nabla \times \frac{\mathbf{B}}{\mu_0} = \frac{1}{\mu_0}\nabla \times \nabla \times \mathbf{A} \tag{10}$$

We now need the expansion in cartesian coordinates for $\nabla \times \nabla \times \mathbf{A}$. Performing the indicated partial differentiations and collecting the resulting terms, we may write the result as

$$\nabla \times \nabla \times \mathbf{A} \equiv \nabla(\nabla \cdot \mathbf{A}) - \nabla^2\mathbf{A} \tag{11}$$

where

$$\nabla^2\mathbf{A} \equiv \nabla^2 A_x\mathbf{a}_x + \nabla^2 A_y\mathbf{a}_y + \nabla^2 A_z\mathbf{a}_z \tag{12}$$

Equation (12) is the definition (in cartesian coordinates) of the *Laplacian of a vector*.

Substituting (11) into (10), we have

$$\nabla \times \mathbf{H} = \frac{1}{\mu_0}[\nabla(\nabla \cdot \mathbf{A}) - \nabla^2\mathbf{A}] \tag{13}$$

and now require expressions for the divergence and the Laplacian of $\mathbf{A}$.

We may find the divergence of $\mathbf{A}$ by applying the divergence operation to (5):

$$\nabla_2 \cdot \mathbf{A}_2 = \frac{\mu_0}{4\pi} \int_{\text{vol}} \nabla_2 \cdot \frac{\mathbf{i}_1}{R_{12}} \, dv_1 \tag{14}$$

and using the vector identity (5) of Sec. 4.8,

$$\nabla \cdot (S\mathbf{V}) \equiv \mathbf{V} \cdot (\nabla S) + S(\nabla \cdot \mathbf{V})$$

producing

$$\nabla_2 \cdot \mathbf{A}_2 = \frac{\mu_0}{4\pi} \int_{\text{vol}} \left[\mathbf{i}_1 \cdot \left(\nabla_2 \frac{1}{R_{12}} \right) + \frac{1}{R_{12}} (\nabla_2 \cdot \mathbf{i}_1) \right] dv_1 \tag{15}$$

The second part of the integrand is zero because $\mathbf{i}_1$ is not a function of x_2, y_2, and z_2.

We have already shown that $\nabla_2(1/R_{12}) = -\mathbf{R}_{12}/R_{12}{}^3$, and it is just as easily shown that

$$\nabla_1 \frac{1}{R_{12}} = \frac{\mathbf{R}_{12}}{R_{12}{}^3}$$

or that

$$\nabla_1 \frac{1}{R_{12}} = -\nabla_2 \frac{1}{R_{12}}$$

Equation (15) can therefore be written

$$\nabla_2 \cdot \mathbf{A}_2 = \frac{\mu_0}{4\pi} \int_{\text{vol}} \left[-\mathbf{i}_1 \cdot \left(\nabla_1 \frac{1}{R_{12}} \right) \right] dv_1$$

and the vector identity applied again:

$$\nabla_2 \cdot \mathbf{A}_2 = \frac{\mu_0}{4\pi} \int_{\text{vol}} \left[\frac{1}{R_{12}} (\nabla_1 \cdot \mathbf{i}_1) - \nabla_1 \cdot \left(\frac{\mathbf{i}_1}{R_{12}} \right) \right] dv_1 \tag{16}$$

Since we are concerned with steady magnetic fields only, the continuity equation shows that the first term of (16) is zero. Application of the divergence theorem to the second term gives

$$\nabla_2 \cdot \mathbf{A}_2 = -\frac{\mu_0}{4\pi} \oint_{S_1} \frac{\mathbf{i}_1}{R_{12}} \cdot d\mathbf{S}_1$$

where the surface S_1 encloses the volume throughout which we are integrating. This volume must include all the current, for the original integral expression for $\mathbf{A}$ was an integration such as to include the effect of all the current. Since there is no current outside of this volume (or otherwise we should have had to increase the volume to include it), we may integrate over a slightly larger volume or a slightly larger enclosing surface without changing $\mathbf{A}$. On this larger surface the current density $\mathbf{i}_1$ must be zero, and therefore the closed surface integral is zero since the integrand is zero. Hence, the divergence of $\mathbf{A}$ is zero.

In order to find the Laplacian of the vector $\mathbf{A}$, let us compare the x

component of (4) with the similar expression for electrostatic potential:

$$A_x = \int_{\text{vol}} \frac{\mu_0 i_x\, dv}{4\pi R} \qquad V = \int_{\text{vol}} \frac{\rho\, dv}{4\pi\epsilon_0 R}$$

We note that one expression can be obtained from the other by a straightforward change of variable, i_x for ρ, μ_0 for $1/\epsilon_0$, and A_x for V. However, we have derived some additional information about the electrostatic potential which we shall not have to repeat now for the x component of the vector magnetic potential. This takes the form of Poisson's equation:

$$\nabla^2 V = -\frac{\rho}{\epsilon_0}$$

which becomes, after the change of variables,

$$\nabla^2 A_x = -\mu_0 i_x$$

Similarly, we have

$$\nabla^2 A_y = -\mu_0 i_y$$

and

$$\nabla^2 A_z = -\mu_0 i_z$$

or

$$\nabla^2 \mathbf{A} = -\mu_0 \mathbf{i} \qquad (17)$$

Returning to (13), we can now substitute for the divergence and Laplacian of **A** and obtain the desired answer:

$$\nabla \times \mathbf{H} = \mathbf{i} \qquad (9)$$

We have already shown the use of Stokes' theorem in obtaining the integral form of Ampère's circuital law from (9) and need not repeat that labor here.

We thus have succeeded in showing that every result we have essentially "pulled from free space" for magnetic fields follows from the basic definitions of **H**, **B**, and **A**. The derivations are not simple, but they should be understandable on a step-by-step basis. It is hoped that the procedure need never be committed to memory!

SUGGESTED REFERENCES

1. Attwood, S. S.: (see Suggested References for Chap. 4). Simple magnetic fields and the concept of the magnetic pole appear in chaps. 9 and 10.
2. Boast, W. B.: (see Suggested References for Chap. 2). Numerous simple problems are solved.
3. Jordan, E. C.: "Electromagnetic Waves and Radiating Systems," Prentice-Hall, Inc., Englewood Cliffs, N.J., 1950. Vector magnetic potential is discussed on pages 82–91.
4. Ramo, S., and J. R. Whinnery: (see Suggested References for Chap. 6). Vector magnetic potential and the derivation of the magnetic-field equations are given on pages 99–106.
5. Skilling, H. H.: (see Suggested References for Chap. 3). The "paddle wheel" is discussed on pages 23–25.

PROBLEMS

1. Write the integral form of the Biot-Savart law as it applies to current flow throughout a volume with density i amp/m² and also as it applies to the flow of surface current of density J_s. The vector sense should in each case be given to the current.

2. Use the Biot-Savart law to find the magnetic field intensity produced by a sheet of current $J_s = J_{sz}a_z$ in the $x = 0$ plane.

3. Find the magnetic field intensity produced by a sheet of current $J_s = J_{sz}a_z$ in the $x = 0$ plane by dividing the sheet into current filaments of $I = J_{sz}\,dy$ amp. Use the known field of the filaments, and work in cartesian coordinates.

4. A filamentary current of I amp flows in the a_ϕ direction about a circular path of radius a in the $z = 0$ plane. Find the magnetic field intensity at a point on the z axis, h m from the plane of the loop.

5. A filamentary current of I amp flows about a square path in the $z = 0$ plane, a m on a side, centered at the origin. Find the magnetic field intensity at the origin.

6. Find the magnetic field intensity at $(0,y,z)$ produced by a blade of current located at the x axis. This current blade may be thought of as that portion of the $y = 0$ plane extending from $z = -\frac{1}{2}\Delta z$ to $z = \frac{1}{2}\Delta z$ and carrying a uniform surface current density of $J_s = J_{sz}a_z$ amp/m. The answer should be expressed in terms of the width of the blade Δz.

7. Using the magnetic field intensity produced by the current blade of Prob. 6, find H produced by a sheet of current $J_s = J_{sz}a_z$ extending over the entire $y = 0$ plane.

8. A tubular conductor of inner radius a and outer radius b is centered along the z axis and carries a uniformly distributed current in the a_z direction of I amp. Find H in each of the three regions, $r < a$, $a < r < b$, $b < r$.

9. An infinitely long solenoid of radius a extends along the z axis. The solenoid has n turns/m length and carries a current of I amp. Assume that the current flows only in the a_ϕ direction, neglecting the a_z component. (a) Show that H is not a function of ϕ or z. (b) Show that H_ϕ and H_r are everywhere zero. (c) Show that $H_z = 0$ for $r > a$. (d) Show that $H_z = nI$ for $r < a$.

10. A toroid whose axis is the z axis has an inner radius a and an outer radius b. The cross section of the toroid is a circle of radius $\frac{1}{2}(b - a)$. The toroid is wound with N turns of a filamentary conductor carrying a current of I amp. Assume that the current flows only around the perimeter of the cross section, neglecting the effective single turn carrying I amp around the mean radius of the toroid itself. (a) Show that H is not a function of ϕ. (b) Show that $H_\phi = NI/2\pi r$ at any point within the toroid cross section and is zero outside.

11. A hollow spherical conducting shell of radius a has filamentary connections made at the top ($r = a$, $\theta = 0$) and bottom ($r = a$, $\theta = \pi$). A direct current of 5 amp flows down the upper filament, down the spherical surface, and out the lower filament. (a) Show that for any point inside the sphere, $H = 0$. (b) Show that for any point outside the sphere, $H = -5a_\phi/(2\pi r \sin \theta)$.

12. In spherical coordinates the surface of a solid conducting cone is described by $\theta = \pi/4$ and a conducting plane by $\theta = \pi/2$. Each carries a total current of 10 amp. The current flows as a surface current radially inward on the plane to the vertex of the cone, and then flows radially outward throughout the cross section of the conical conductor. (a) Express the surface current as a function of r. (b)

Express the current density in the conical conductor as a function of r. (c) Show that $H = 5a_\phi/(\pi r \sin \theta)$ for $\pi/4 < \theta < \pi/2$. (d) Show that $H = 5(1 - \cos \theta)a_\phi/[\pi r \sin \theta (1 - 1/\sqrt{2})]$ for $0 < \theta < \pi/4$.

13. By applying the definition of curl [Sec. 8.3, Eq. (4)] to the vector water velocity U at a point where this velocity has only a U_ϕ component in cylindrical coordinates, show that $\nabla \times U = 2\omega a_z$, where $\omega r = U_\phi$.

14. A certain field is investigated by measuring its circulation about a very small closed path. The path lies in the xy plane and is moved about this plane during the investigation. It is found that the circulation is proportional to the square of the distance of the small closed path from the x axis. What information does this provide about the curl of this vector field?

15. Show that the curl of the gradient of S is identically equal to zero by expansion in cartesian coordinates. S is a scalar function of x, y, and z.

16. Evaluate curl H (a) in cartesian coordinates for $H = ya_x - xa_y$; (b) in cylindrical coordinates for $H = (a_r \cos \phi)/r - (a_z \sin \phi)/r$; (c) in spherical coordinates for $H = \csc \theta \, a_\theta + \sin \theta \, a_\phi$.

17. Use Stokes' theorem to show that if $\oint E \cdot dL = 0$, then $\nabla \times E = 0$.

18. Show that the total magnetic flux surrounding an infinitely long straight conductor of circular cross section carrying a direct current is infinite, even on a per-meter-length basis.

19. Apply Maxwell's equations for non-time-varying conditions to a conducting material for which $i = \sigma E$, and show that E_x, E_y, E_z, H_x, H_y, and H_z all satisfy Laplace's equation. [HINT: Using Sec. 8.5, Eqs. (6), take the curl of the third equation and use the identities of Sec. 8.7, Eqs. (11) and (12)].

20. Show that each of the fields given below does *not* satisfy Maxwell's equations as given for non-time-varying conditions: (a) $E = 10xa_y$; (b) $H = 5ra_r$; (c) $i = 10^3 e^{-2x} a_x$.

21. Assume a direct current of I amp flowing in the a_z direction in a filament extending from $z = -L$ to $z = L$ on the z axis. (a) Using cylindrical coordinates, find A at any general point $(r,0°,z)$. (b) From (a) find B and H. (c) Let $L \to \infty$ and show that the expression for H is then the same as for an infinitely long filament.

22. A filamentary ring of radius a carries a direct current I. (a) Find A at the center of the ring. (b) Using the Biot-Savart law (or the answer to Prob. 4), find H at the center of the ring. (c) How can both of the above answers be correct if $B = \nabla \times A$?

23. Using $B = \nabla \times A$, $\int_s B \cdot dS = \Phi$, and Stokes' theorem, show that the line integral of A about any closed path is equal to the magnetic flux enclosed by the path, or $\oint A \cdot dL = \Phi$.

24. Given $\oint A \cdot dL = \Phi$ (see Prob. 23), choose an appropriate path and show that the vector magnetic potential difference between points radially distant a and b from an infinite filament on the z axis is $[\mu_0 I \ln (b/a)]/2\pi$.

25. Given $\oint A \cdot dL = \Phi$ (see Prob. 23), choose an appropriate path and show that the vector magnetic potential at a point x m distant from a current sheet $J_s = J_{sz} a_z$ at $x = 0$ is $A_z = -\frac{1}{2}\mu_0 J_{sz} x$ if the zero reference potential is chosen at $x = 0$.

26. Given the field $G = (r + z^2)a_r + \phi a_\phi$, evaluate both sides of Stokes' theorem independently for a circular disk of radius a at $z = h$.

CHAPTER 9

FORCES IN STEADY MAGNETIC FIELDS

The magnetic field quantities **H**, **B**, Φ, and **A** introduced in the last chapter have not as yet been given any physical significance. Each of these quantities is merely defined in terms of the distribution of current sources throughout space. If the current distribution is known, we should feel that **H**, **B**, and **A** are determined at every point in space, even though we may not be able to evaluate the defining integrals because of mathematical complexity.

We are now ready to undertake the second half of the magnetic field problem, that of determining the forces and torques exerted by the magnetic field on other charges. The electric field causes a force to be exerted on a charge which may be either stationary or in motion; we shall see that the magnetic field is capable of exerting a force only on a *moving* charge. This result appears logical; a magnetic field may be produced by moving charges and may exert forces on moving charges; a magnetic field cannot arise from stationary charges and cannot exert any force on a stationary charge.

This chapter is concerned primarily with the forces and torques on current-carrying conductors which may either be of a filamentary nature or possess a finite cross section with a known current density distribution. The problems associated with the motion of particles in a vacuum are largely avoided.

9.1. Force on a Moving Charge. In an electric field the definition of the electric field intensity shows us that the force on a charged particle is

$$\mathbf{F} = Q\mathbf{E} \tag{1}$$

The force is in the same direction as the electric field intensity (for a positive charge) and is directly proportional to both **E** and Q. If the charge is in motion, the force at any point in its trajectory is then given by (1).

A charged particle in motion in a magnetic field of flux density **B** is found experimentally to experience a force which is proportional to the charge Q, its velocity U, the flux density B, and to the sine of the

213

angle between the vectors **U** and **B**. The direction of the force is perpendicular to both **U** and **B** and is given by a unit vector in the direction of **U** × **B**. The force may therefore be expressed as

$$\mathbf{F} = Q\mathbf{U} \times \mathbf{B} \tag{2}$$

A fundamental difference in the effect of the electric and magnetic fields on charged particles is now apparent, for a force which is always applied in a direction at right angles to the direction in which the particle is proceeding can never change the magnitude of the particle velocity. In other words, the *acceleration* vector is always normal to the velocity vector. The kinetic energy of the particle thus remains unchanged, and the steady magnetic field is therefore incapable of transferring energy to the moving charge. The electric field, on the other hand, exerts a force on the particle which is independent of the direction in which the particle is progressing and therefore effects an energy transfer between field and particle in general.

D9.1. An electron ($Q = -e$) at (1,0,0) has a velocity of 3×10^5 m/sec in the positive z direction. Find the vector force on the electron caused by the magnetic field resulting from:

(a) A current filament on the z axis carrying a current of 4 amp in the positive z direction.

(b) Infinite current sheets of $\mathbf{J}_{s1} = \dfrac{3}{\pi} \mathbf{a}_z$ amp/m in the plane $x = 0$ and $\mathbf{J}_{s2} = -\dfrac{3}{\pi} \mathbf{a}_z$ amp/m in the plane $x = 1.5$.

(c) A filamentary current ring of unit radius in the plane $x = 1$, centered at (1,0,0) and carrying a current of $\dfrac{4}{\pi}$ amp. The direction of the current is clockwise when viewed from (2,0,0).

Ans. $\mathbf{F} = 0.60e\mathbf{a}_x + 0.24e\mathbf{a}_y$.

9.2. Force on a Differential Current Element.

The force on a charged particle moving through a steady magnetic field,

$$\mathbf{F} = Q\mathbf{U} \times \mathbf{B} \tag{1}$$

may be used to obtain the expression for the differential amount of force exerted on a differential element of charge:

$$d\mathbf{F} = dQ\,\mathbf{U} \times \mathbf{B} \tag{2}$$

Physically, the differential element of charge consists of a large number of very small discrete charges occupying a volume which, although small, is much larger than the average separation between the charges. The differential force expressed by (2) is thus merely the sum of the forces on the individual charges. This sum, or resultant force, is not a force applied to a single object. In an analogous way we might consider the differential gravitational force experienced by a small volume taken in a shower of falling sand. The small volume contains a large number of sand grains, and the differential force is the sum of the forces on the individual grains within the small volume.

If our charges are electrons in motion in a conductor, however, we can show that the force is transferred to the conductor and that the sum of this extremely large number of extremely small forces is of practical importance. Within the conductor electrons are in motion throughout a region of immobile positive ions which form a crystalline array giving the conductor its solid properties. A magnetic field which exerts forces on the electrons tends to cause them to shift position slightly and produces a small displacement between the centers of "gravity" of the positive and negative charges. The Coulomb forces between electrons and positive ions, however, tend to resist such a displacement. Any attempt to move the electrons, therefore, results in an attractive force between electrons and the positive ions of the crystalline lattice. The magnetic force is thus transferred to the crystalline lattice, or to the conductor itself. The Coulomb forces are so much greater than the magnetic forces in good conductors that the actual displacement of the electrons is almost immeasurable. This effect is called the *Hall effect*.

Returning to (2), we therefore may say that if we are considering an element of moving charge in an electron beam, the force is merely the sum of the forces on the individual electrons in that small volume element, but if we are considering an element of moving charge within a conductor, the total force is applied to the solid conductor itself. In this chapter we shall now limit our attention to the forces on current-carrying conductors.

Let us assume that charge is moving in a differential length of a conductor $d\mathbf{L}$ with a velocity $\mathbf{U}$:

$$\mathbf{U} = \frac{d\mathbf{L}}{dt}$$

and express the differential force as

$$d\mathbf{F} = dQ\,\frac{d\mathbf{L}}{dt} \times \mathbf{B}$$

The time differential may be associated with the element of charge:

$$d\mathbf{F} = \frac{dQ}{dt}\,d\mathbf{L} \times \mathbf{B}$$

or
$$= I\,d\mathbf{L} \times \mathbf{B} \tag{3}$$

Equation (3) is expressed in terms of a filamentary current I. If the current element is a portion of a sheet of current, $I\ d\mathbf{L}$ is replaced by $\mathbf{J}_s\ dS$, and the differential force becomes

$$d\mathbf{F} = \mathbf{J}_s \times \mathbf{B}\ dS \qquad (4)$$

In a similar manner, the force on a differential volume element containing current density $\mathbf{i}$ is

$$d\mathbf{F} = \mathbf{i} \times \mathbf{B}\ dv \qquad (5)$$

Each of the expressions for the differential force on a current element, (3), (4), or (5), leads to results which may be verified experimentally only when the entire physical current distribution is considered. This is exactly analogous to the interpretation of the expressions for the differential field $d\mathbf{H}$ produced by differential current elements, as discussed in the first section of the previous chapter.

Integrating (3), (4), and (5) over a closed path, a surface which may be either open or closed (why?), or a volume, respectively, leads to the integral formulations:

$$\mathbf{F} = \oint I\ d\mathbf{L} \times \mathbf{B} = -I \oint \mathbf{B} \times d\mathbf{L} \qquad (6)$$

$$= \int_s \mathbf{J}_s \times \mathbf{B}\ dS \qquad (7)$$

and

$$= \int_{\text{vol}} \mathbf{i} \times \mathbf{B}\ dv \qquad (8)$$

One simple result is obtained by applying (3) or (6) to a straight conductor in a uniform magnetic field:

$$\mathbf{F} = I\mathbf{L} \times \mathbf{B} \qquad (9)$$

The magnitude of the force is given by the familiar equation

$$F = BIL \sin \theta \qquad (10)$$

where the angle between the vectors representing the direction of the current flow and the direction of the magnetic flux density is θ. Equation (9) or (10) applies only to a portion of the closed circuit, and the remainder of the circuit must be considered in any practical problem.

D9.2. A uniform magnetic flux density is given in cylindrical coordinates by $\mathbf{B} = 0.01\mathbf{a}_z$. Find the vector force exerted on a current-carrying element of a conductor at point P ($r = 1$, $\phi = 0$, $z = 0$) if:

(a) The element is a 1-mm length of a filamentary conductor in the $z = 0$ plane carrying 10^{-3} amp radially outward from the origin through P.

(b) The element is 1 mm^2 of the $z = 0$ plane carrying a surface current $\mathbf{J}_s = -1\mathbf{a}_r + 2\mathbf{a}_\phi$ amp/m.

(c) The element is 1 mm^3 of a conductor with current density $\mathbf{i} = -10^3 \cos \phi\ \mathbf{a}_\phi - 10^3 \sin \phi\ \mathbf{a}_r$.

Ans. $d\mathbf{F} = 10^{-8}\mathbf{a}_r$.

D9.3. Find the total vector force on a filamentary conductor in the $z = 0$ plane forming a square, centered at the origin, 1 m on a side. The current is 10 amp and flows in a clockwise direction as viewed from a point on the negative z axis. The magnetic flux density is:

(a) $\mathbf{B} = \mathbf{a}_z$.

(b) $\mathbf{B} = \mathbf{a}_x$.

(c) $\mathbf{B} = \mathbf{a}_y - 2\mathbf{a}_z$.

Ans. $\mathbf{F} = 0$.

9.3. Force between Differential Current Elements.

The concept of the magnetic field was introduced to break into two parts the problem of finding the interaction of one current distribution on a second current distribution. It is possible to express the force on one current element directly in terms of a second current element without finding the magnetic field. Since we have claimed that the magnetic-field concept simplifies our work, it then behooves us to show that avoidance of this intermediate step leads to more complicated expressions.

The magnetic field at point 2 due to a current element at point 1 has been found to be

$$d\mathbf{H}_2 = \frac{I_1\, d\mathbf{L}_1 \times \mathbf{a}_{R12}}{4\pi R_{12}{}^2}$$

and the resultant force on a second current element located at point 2 is

$$d\mathbf{F}_2 = I_2\, d\mathbf{L}_2 \times \mathbf{B}_2$$

Replacing $\mathbf{B}_2$ by $d\mathbf{B}_2$, we have only a differential amount of our differential force, and we indicate this by $d(d\mathbf{F}_2)$:

$$d(d\mathbf{F}_2) = I_2\, d\mathbf{L}_2 \times d\mathbf{B}_2$$

Since $d\mathbf{B}_2 = \mu_0\, d\mathbf{H}_2$, we obtain the force between two differential current elements:

$$d(d\mathbf{F}_2) = \mu_0 \frac{I_1 I_2}{4\pi R_{12}{}^2}\, d\mathbf{L}_2 \times (d\mathbf{L}_1 \times \mathbf{a}_{R12}) \tag{1}$$

The total force between the two filamentary circuits is obtained by integrating twice:

$$\mathbf{F}_2 = \mu_0 \frac{I_1 I_2}{4\pi} \oint \left[d\mathbf{L}_2 \times \oint \frac{d\mathbf{L}_1 \times \mathbf{a}_{R12}}{R_{12}{}^2} \right]$$

$$= \mu_0 \frac{I_1 I_2}{4\pi} \oint \left[\oint \frac{\mathbf{a}_{R12} \times d\mathbf{L}_1}{R_{12}{}^2} \right] \times d\mathbf{L}_2 \tag{2}$$

Equation (2) is quite formidable, but our familiarity with the magnetic field gained in the last chapter should enable us to recognize the inner integral as the integral necessary to find the magnetic field at point 2 due to the current element at point 1.

One of the problems at the end of the chapter uses (2) to show that the force of repulsion between infinitely long, straight, parallel, filamentary conductors carrying equal but opposite currents of I amp is

$$F = \mu_0 \frac{I^2}{2\pi d} \qquad \text{newtons/m length}$$

where the conductor separation is d m.

D9.4. A differential current element $I_A \, d\mathbf{L}_A = I_A \, dx \, \mathbf{a}_x$ is located at $(0,0,0)$, and a second current element $I_B \, d\mathbf{L}_B = I_B \, dy \, \mathbf{a}_y$ is at $(0,1,0)$.

(a) Find the force exerted on $I_B \, d\mathbf{L}_B$ by $I_A \, d\mathbf{L}_A$.

(b) Find the force exerted on $I_A \, d\mathbf{L}_A$ by $I_B \, d\mathbf{L}_B$.

(c) Demonstrate the ridiculous nature of these answers, obtained by considering only portions of complete circuits, by stating the result which Newton's third law demands for the sum of the force of $I_B \, d\mathbf{L}_B$ on $I_A \, d\mathbf{L}_A$ and of $I_A \, d\mathbf{L}_A$ on $I_B \, d\mathbf{L}_B$.

$$Ans. \quad d(d\mathbf{F}) = \mu_0 \frac{I_A I_B \, dx \, dy}{4\pi} \mathbf{a}_x.$$

9.4. Force on a Closed Circuit in a Uniform Field. The force on a filamentary closed circuit is given by Sec. 9.2, Eq. (6):

$$\mathbf{F} = -I \oint \mathbf{B} \times d\mathbf{L}$$

and if we assume a uniform magnetic flux density, $\mathbf{B}$ may be removed from the integral:

$$\mathbf{F} = -I\mathbf{B} \times \oint d\mathbf{L}$$

However, we discovered during our investigation of closed line integrals in the electrostatic potential field that $\oint d\mathbf{L} = 0$, and therefore the force on a closed filamentary circuit in a uniform magnetic field is zero.

We need not restrict this result to filamentary circuits only. The circuit may contain surface currents or volume current density as well. If the total current is divided into filaments, the force on each one is zero and the total force is again zero. Therefore any real closed circuit carrying direct currents experiences a total vector force of zero in a uniform magnetic field.

If the field is not uniform, the total force need not be zero.

9.5. Torque on a Differential Current Loop. The *torque*, or *moment*, of a force may be defined as a vector. The magnitude of the vector torque is the product of the magnitudes of the vector force, the vector lever arm, and the sine of the angle between these two vectors. The direction of the vector torque is normal to both the force and lever arm and is in the direction of progress of a right-handed screw as the lever arm is rotated into the force vector through the smaller angle. The torque is expressible as a cross product:

$$\mathbf{T} = \mathbf{r} \times \mathbf{F}$$

Let us assume that two forces $\mathbf{F}_1$ and $\mathbf{F}_2$ with lever arms $\mathbf{r}_1$ and $\mathbf{r}_2$ are applied to an object of fixed shape and that the object does not undergo any translation. Then

$$\mathbf{T} = \mathbf{r}_1 \times \mathbf{F}_1 + \mathbf{r}_2 \times \mathbf{F}_2$$

where
$$\mathbf{F}_1 + \mathbf{F}_2 = 0$$

and therefore
$$\mathbf{T} = (\mathbf{r}_1 - \mathbf{r}_2) \times \mathbf{F}_1$$

The vector $(\mathbf{r}_1 - \mathbf{r}_2)$ joins the point of application of $\mathbf{F}_2$ to that of $\mathbf{F}_1$ and is independent of the choice of origin for the two vectors $\mathbf{r}_1$ and $\mathbf{r}_2$. We are therefore free to choose any common origin for the lever arms $\mathbf{r}_1$ and $\mathbf{r}_2$, provided that the total force is zero.   This may be extended to any number of forces.

Consider the application of a vertically upward force at the end of a horizontal crank handle on an elderly automobile.   This cannot be the only applied force, for, if it were, the entire handle would be accelerated in an upward direction.   A second force, equal in magnitude to that exerted at the end of the handle, is applied in a downward direction by the bearing surface at the axis of rotation.   For a 10-lb force on a crank handle 1 ft in length, the torque is 10 lb-ft.   This figure is obtained no matter whether the origin is considered to be on the axis of rotation (leading to 10 lb-ft plus 0 lb-ft), at the mid-point of the handle (leading to 5 lb-ft plus 5 lb-ft), or at some point not even on the handle or an extension of the handle.

We may therefore choose the most convenient origin, and this is usually on the axis of rotation and in the plane containing the applied forces if the several forces are coplanar.

With this introduction to the concept of torque, let us now consider the torque on a differential current loop in a magnetic field $\mathbf{B}$.   The loop lies in the xy plane (Fig. 9.1); the sides of the loop are parallel to the x and y axes and are of length dx and dy.   The value of the magnetic field at the center of the loop is taken as $\mathbf{B}_0$.   Since the loop is of differential size, the value of $\mathbf{B}$ at all points on the loop may be taken as $\mathbf{B}_0$.   (Why was this not possible in the discussion of curl and divergence?)   The total force on the loop is therefore zero, and we are free to choose the origin for the lever arms at the center of the loop.

The vector force on side 1 is obtained by applying Sec. 9.2, Eq. (3):

$$d\mathbf{F} = I\, d\mathbf{L} \times \mathbf{B}$$

leading to
$$d\mathbf{F}_1 = I\, dx\, \mathbf{a}_x \times \mathbf{B}_0$$

or
$$= I\, dx\, (B_{0y}\mathbf{a}_z - B_{0z}\mathbf{a}_y)$$

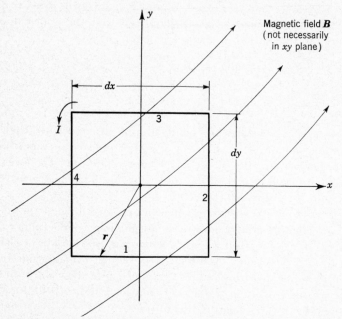

FIG. 9.1. A differential current loop in a magnetic field **B**.   The center of the loop is at the origin of a cartesian coordinate system, and the sides of the loop are parallel to the x and y axes.

For this side of the loop the average lever arm **r** extends from the origin to the mid-point of the side, $\mathbf{r}_1 = -\frac{1}{2}dy\,\mathbf{a}_y$, and the contribution to the total torque is

$$d\mathbf{T}_1 = \mathbf{r}_1 \times d\mathbf{F}_1$$
$$= -\tfrac{1}{2}dy\,\mathbf{a}_y \times I\,dx\,(B_{0y}\mathbf{a}_z - B_{0z}\mathbf{a}_y)$$
$$= -\tfrac{1}{2}dx\,dy\,IB_{0y}\mathbf{a}_x$$

Similarly, the torque contribution on side 3 is found to be equal to the above expression:

$$d\mathbf{T}_3 = d\mathbf{T}_1$$
and
$$d\mathbf{T}_1 + d\mathbf{T}_3 = -dx\,dy\,IB_{0y}\mathbf{a}_x$$

Evaluating the torque on sides 2 and 4, we find

$$d\mathbf{T}_2 + d\mathbf{T}_4 = dx\,dy\,IB_{0x}\mathbf{a}_y$$

and the total torque is, then,

$$d\mathbf{T} = I\,dx\,dy\,(B_{0x}\mathbf{a}_y - B_{0y}\mathbf{a}_x)$$

The quantity within the parentheses may be represented by a cross product:

$$dT = I \, dx \, dy \, (\mathbf{a}_z \times \mathbf{B}_0)$$
$$= I(dx \, dy \, \mathbf{a}_z \times \mathbf{B}_0)$$
$$= I \, d\mathbf{S} \times \mathbf{B} \tag{1a}$$
$$= d\mathbf{M} \times \mathbf{B} \tag{1b}$$

where $d\mathbf{S}$ is the vector differential area of the current, $I \, d\mathbf{S}$ is replaced by $d\mathbf{M}$, the differential *moment* of the current loop, and the subscript on $\mathbf{B}_0$ has been dropped. The moment of a current loop, given by the product of the loop current and the area enclosed, produces a torque, or moment of forces, in a magnetic field. These two uses of the term *moment* are only slightly related.

Equation (1) is a general result which holds for a differential loop of any shape, not necessarily rectangular. The torque on a circular or triangular loop is also given in terms of its vector surface by (1a) or (1b).

It should be noticed that (1) shows that the torque produced in a current-carrying loop in a magnetic field is in such a direction as to align the magnetic field produced by the loop with the applied magnetic field. This fact will help us to understand the nature of magnetic materials in Sec. 9.7 below.

D9.5. Find the incremental torque produced:

(a) On the loop of Fig. 9.1 if $I = 1$ amp and the sides are 1 mm in length, $\mathbf{B}_0 = 0.01\mathbf{a}_x$ webers/m^2.

(b) On a circular loop, 1 mm radius, center at the origin, lying in the xy plane, $I = 1$ amp in $\mathbf{a}_\phi$ direction, $\mathbf{B} = 10^{-4}[(100 + y)\mathbf{a}_x + (50 - x)\mathbf{a}_y]$.

(c) On an electric dipole (discussed in Sec. 4.7), $q = 10^{-6}$ coulomb at $(0,0,10^{-3})$, $q = -10^{-6}$ coulomb at $(0,0,-10^{-3})$, $\mathbf{E} = 10\mathbf{a}_y$ volts/m.

$Ans.$ $(4.14\mathbf{a}_y - 3.57\mathbf{a}_x)10^{-8}$ newton-m.

9.6. Torque on a Closed Circuit.

In this section we shall consider loops of finite size and in particular those lying entirely in one plane (*planar* loops). Let us temporarily assume that the planar loop lies in a region of uniform magnetic flux density $\mathbf{B}_0$. Such a loop is shown in Fig. 9.2.

The interior of the loop is shown divided into differential elements of area. The sides of each of these differential area elements may be considered to be filamentary conductors carrying a current I in a counterclockwise direction, for the sum of the currents in two adjacent loops is then zero along every common boundary. The sum of the forces produced on such a common boundary is, therefore, also zero. Since the elemental forces on both the original and subdivided systems are identical, it is evident that the total torque on the finite-sized

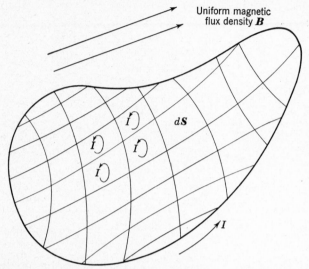

Fɪɢ. 9.2. A planar current loop carrying a direct current I lies in a uniform magnetic field $\mathbf{B}_0$. The loop interior is divided into differential area elements, each of vector area $d\mathbf{S}$.

loop is therefore the sum of the torques produced on the differential elements:

$$
\begin{aligned}
\mathbf{T} &= \int d\mathbf{T} \\
&= I \int_s d\mathbf{S} \times \mathbf{B}_0 \\
&= -I\mathbf{B}_0 \times \int_s d\mathbf{S} \\
&= I\mathbf{S} \times \mathbf{B}_0 = \mathbf{M} \times \mathbf{B}_0
\end{aligned}
\tag{1}
$$

If the magnetic flux density is not uniform, the result must be expressed in terms of an integral:

$$
\mathbf{T} = -I \int_s \mathbf{B} \times d\mathbf{S}
\tag{2}
$$

Equation (2) evidently also applies in the case of a nonplanar loop in a nonuniform magnetic field. The loop may now be considered as the perimeter of an infinite number of surfaces, and any of these surfaces may be chosen for the evaluation of the integral.

In general (1) shows us that the torque on a planar current loop in a uniform magnetic field tends to produce a rotation of the loop in such a way as to align the flux in the interior of the loop with the applied flux.

D9.6. A circular filamentary current loop in the $z = 0$ plane, radius 0.10 m, center at the origin, carries a current of 30 amp in the $\mathbf{a}_\phi$ direction. Find the vector torque produced on this loop by the given magnetic flux density. Remember that $\oint d\mathbf{L} = 0$.

(a) $\mathbf{B} = 0.05\mathbf{a}_x$.

(b) $\mathbf{B} = 0$, $0 < r < 0.09$; $\mathbf{B} = \dfrac{-0.09}{r}\mathbf{a}_r$, $0.09 < r < 1.10$; $\mathbf{B} = 0$, $r > 1.10$.

(c) $\mathbf{B} = \dfrac{0.10\mathbf{a}_\phi}{r}$.

Ans. $4.71 \times 10^{-2}\mathbf{a}_y$ newton-m.

9.7. Magnetic Materials and Boundary Conditions.

We are now in a position to combine our knowledge of the action of a magnetic field on a current loop with the simple model of an atom and obtain some appreciation of the difference in behavior of various materials in magnetic fields.

We may use the atomic model consisting of a central positive nucleus surrounded by electrons in various orbits. An electron in an orbit is analogous to a small current loop (in which the current is directed oppositely to the direction of electron travel) and as such experiences a torque in an external magnetic field, the torque tending to align the magnetic field produced by the orbiting electron with the external field. Since the magnetic field of the electron then adds to the external field, this simple picture would lead us to believe that the magnetic field in any material is always greater than it would be without the material present. This is true only in some cases, however, and a second motion of the electrons must be taken into account, *electron spin*.

The physicists have obtained experimental evidence which may be explained theoretically by assuming that the electron spins about an axis passing through the electron itself as it orbits about the nucleus. This model is evidently patterned after the motion of a planet such as the earth about its sun. The spinning electron is thus the equivalent of a second current loop, and the torque on this loop must also be considered in the presence of an external magnetic field. It turns out that these effects very nearly cancel each other in most atoms, the notable class of exceptions being ferromagnetic materials.

Let us first consider those atoms in which the small magnetic fields produced by the motion of the electrons in their orbits and the fields produced by the electron spin combine to produce a net field of zero. Note that we here are considering the fields produced by the electron motion itself in the absence of any external magnetic field. We might also describe this material as one in which the moment $I\,d\mathbf{S}$ of each atom is zero. Such a material is termed *diamagnetic*. An external magnetic field produces a torque on each electron in the atom because of both its orbital motion and its spin. The net sum of these torques is zero, and no realignment of the atom occurs. To a good approximation, then, the magnetic field within the material is the same as the external field. A more complete analysis shows that as the applied magnetic field initially increases from zero it produces an electric field (by Faraday's law, discussed in Chap. 10) which changes the velocity of the electron in its orbit, and thus changes the magnetic field produced by the orbiting electron slightly, but in such a way as to *oppose* the externally applied field. The resultant value of **B** is thus slightly smaller in a diamagnetic material than it would be without the diamagnetic material being present. This decrease is seldom greater than one-hundredth of one per cent.

Now let us consider an atom in which the effects of electron spin and orbital motion do not quite cancel. The atom as a whole behaves as a rather weak current loop, but the random orientation of the atoms in a larger sample produces an *average* magnetic moment of zero. The material shows no magnetic effects in the absence of an external field. If the sample is subjected to a torque by an externally applied magnetic field, then, as we have seen above, the action of the torque results in the small magnetic field of the atom adding to the external field. The diamagnetic effect is still present and serves to decrease the external field. If the net effect is an increase in **B**, the material is termed *paramagnetic*. If **B** decreases, the material is still called diamagnetic.

Finally, there is a class of materials in which the orbital motion and electron spin fail to counteract each other by an amount equal to the spin of several electrons. Each atom has a relatively large magnetic moment, and, in a magnetic field, **B** increases to many times the value it would have in free space. These materials are called *ferromagnetic*. Molecular forces may also act to maintain some alignment of the current loops after the external field is removed. Such permanent magnets are possible only with ferromagnetic materials.

Most atoms and molecules are either diamagnetic or paramagnetic, showing very little effect in a magnetic field. The ferromagnetic materials include iron, cobalt, nickel, gadolinium, and many alloys of these with other metals.

In order to place our description of magnetic materials on a more quantitative basis, let us place the material in a uniform magnetic field. Such a field may be established simply by providing two infinite current sheets, carrying oppositely directed currents, as shown in Fig. 9.3. We place an infinite slab of material between these parallel sheets, leaving an air gap between the material and each sheet

for reference purposes.   Given a surface current of J_s amp/m, the
results obtained in Sec. 8.2 (or a simple application of Ampère's circuital law) show that the magnetic field intensity in the air gap, H_0,
is given by $H_0 = J_s$.   In this region B is then $B_0 = \mu_0 H_0$.   The magnetic flux density within the added material depends on the type of
material, which we shall assume is paramagnetic (or ferromagnetic,
but linear).   The torque applied to the atomic current loops thus
tends to align the atoms in such a way as to make the **B** produced by

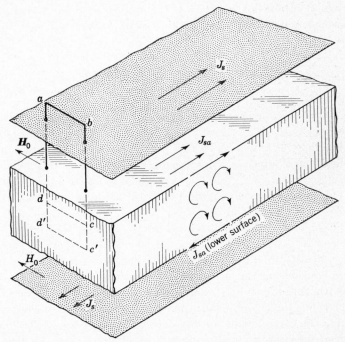

FIG. 9.3. Two parallel infinite current sheets carrying oppositely directed surface
currents of J_s amp/m produce magnetic fields in the adjacent air gaps of $H_0 = J_s$.
An infinite slab of material whose magnetic properties are to be investigated
occupies the remainder of the space between the current sheets.

the loops add to the external field.   The current flow in several loops
is indicated in Fig. 9.3.   These currents are called *Amperian currents*
and result from the movement of *bound* electrons.   The increase in
magnetic flux density and magnetic field intensity is thus directly due
to these Amperian currents.   Adjacent internal loops produce can-
celing currents along a common boundary, leaving a net current flow
only along the upper and lower surfaces of the slab.   The Amperian
currents may thus be represented by two additional surface currents,

in this case on the surfaces of the slab, and are indicated in Fig. 9.3 by J_{sa}.

Applying Ampère's circuital law to the paths $abcd$ and $abc'd'$ shows that the magnetic field within the slab is uniform and given by

$$H_i = J_s + J_{sa} \tag{1}$$

$$B_i = \mu_0 H_i = \mu_0 H_0 \left(1 + \frac{J_{sa}}{J_s}\right) \tag{2}$$

The factor $1 + J_{sa}/J_s$ depends on the material and in ferromagnetic materials also depends on H_0 (or J_s) to a large extent. Let us set this factor equal to the dimensionless constant μ_r:

$$1 + \frac{J_{sa}}{J_s} = \mu_r \tag{3}$$

and then

$$B_i = \mu_r \mu_0 H_0 \tag{4}$$

Our initial investigation of this magnetic material has thus produced these three steps:

1. The flow of Amperian surface currents increases the net surface current which is effective in producing a field within the sample by a factor of μ_r.

2. The magnetic field intensity within the material therefore increases by a factor of μ_r.

3. The magnetic flux density within the material also increases by a factor of μ_r.

The difficulty in this method of analysis lies with the necessity of directly considering the Amperian surface currents. These currents are not the motion of free charge, and an engineer would be much happier if he could ignore the Amperian currents and still be sure of obtaining the correct value of flux density.

Such a procedure is possible if we are willing to say that the permeability of the material is not that of free space. In the analysis above we considered the material as free space in which were embedded countless orbiting and spinning electrons and positive nuclei. Hence, in going from (1) to (2), we let $B_i = \mu_0 H_i$. Now we shall ascribe a permeability $\mu = \mu_r \mu_0$ to the magnetic material and let

$$\mathbf{B} = \mu \mathbf{H} \tag{5}$$

everywhere, and in particular,

$$B_i = \mu H_i \tag{6}$$

We now neglect the Amperian surface currents and find, therefore, that H_i and $\bar{H}_0$ are equal. The paths $abcd$ and $abc'd'$ both include only J_s. Equation (6) therefore becomes

$$B_i = \mu H_0 = \mu_r \mu_0 H_0 \tag{7}$$

and agrees with (4). The only difference between the two viewpoints lies in the value of H obtained within the material. If the Amperian currents are considered, $H_i = \mu_r H_0$, and if they are not considered, $H_i = H_0$. This disagreement is of no consequence because the force, or torque, produced by the magnetic field is a function of **B** and not of **H**, and **B** is unchanged.

The "engineer's viewpoint" may then be summarized by these three steps:

1. There are no Amperian surface currents (or perhaps we concede their existence but then do not consider them as sources of the magnetic field intensity).

2. The value of magnetic field intensity within the material is therefore unchanged.

3. The material is described by its *relative permeability*, $\mu_r = \mu/\mu_0$, and the magnetic flux density within the material therefore increases by a factor of μ_r.

Most of us probably recognize the similarity of this description of the magnetic properties of materials with that of the dielectric properties in Chap. 5. At that time we were confronted with an induced surface charge which changed the electric flux density **D** within the dielectric. We then agreed to describe the material by a relative dielectric constant, ignore the bound surface charge, and accept a different value of internal electric flux density. The forces in the electric field are proportional to the electric field intensity, and not to the electric flux density.

An important difference in the electric and magnetic properties of materials lies in the fact that the common dielectric materials possess a relative permittivity which is essentially not a function of the electric field intensity, but all ferromagnetic materials have a relative permeability which varies greatly with the magnetic field intensity. In other words, the relationship of B to H is nonlinear.

As a final example, let us consider an air-filled infinitely long solenoid of radius a provided with n turns/m, each turn carrying I amp. The field was found to be (Chap. 8, Prob. 9)

$$H = nI \qquad r < a$$

and
$$B = \mu_0 nI$$

If now we place a cylinder of permeability μ within the solenoid, the value of H is unchanged since the current distribution is unchanged

(Amperian currents ignored).   The value of B, however, is now

$$B = \mu n I$$

The boundary conditions for **B** and **H** at the boundary between two media of different permeabilities are now easily established.   Figure 9.4 shows such a boundary between regions of permeability μ_1 and μ_2. The boundary condition on the normal components is determined by

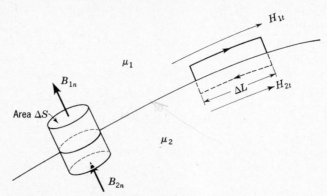

FIG. 9.4. A Gaussian surface and a closed path are constructed at the boundary between media 1 and 2, having permeabilities of μ_1 and μ_2, respectively.

allowing the surface to cut a small, cylindrical Gaussian surface. Applying Gauss's law for the magnetic field [Sec. 8.5, Eq. (4)],

$$\oint_s \mathbf{B} \cdot d\mathbf{S} = 0$$

we find that

$$B_{1n}\,\Delta S - B_{2n}\,\Delta S = 0$$

or
$$B_{1n} = B_{2n} \tag{8}$$
and
$$\mu_1 H_{1n} = \mu_2 H_{2n} \tag{9}$$

The normal component of **B** is continuous, and the normal component of **H** is discontinuous by the ratio μ_2/μ_1.

Application of Ampère's circuital law,

$$\oint \mathbf{H} \cdot d\mathbf{L} = I$$

to a small closed path in a plane normal to the boundary surface indicates that

$$H_{t1}\,\Delta L - H_{t2}\,\Delta L = 0$$

or
$$H_{t1} = H_{t2} \tag{10}$$

if no current is enclosed by the path.   As the dimension of the path normal to the surface approaches zero, the enclosed current due to volume current density also approaches zero. Unless the path encloses a surface current or filamentary current, (10) is true. For a surface current J_s on the boundary surface, where $\mathbf{J}_s$ is perpendicular to $\mathbf{H}$,

$$H_{t1}\,\Delta L - H_{t2}\,\Delta L = J_s\,\Delta L$$

or
$$H_{t1} - H_{t2} = J_s \tag{11}$$

and
$$\frac{B_{t1}}{\mu_1} - \frac{B_{t2}}{\mu_2} = J_s \tag{12}$$

At this point all the fundamental concepts have been laid for the study of the magnetic circuit, which may be shown to be analogous to the electric circuit. Circuit theory, however, whether it concerns magnetic or electric circuits, is a specialized (but important) branch of field theory. In Chap. 11 the general equations of Maxwell are used to show the assumptions upon which all circuit theory is based and to show its restrictions, but neither the magnetic nor the electric circuit will receive any further discussion.

D9.7. In Fig. 9.3 let the current sheets be $J_s = 5$ amp/m and let the magnetic material have a relative permeability of 5.

(a) Find the magnetic field intensity which would exist throughout the region between the current sheets if the magnetic material were not present.

(b) Find the magnetic field intensity within the magnetic material if Amperian currents are considered.

(c) Find the magnetic field intensity within the magnetic material using the practical engineering approach.

Ans. 35 amp/m.

D9.8. Repeat the above problem in terms of magnetic flux density.

Ans. 69.1×10^{-6} weber/m².

D9.9. The $z = 0$ plane is the boundary between region 1 ($z > 0$) and region 2 ($z < 0$). The magnetic flux density in region 1 is given by $\mathbf{B}_1 = 2\mathbf{a}_x - 3\mathbf{a}_y - 5\mathbf{a}_z$. Find $\mathbf{B}_2$ if:

(a) $\mu_{r1} = 1$, $\mu_{r2} = 2$.

(b) $\mu_{r1} = 2$, $\mu_{r2} = 1$.

(c) $\mu_{r1} = 2$, $\mu_{r2} = 1$, and $\mathbf{J}_s = 10^6\mathbf{a}_x$ on the boundary surface.

Ans. $\mathbf{B}_2 = 6\mathbf{a}_x - 7.74\mathbf{a}_y - 15\mathbf{a}_z$.

9.8. Potential Energy of Magnetic Fields. In the electrostatic field we first introduced the point charge and the experimental law of force between point charges. After defining electric field intensity, electric flux density, and electric potential, we were able to find an expression for the energy in an electrostatic field by establishing the work necessary to bring the necessary point charges from infinity to their final positions. The general expression for energy is

$$W_E = \frac{1}{2} \int_{\text{vol}} \mathbf{D} \cdot \mathbf{E}\, dv \tag{1}$$

A magnetostatic field might have been defined along similar methods by assuming the existence of a unit magnetic pole and defining a scalar potential. If this had been done, an energy expression analogous to (1) would have been obtained:

$$W_H = \frac{1}{2} \int_{\text{vol}} \mathbf{B} \cdot \mathbf{H} \, dv \tag{2}$$

Although this could still be done very easily, the new *magnetostatic* quantities we should have to introduce would be too great a price to pay for one simple result. In addition, the relationship of the magnetic field to current sources would still have to be established. For these reasons (2) is offered without proof[1] as the energy stored in the steady magnetic field.

Letting $\mathbf{B} = \mu\mathbf{H}$, we have the equivalent formulations

$$W_H = \frac{1}{2} \int_{\text{vol}} \mu H^2 \, dv \tag{3}$$

or

$$= \frac{1}{2} \int_{\text{vol}} \frac{B^2}{\mu} \, dv \tag{4}$$

It is again convenient to think of this energy as being distributed throughout the volume with an energy density of $\frac{1}{2}\mathbf{B} \cdot \mathbf{H}$ joules/m³, although we have no mathematical justification for such a statement.

D9.10. Find the energy density of the magnetic field in joules per cubic meter:

(*a*) 1 cm from an infinitely long straight conductor of 1 mm radius carrying a total direct current of 1 amp.

(*b*) In free space between two infinite current sheets carrying oppositely directed surface currents of 10 amp/m.

(*c*) Between the above two current sheets in a magnetic material of relative permeability $\mu_r = 5$.

Ans. 5.36×10^{-4} joule/m³.

9.9. Inductance.

Inductance is the last of the three familiar constants from circuit theory, which we should now define in more general terms. Resistance was defined in the fifth chapter as the ratio of the potential difference between two equipotential surfaces of a conducting material to the total current crossing either equipotential surface. The resistance is a function of conductor geometry and conductivity only. Capacitance was defined in the same chapter as the ratio of the total charge on either of two equipotential conducting surfaces to the potential difference between the surfaces. Capacitance is a function only of the geometry of the two conducting surfaces and the permittivity of the dielectric medium between or surrounding them.

---

[1] A proof of (2) is offered in the references which are listed at the end of this chapter.

Let us now define inductance from an energy point of view as

$$L = \frac{2W_H}{I^2} \tag{1}$$

where I = total current flowing in closed path, and W_H = energy in magnetic field produced by this current. The unit of inductance is the henry, and this is evidently equivalent to one joule per ampere squared.

As an example of the application of (1), we may calculate the inductance per meter length of a coaxial cable of inner radius a and outer radius b. In the region between conductors, the flux density is given in Sec. 8.2 as

$$H_\phi = \frac{I}{2\pi r} \qquad a < r < b$$

and the energy stored in the magnetic field per meter length is found through Sec. 9.8, Eq. (2), as

$$W_H = \frac{1}{2} \int_{z=0}^{z=1} \int_{\phi=0}^{\phi=2\pi} \int_{r=a}^{r=b} \frac{\mu I^2}{4\pi^2 r^2} r \, dr \, d\phi \, dz$$
$$= \frac{\mu I^2}{4\pi} \ln \frac{b}{a}$$

The inductance is, then,

$$L = \frac{\mu}{2\pi} \ln \frac{b}{a} \qquad \text{henrys/m} \tag{2}$$

This inductance is known as the *external inductance*. It does not include the energy storage within the conductor itself which leads to an *internal inductance*. The total inductance is given by the sum of the internal and external inductances. The internal inductance of a long straight wire of circular cross section with uniform current distribution is $\mu/8\pi$ henrys/m. This is the result of a problem at the end of this chapter.

In Chap. 11 it will be seen that the current distribution in a conductor at high frequencies tends to be concentrated near the surface. The internal flux is reduced, and it is usually sufficient to consider only the external inductance. At lower frequencies, however, internal inductance may become an appreciable part of the total inductance.

Let us now obtain several other expressions for inductance by manipulating (1). Evidently we may write

$$L = \frac{\int_{\text{vol}} \mathbf{B} \cdot \mathbf{H} \, dv}{I^2} \tag{3}$$

and replace **B** by ∇ × **A**:

$$L = \frac{1}{I^2} \int_{\text{vol}} \mathbf{H} \cdot (\nabla \times \mathbf{A}) \, dv$$

The vector identity

$$\nabla \cdot (\mathbf{A} \times \mathbf{H}) \equiv \mathbf{H} \cdot (\nabla \times \mathbf{A}) - \mathbf{A} \cdot (\nabla \times \mathbf{H}) \tag{4}$$

may be proved by expansion in cartesian coordinates. The inductance is, then,

$$L = \frac{1}{I^2} \left[\int_{\text{vol}} \nabla \cdot (\mathbf{A} \times \mathbf{H}) \, dv + \int_{\text{vol}} \mathbf{A} \cdot (\nabla \times \mathbf{H}) \, dv \right] \tag{5}$$

Replacing the first integral by an equivalent closed surface integral (through the use of what theorem?) and replacing ∇ × **H** by **i**, we have

$$L = \frac{1}{I^2} \left[\oint_s (\mathbf{A} \times \mathbf{H}) \cdot d\mathbf{S} + \int_{\text{vol}} \mathbf{A} \cdot \mathbf{i} \, dv \right]$$

The surface integral is zero, since the surface encloses the volume containing all the magnetic energy, and this requires that **A** and **H** be zero on the bounding surface. The inductance may therefore be written:

$$L = \frac{1}{I^2} \int_{\text{vol}} \mathbf{A} \cdot \mathbf{i} \, dv \tag{6}$$

Equation (6) expresses the inductance in terms of an integral of the values of **A** and **i** at every point. Since current density exists only within the conductor, the external vector magnetic potential need not be determined. The vector potential is that which arises from the current **i**, and any other current source contributing a vector potential field in the region of the original current density is to be ignored for the present. Later we shall see that this leads to a *mutual inductance*.

The vector magnetic potential **A** due to **i** is given by Sec. 8.6, Eq. (7):

$$\mathbf{A} = \int_{\text{vol}} \frac{\mu \mathbf{i}}{4\pi R} \, dv$$

and the inductance may therefore be expressed more basically as a rather formidable double volume integral:

$$L = \frac{1}{I^2} \int_{\text{vol}} \left(\int_{\text{vol}} \frac{\mu \mathbf{i}}{4\pi R} \, dv \right) \cdot \mathbf{i} \, dv \tag{7}$$

A slightly simpler integral expression is obtained by restricting our attention to current filaments of small cross section for which **i** *dv* may be replaced by $I\,d\mathbf{L}$ and the volume integral replaced by a closed line integral along the axis of the filament:

$$L = \frac{1}{I^2} \oint \left(\oint \frac{\mu I\,d\mathbf{L}}{4\pi R} \right) \cdot I\,d\mathbf{L}$$

$$= \frac{\mu}{4\pi} \oint \left(\oint \frac{d\mathbf{L}}{R} \right) \cdot d\mathbf{L} \tag{8}$$

Our only present interest in Eqs. (7) and (8) lies in their implication that the inductance is a function of the distribution of the current in space or the geometry of the conductor configuration.

Finally, we wish to express inductance in a form which is probably more familiar than any of the previous expressions.   Let us hypothesize a uniform current distribution in a filamentary conductor of small cross section so that $\mathbf{i}\,dv$ in (6) may be replaced by $I\,d\mathbf{L}$:

$$L = \frac{1}{I} \oint \mathbf{A} \cdot d\mathbf{L} \tag{9}$$

For a small cross section, $d\mathbf{L}$ may be taken along the center of the filament.   We now apply Stokes' theorem and obtain

$$L = \frac{1}{I} \int_s (\nabla \times \mathbf{A}) \cdot d\mathbf{S}$$

or

$$= \frac{1}{I} \int_s \mathbf{B} \cdot d\mathbf{S}$$

or

$$= \frac{\Phi}{I} \tag{10}$$

Retracing the steps by which (10) has been obtained, we should see that the flux Φ is that portion of the total flux which passes through any open surface whose perimeter is the filamentary current path.

If we now let the filament make N turns about the same path, an idealization which may be closely realized in practice, the closed line integral must consist of N laps about this path and (10) becomes

$$L = \frac{N\Phi}{I} \qquad \Phi/_{amp} = \overset{must}{constant} \tag{11}$$

The flux Φ is now the flux crossing any surface whose perimeter is the path occupied by each of the N turns.   The inductance of an N-turn coil may still be obtained from (10), however, if we realize that the flux is that which crosses the complicated surface whose perimeter consists of all N turns.

Use of any of the inductance expressions for a true filamentary conductor (having zero radius) leads to an infinite value of inductance, regardless of the configuration of the filament. The magnetic field intensity varies inversely as the distance from the conductor, and a simple integration soon shows that an infinite amount of energy and an infinite amount of flux are contained within any finite cylinder about the filament. This difficulty is eliminated by specifying a small but finite filamentary radius.

The use of (11) leads to the rather restricted definition of inductance as "flux linkages per unit current," a definition which allows the computation of external inductance in circuits involving conductors of very small cross-sectional dimensions. In some symmetrical problems of conductors of larger dimensions in which the path of the line integral of (9) is obvious, (10) and (11) are also applicable. For instance, the magnetic flux between the inner and outer conductors of a coaxial transmission line is given in Sec. 8.5, Eq. (8), as

$$\Phi = \frac{\mu_0 I}{2\pi} \ln \frac{b}{a}$$

This flux links the total current I carried by the inner conductor, and the inductance from (10) is, simply,

$$L = \frac{\mu_0}{2\pi} \ln \frac{b}{a}$$

as before. Here symmetry has established the path of the total current as the axis of the coaxial line. In the case of a ring formed from a conductor of appreciable cross section, the question of the location of the path is very difficult to answer, for the flux is not uniformly distributed about the perimeter of the conductor cross section.

Finally, we shall define the *mutual inductance* between circuits 1 and 2, L_{12}, in terms of a mutual energy:

$$L_{12} = \frac{1}{I_1 I_2} \int_{\text{vol}} (\mathbf{B}_1 \cdot \mathbf{H}_2) \, dv$$

$$= \frac{1}{I_1 I_2} \int_{\text{vol}} (\mu \mathbf{H}_1 \cdot \mathbf{H}_2) \, dv \tag{12}$$

where $\mathbf{B}_1$ = field resulting from I_1 (with $I_2 = 0$), and $\mathbf{H}_2$ = field due to I_2 (with $I_1 = 0$). Interchange of the subscripts does not change the right-hand side of (12), and therefore

$$L_{12} = L_{21}$$

Equivalent expressions for (12) may be obtained by the same general methods used in the study of inductance or *self-inductance* above:

$$L_{12} = \frac{1}{I_1 I_2} \int_{vol} [(\nabla \times \mathbf{A}_1) \cdot \mathbf{H}_2]\, dv$$

$$= \frac{1}{I_1 I_2} \int_{vol} (\mathbf{A}_1 \cdot \mathbf{i}_2)\, dv$$

$$= \frac{1}{I_1} \oint \mathbf{A}_1 \cdot d\mathbf{L}_2$$

$$= \oint \left(\oint \frac{\mu}{4\pi R}\, d\mathbf{L}_1 \right) \cdot d\mathbf{L}_2$$

where R = distance between differential elements $d\mathbf{L}_1$ and $d\mathbf{L}_2$.

In terms of flux linkages,

$$L_{12} = \frac{1}{I_1} \oint \mathbf{A}_1 \cdot d\mathbf{L}_2$$

$$= \frac{1}{I_1} \int_s (\nabla \times \mathbf{A}_1) \cdot d\mathbf{S}_2$$

$$= \frac{1}{I_1} \int_s \mathbf{B}_1 \cdot d\mathbf{S}_2$$

$$= \frac{\Phi_{12}}{I_1}$$

where Φ_{12} signifies the flux produced by I_1 which links the path of the filamentary current I_2.

We see, therefore, that there are many methods available for the calculation of self-inductance and mutual inductance. Unfortunately, even problems possessing a high degree of symmetry present very challenging integrals for evaluation, and only a few problems are available for us to try our skill on.

Inductance will be met again in the following chapter and also in the discussion of circuit concepts in Chap. 11.

D9.11. Find the inductance of a filamentary current loop carrying a current of 6 amp if:

(a) The total energy stored in the magnetic field of the loop is 9×10^{-3} joule.

(b) The total flux enclosed by the loop is 0.006 weber.

(c) The average value of the component of the vector magnetic potential which is tangential to the loop is 0.1 weber/m, and the length of the loop perimeter is 3 cm.

$Ans.\ 2 \times 10^{-3}$ henry.

SUGGESTED REFERENCES

1. Kraus, J. D.: (see Suggested References for Chap. 4). The magnetic field is described with numerous examples in chaps. 4 and 5.

2. Winch, R. P.: (see Suggested References for Chap. 3).   Discusses the magnetic field from the physicist's viewpoint at an introductory level in chaps. 13 and 14.

PROBLEMS

1. Show that a particle of charge Q and mass m moving in a magnetic field of uniform density **B** must move in a circular path.   Describe the orientation of the path with respect to **B**, and show that the angular velocity ω of the particle is QB/m by relating centrifugal and centripetal forces.

2. A uniform magnetic field, $B = 10^{-3}a_x$ weber/m², is present in the region $y > 0$.   Particles are injected into the field at the origin with velocity $U = 3 \times 10^6 a_y$ m/sec.   Using the results of Prob. 1, determine the z coordinate of the particle as it leaves the field and the time spent in the field as a function of the particle charge and mass.   Determine numerical answers for a proton and an alpha particle.

3. An electron of charge $Q = -e$ is electrostatically accelerated to a velocity U_0 in a cathode-ray tube.   The electron then enters a uniform magnetic field of flux density B_0, where $B_0 \cdot U_0 = 0$, which extends a distance d along the tube axis.   If the fluorescent screen is L m from the center of the region of magnetic flux and if the deflection of the electron produced by the magnetic field is small, show that this deflection at the screen is eB_0Ld/mU_0 m.

4. A circular conductor of radius a carries a uniformly distributed current of I amp.   Find the force on the current elements comprising the conductor as a force per unit volume at every point.   Show the direction and magnitude of the force throughout the cross section by a small sketch.   Why does this force not cause the current distribution to become noticeably nonuniform?   Integrate over the cross section, and show that the total force per meter length is zero.

5. In Sec. 9.3, Eq. (1), the triple cross product appears.   Show that the parentheses are necessary by demonstrating that $A \times (B \times C)$ is not in general equal to $(A \times B) \times C$.

6. Two infinitely long, straight, filamentary conductors are parallel and separated d m.   The conductors carry oppositely directed currents of I amp.   Use Sec. 9.3, Eq. (2), to show that the force of repulsion between the conductors is $\mu_0 I^2/2\pi d$ newtons/m length.

7. Find the pressure tending to separate two parallel conducting planes carrying equal and opposite uniform currents of J_s amp/m.

8. A square filamentary current loop, a m on a side and carrying I amp, lies in the xy plane and is centered at the origin.   The current direction is given generally by a_ϕ.   Show that the total force on the loop is zero in a uniform field of $B = B_0 a_x$.   Find the total force on the loop in the nonuniform field $B = B_0 \sin (\pi y/a)\, a_x$.

9. Show that the total force on a simple parallel circuit in a uniform magnetic field is zero.   Assume a battery of open-circuit voltage V_0 and internal resistance R_0 is connected to the parallel combination of R_1 and R_2.

10. Show that Sec. 9.5, Eq. (1), is also obtained for a circular loop.   For simplicity consider a uniform magnetic field in the plane of the loop.

11. Find the vector torque on the loop described in Prob. 8 for each of the given magnetic fields.

12. Assume a simple atomic model in which a single electron rotates about a nucleus of equal and opposite charge.   Let the radius of the circular path be a and the angular velocity of the electron ω (neglect relativistic effects).   Find the moment of this "current loop" and the torque produced by a magnetic flux density of B parallel to the plane of rotation.

13. The relative permeability of crystallized carbon is 0.999978, and that of aluminum is 1.000022. Refer to Fig. 9.3, and determine the magnitude and direction of the Amperian surface currents for each material if $J_s = 1$ amp/m. State whether each material is diamagnetic, paramagnetic, or ferromagnetic.

14. An infinitely long, straight, filamentary conductor carries a current of I amp in the $\mathbf{a}_z$ direction. A cylindrical shell of inner radius a and outer radius b surrounds the wire and has a relative permeability of 10. Using the Amperian currents, find the Amperian surface current density $\mathbf{J}_{sa}$ on the shell at $r = a$ and $r = b$, and find the value of $\mathbf{B}$ and $\mathbf{H}$ at all radii if the effect of Amperian currents is included. Now neglect the Amperian currents, and find $\mathbf{B}$ and $\mathbf{H}$ at all radii.

15. At the plane interface between two regions of relative permeability μ_{r1} and μ_{r2}, $\mathbf{B}_1$ makes an angle of θ_1 with the normal to the plane boundary. Show that the angle θ_2 which $\mathbf{B}_2$ makes with the normal in the second region is given by $\tan \theta_2 = (\mu_2/\mu_1) \tan \theta_1$.

16. An infinitely long solenoid of radius b and n turns/m, each turn carrying I amp, surrounds two different media. Medium 1 extends from $r = 0$ to $r = a$ and has a permeability of μ_1; medium 2 extends from $r = a$ to $r = b$ and has a permeability μ_2. Find B and H in each medium.

17. Show that the energy stored per unit length in the external magnetic field of an infinitely long, straight conductor of radius a is infinite.

18. Show that the energy stored per unit length in the internal magnetic field of an infinitely long, straight conductor of radius a, carrying a current I, is $\mu_0 I^2/16\pi$ joules/m.

19. Use the results of Probs. 17 and 18 to determine the external and internal inductance per unit length of an infinitely long, straight conductor of radius a.

20. Show that the external inductance per unit length of a two-wire transmission line, each conductor of radius a, center-to-center separation d, equal and opposite currents, is $(\mu/\pi) \ln (d/a)$, approximately.

21. Show that the inductance per unit length per unit width of a planar transmission line is $\mu_0 d$ henrys. The planar transmission line consists of two infinite, parallel, conducting planes (of zero thickness), separated d m, carrying equal and opposite surface currents of J_s amp/m.

22. Find the mutual inductance between filament A extending along the z axis and filament B, forming a square with corners at (1,0,0), (2,0,0), (2,0,1), and (1,0,1).

23. Find the mutual inductance between two filaments forming circular rings of radius a and Δa, where $\Delta a \ll a$. The field should be determined by approximate methods. The rings are coplanar and concentric.

24. Given a certain magnetic field intensity $\mathbf{H}$, it is found that both $\nabla \cdot \mathbf{H} = 0$ and $\nabla \times \mathbf{H} = 0$ at all points in a certain region. Explain these results, stating whether or not each is always true or whether it is a special case, and if so, what is special about it.

CHAPTER 10

TIME-VARYING FIELDS AND MAXWELL'S EQUATIONS

The basic relationships of the electrostatic and the steady magnetic field have been obtained in the previous nine chapters, and we are now ready to discuss time-varying fields. The discussion will be short for several reasons: vector analysis and vector calculus should now be more familiar tools, some of the relationships are unchanged, and most of the relationships are changed only slightly.

Two new concepts will be introduced: the electric field produced by a changing magnetic field and the magnetic field produced by a changing electric field. The first of these concepts resulted from directed experimental research by Michael Faraday, and the second from the theoretical efforts of James Clerk Maxwell. Maxwell was also responsible for collecting and unifying previously known relationships, and the four basic equations of electromagnetic theory presented in this chapter bear his name.

10.1. Faraday's Law. After Oersted demonstrated in 1820 that an electric current affected a compass needle, Faraday professed his belief that if a current could produce a magnetic field, then a magnetic field should be able to produce a current. The concept of the "field" was not available at that time, and Faraday's goal was to show that a current could be produced by "magnetism."

He worked on this problem intermittently over a period of ten years until he was finally successful in 1831. He wound two separate windings on an iron toroid, placed a galvanometer in one circuit and a battery in the other. Upon closing the battery circuit, a momentary deflection of the galvanometer was noted; a similar deflection in the opposite direction occurred when the battery was disconnected. This, of course, was the first experiment he had made involving a *changing* current, and he followed it with a demonstration that either a *moving* magnetic field or a moving coil could also produce a galvanometer deflection.

In terms of fields, we now say that a time-varying magnetic field produces an *electromotive force* which may establish a current in a suitable closed circuit.   Faraday's law is customarily stated as

$$\text{emf} = - \frac{d\Phi}{dt} \quad \text{volts} \tag{1}$$

Equation (1) implies a closed path, although not necessarily a closed conducting path.   The magnetic flux is that flux which passes through any and every surface whose perimeter is the closed path, and $d\Phi/dt$ is the time rate of change of this flux.   A nonzero value of $d\Phi/dt$ may result from either a time-changing flux linking a stationary closed path, relative motion between a steady flux and a closed path, or a combination of the two.   The minus sign is an indication that the emf is in such a direction as to produce a current whose flux, if added to the original flux, would reduce the magnitude of the emf.   A more satisfactory and simpler interpretation of the minus sign will be apparent after "emf" has been defined and vector analysis is applied to (1).

If the closed path is that taken by an N-turn filamentary conductor, it is sufficiently accurate to consider the turns as coincident and let

$$\text{emf} = - N \frac{d\Phi}{dt} \tag{2}$$

where $\Phi = $ flux passing through any one of N coincident paths.

We must now define emf as used in (1) or (2).   The emf is obviously a scalar, and (perhaps not so obviously) a dimensional check shows it is measured in volts.   We shall define the emf as

$$\text{emf} = \oint \mathbf{E} \cdot d\mathbf{L} \tag{3}$$

and note that it is the potential difference about a specific *closed path*. If any part of the path is changed, the emf in general changes.   The departure from static results is clearly shown by (3), for an electric field intensity resulting from a static charge distribution must lead to zero potential difference about a closed path.

Replacing Φ by the surface integral of $\mathbf{B}$, we have

$$\oint \mathbf{E} \cdot d\mathbf{L} = - \frac{d}{dt} \int_s \mathbf{B} \cdot d\mathbf{S} \tag{4}$$

and interpret the minus sign by remembering that, as in Ampère's circuital law, we may use the fingers of our right hand to indicate the direction of the closed path, and our thumb then indicates the direction of $d\mathbf{S}$.   A flux density $\mathbf{B}$ in the direction of $d\mathbf{S}$ and increasing with time thus produces an average value of $\mathbf{E}$ which is *opposite* to the positive direction about the closed path.

Let us first restrict our investigation to a stationary path.   The magnetic flux is then the only time-varying quantity on the right side of (4) and may be differentiated partially under the integral sign:

$$\oint \mathbf{E} \cdot d\mathbf{L} = - \int_s \frac{\partial \mathbf{B}}{\partial t} \cdot d\mathbf{S} \tag{5}$$

Applying Stokes' theorem to the left side of this equation, we have

$$\int_s (\nabla \times \mathbf{E}) \cdot d\mathbf{S} = - \int_s \frac{\partial \mathbf{B}}{\partial t} \cdot d\mathbf{S}$$

where the surface integrals may be taken over identical surfaces. The surfaces are perfectly general and may be chosen as differentials:

$$(\nabla \times \mathbf{E}) \cdot d\mathbf{S} = - \frac{\partial \mathbf{B}}{\partial t} \cdot d\mathbf{S}$$

and
$$\nabla \times \mathbf{E} = - \frac{\partial \mathbf{B}}{\partial t} \tag{6}$$

This is one of Maxwell's four equations as written in differential or point form, the form in which they are most generally used. Equation (5) is the integral form of this equation and is equivalent to Faraday's law as applied to a fixed path. If $\mathbf{B}$ is not a function of time, (5) and (6) evidently reduce to the equations obtained in electrostatics:

$$\oint \mathbf{E} \cdot d\mathbf{L} = 0$$
$$\nabla \times \mathbf{E} = 0$$

As an example of the interpretation of (5) and (6), let us assume a simple magnetic field which increases exponentially with time:

$$\mathbf{B} = B_0 e^{bt} \mathbf{a}_z$$

where $B_0 = $ constant. Choosing a circular path of radius a in the $z = 0$ plane, along which $\mathbf{E}$ must be constant by symmetry, we then have from (5)

$$2\pi a E_\phi = -b B_0 e^{bt} \pi a^2$$

The emf around this closed path is $-b B_0 e^{bt} \pi a^2$ volts. It is proportional to a^2 since the magnetic flux density is uniform and the flux passing through the surface at any instant is proportional to the area. The emf is evidently the same for any other path in the $z = 0$ plane enclosing the same area.

If we now replace a by r, the electric field intensity at any point is

$$\mathbf{E} = -\tfrac{1}{2} b B_0 e^{bt} r \mathbf{a}_\phi$$

Let us now attempt to obtain the same answer from (6), which becomes

$$(\nabla \times \mathbf{E})_z = -bB_0 e^{bt} = \frac{1}{r}\frac{\partial(rE_\phi)}{\partial r}$$

Multiplying by r and integrating (treating t as a constant since the derivative is a partial derivative),

$$-\tfrac{1}{2}bB_0 e^{bt} r^2 = rE_\phi + K$$

where K = constant of integration and is set equal to zero in order that E_ϕ approach zero as t approaches negative infinity.

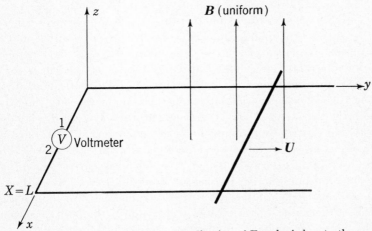

Fig. 10.1. An example illustrating the application of Faraday's law to the case of a constant magnetic flux density and a moving path. The shorting bar moves to the right with a velocity $\mathbf{U}$, and the circuit is completed through the two rails and an extremely small, high-resistance voltmeter.

If B_0 is considered positive, a filamentary conductor of resistance R would have a current flowing in the negative $\mathbf{a}_\phi$ direction, and this current would establish a flux within the circular loop in the negative $\mathbf{a}_z$ direction. Since E_ϕ increases exponentially with time, the current and flux do also, and thus tend to reduce the time rate of increase of the applied flux and the resultant emf.

Now let us apply Faraday's law (1) to the case of a time-constant flux and a moving closed path. Consider the simple problem outlined in Fig. 10.1. The closed circuit consists of two parallel conductors which are connected at one end by a high-resistance voltmeter of negligible dimensions and at the other end by a sliding bar moving at a velocity $\mathbf{U}$. The magnetic flux density is constant (in space and time) and is normal to the plane containing the closed path.

Let the position of the shorting bar be given by y, and the flux passing through the surface within the closed path at any time t is

$$\Phi = BLy$$

From (1),

$$\text{emf} = -\frac{d\Phi}{dt}$$

we obtain

$$\text{emf} = -BL\frac{dy}{dt} = -BLU \qquad (7)$$

Since the emf is defined as $\oint \mathbf{E} \cdot d\mathbf{L}$ and we have a conducting path, we may actually determine $\mathbf{E}$ at every point along the closed path. We found in electrostatics that the tangential component of $\mathbf{E}$ is zero at the surface of a conductor, and we shall show in Sec. 10.4 that the tangential component is zero at the surface of a *perfect* conductor ($\sigma = \infty$) for all time-varying conditions. This is equivalent to saying that a perfect conductor is a "short circuit." The entire closed path in Fig. 10.1 may be considered as a perfect conductor with the exception of the voltmeter. The actual computation of $\oint \mathbf{E} \cdot d\mathbf{L}$ then must involve no contribution along the entire moving bar, both rails, and the voltmeter leads. Since we are moving in a counterclockwise direction (keeping the interior of the positive side of the surface on our left), the contribution $E \, \Delta L$ across the voltmeter must be $-BLU$, showing that the electric field intensity in the instrument is directed from terminal 2 to terminal 1. For an up-scale reading, the positive terminal of the voltmeter should therefore be terminal 2.

The direction of the resultant small current flow may be confirmed by noting that the enclosed flux is reduced by a clockwise current. The voltmeter terminal 2 is again seen to be the positive terminal.

This example offers us the opportunity of applying the concept of *motional emf*. The force on a charge Q moving at a velocity $\mathbf{U}$ in a magnetic field $\mathbf{B}$ is

$$\mathbf{F} = Q\mathbf{U} \times \mathbf{B}$$

or

$$\frac{\mathbf{F}}{Q} = \mathbf{U} \times \mathbf{B} \qquad (8)$$

The sliding conducting bar is composed of positive and negative charges, and each experiences this force. The force per unit charge, as given by (8), is by definition the electric field intensity $\mathbf{E}$:

$$\mathbf{E} = \mathbf{U} \times \mathbf{B} \qquad (9)$$

If the moving conductor were isolated, this electric field intensity would force electrons to one end of the bar until the *static field* due to these charges just balanced the field induced by the motion of the bar. The resultant tangential electric field intensity would then be zero along the length of the bar.

The motional emf produced by the moving conductor is, then,

$$\text{Motional emf} = \oint (\mathbf{U} \times \mathbf{B}) \cdot d\mathbf{L} \tag{10}$$

where the integral may have a nonzero value only along that portion of the path which is in motion, or along which $\mathbf{U}$ has some nonzero value. Again setting the emf equal to the circulation of $\mathbf{E}$ as in (3), we have

$$\oint \mathbf{E} \cdot d\mathbf{L} = \oint (\mathbf{U} \times \mathbf{B}) \cdot d\mathbf{L} \tag{11}$$

Evaluating the right side of (11), we obtain

$$\oint (\mathbf{U} \times \mathbf{B}) \cdot d\mathbf{L} = \int_{L}^{0} UB \, dx = -BLU$$

as before, and this result corresponds to that portion of the closed line integral on the left side of (11) taken across the voltmeter, for E_{tan} must be zero along all the other conductors. The objection may be raised that $\mathbf{E}$ should have the value given by (9) along the moving bar, but we must remember that this is the force which sets the charges into motion, and the charges will move in such a way as to satisfy the boundary conditions requiring tangential $\mathbf{E}$ to be zero along all perfect conductors. Thus each side of (11) is equal to $-BLU$, but this value is obtained along different portions of the closed path.

In the case of a conductor moving in a magnetic field we may therefore ascribe an induced electric field intensity

$$\mathbf{E} = \mathbf{U} \times \mathbf{B}$$

to every portion of the moving conductor and evaluate the resultant emf by

$$\text{emf} = \oint \mathbf{E} \cdot d\mathbf{L} = \oint (\mathbf{U} \times \mathbf{B}) \cdot d\mathbf{L} \tag{12}$$

or we may continue to apply the concept of changing flux:

$$\text{emf} = \oint \mathbf{E} \cdot d\mathbf{L} = -\frac{d\Phi}{dt} \tag{13}$$

Each yields the same answer, and the two viewpoints merely correspond to a change in the *frame of reference*, a subject which we shall discuss later in connection with relativity.

It should be realized that although either concept may be used in problems involving moving conductors, only (13) may be applied when the path is fixed. Thus it is preferable to use the single relationship, $\text{emf} = -d\Phi/dt$, consistently in all problems. The first problem at the end of this chapter is similar to the sliding-bar example just considered, except that the magnetic flux density is a function of time. It is therefore necessary to consider the time-varying magnetic field by (13), although the movement of the shorting bar may be taken into account by either (13) or (12). The problem should be checked by each method.

Finally, let us consider a somewhat trickier problem and solve it by each of these methods. In Fig. 10.2 a stationary voltmeter and its connecting leads are shown making sliding contact with a conducting sheet moving at a velocity **U** in a constant magnetic field.

Applying (13), first we must choose a closed path through which Φ is to be measured. At some given instant the path may be chosen,

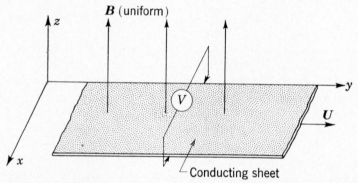

FIG. 10.2. A conducting sheet of width L moves at a velocity **U** in a uniform magnetic flux density **B**. A stationary voltmeter makes sliding contact with the edges of the sheet.

perhaps between the two contacts in Fig. 10.2. Once chosen, we should mentally scribe a line on the conducting sheet so that we do not carelessly change paths. Then dt sec later the scribed line has moved dy m, where $U = dy/dt$, and the flux enclosed increases from zero to $BL\,dy$, or

$$d\Phi = BL\,dy$$
$$\frac{d\Phi}{dt} = BL\,\frac{dy}{dt} = BLU$$

and
$$\text{emf} = -BLU$$

We may also use the moving-charge viewpoint, for the motion of the conducting sheet forces electrons toward the back edge, an effect equivalent to an induced electric field intensity. Thus (12) leads to

$$\text{emf} = \oint (\mathbf{U} \times \mathbf{B}) \cdot d\mathbf{L}$$
$$= \int_{L}^{0} UB\,dx = -BLU$$

The second problem at the end of this chapter considers other aspects of this example and should be worked by both of the two methods.

D10.1. Find the emf at $t = 0$ acting around the closed path consisting of the straight line segments joining the points $(0,0,0)$ to $(1,0,0)$ to $(1,1,0)$ to $(0,1,0)$ to $(0,0,0)$ if:

(a) $\mathbf{B} = 0.1 \sin 377t \; \mathbf{a}_z$.

(b) $\mathbf{B} = (x - 0.5) \sin 377t \; \mathbf{a}_z$.

(c) $\mathbf{B} = 10^{-7} \sin \left(2\pi 10^8 t - \dfrac{2\pi x}{3} \right) \mathbf{a}_z$.

$Ans.\ -63.7$ volts.

D10.2. Find the magnetic flux density at the origin at $t = 0$ if the time-average value of $\mathbf{B}$ is zero and:

(a) $\mathbf{E} = 10^4 \cos (3 \times 10^8 t - x) \; \mathbf{a}_z$.

(b) $\mathbf{E} = 10^4 \cos \left(3 \times 10^8 t + y - \dfrac{\pi}{3} \right) \mathbf{a}_z$.

(c) $\mathbf{E} = 10^4 x \mathbf{a}_x$.

$$Ans.\ \mathbf{B} = - \frac{10^{-4}}{6} (\mathbf{a}_x + 2\mathbf{a}_y)\ \text{amp/m}.$$

10.2. Displacement Current.

Faraday's experimental law has been used to obtain one of Maxwell's equations:

$$\mathbf{\nabla} \times \mathbf{E} = - \frac{\partial \mathbf{B}}{\partial t} \tag{1}$$

which shows us that a time-changing magnetic field produces an electric field. Remembering the definition of curl, we see that this electric field has the special property of circulation; its line integral about a general closed path is not zero. Now let us turn our attention to the time-changing electric field.

We should first look at the point form of Ampère's circuital law as it applies to steady magnetic fields:

$$\mathbf{\nabla} \times \mathbf{H} = \mathbf{i} \tag{2}$$

and show its inadequacy for time-varying conditions by taking the divergence of each side:

$$\mathbf{\nabla} \cdot \mathbf{\nabla} \times \mathbf{H} \equiv 0 = \mathbf{\nabla} \cdot \mathbf{i}$$

Since the divergence of the curl is identically zero, $\mathbf{\nabla} \cdot \mathbf{i}$ is also zero. However, the equation of continuity,

$$\mathbf{\nabla} \cdot \mathbf{i} = - \frac{\partial \rho}{\partial t} \tag{3}$$

then shows us that (2) can be true only if $\partial \rho / \partial t = 0$. This is an unrealistic limitation, and (2) must be amended before we can accept it for time-varying fields.   Suppose we add an unknown term **G** to (2):

$$\nabla \times \mathbf{H} = \mathbf{i} + \mathbf{G}$$

Again taking the divergence, we have

$$0 = \nabla \cdot \mathbf{i} + \nabla \cdot \mathbf{G}$$

or $$\nabla \cdot \mathbf{G} = \frac{\partial \rho}{\partial t}$$

Replacing ρ by $\nabla \cdot \mathbf{D}$,

$$\nabla \cdot \mathbf{G} = \frac{\partial}{\partial t}(\nabla \cdot \mathbf{D}) = \nabla \cdot \frac{\partial \mathbf{D}}{\partial t}$$

from which we obtain the simplest solution for **G**:

$$\mathbf{G} = \frac{\partial \mathbf{D}}{\partial t}$$

Ampère's circuital law in point form therefore becomes

$$\nabla \times \mathbf{H} = \mathbf{i} + \frac{\partial \mathbf{D}}{\partial t} \qquad (4)$$

Equation (4) has not been derived.   It is merely a form we have obtained which does not disagree with the continuity equation.   It is also consistent with all our other results, and we accept it as we did each experimental law and the equations derived from it.   We are building a theory, and we have every right to our equations *until they are proved wrong*.   This has not yet been done.

We now have a second one of Maxwell's equations and shall investigate its significance.   The additional term $\partial \mathbf{D}/\partial t$ has the dimensions of current density, amperes per square meter.   Since it results from a time-varying electric flux density (or displacement density), Maxwell termed it a *displacement current density*.   We sometimes denote it by $\mathbf{i}_d$:

$$\nabla \times \mathbf{H} = \mathbf{i} + \mathbf{i}_d$$
$$\mathbf{i}_d = \frac{\partial \mathbf{D}}{\partial t}$$

This is the third type of current density we have met.   Conduction current density,

$$\mathbf{i} = \sigma \mathbf{E}$$

the motion of charge (usually electrons) in a region of zero net charge density, and convection current density,

$$\mathbf{i} = \rho \mathbf{U}$$

the motion of volume charge density, are both represented by **i** in (4). In a nonconducting medium in which no volume charge density is present, **i** = 0, and then

$$\nabla \times \mathbf{H} = \frac{\partial \mathbf{D}}{\partial t} \tag{5}$$

Notice the symmetry between (5) and (1):

$$\nabla \times \mathbf{E} = - \frac{\partial \mathbf{B}}{\partial t} \tag{1}$$

Again the analogy between the intensity vectors **E** and **H** and the flux density vectors **D** and **B** is apparent. Too much faith cannot be placed in the analogy, however, for it fails when we investigate forces on particles. The force on a charge is related to **E** and to **B**, and some good arguments may be presented showing an analogy between **E** and **B** and between **D** and **H**. We shall omit them, however, and merely say that the concept of displacement current was probably suggested to Maxwell by the symmetry first mentioned above.

The total displacement current crossing any given surface is given by the surface integral:

$$\int_s \mathbf{i}_d \cdot d\mathbf{S} = \int_s \frac{\partial \mathbf{D}}{\partial t} \cdot d\mathbf{S}$$

and we may obtain the time-varying version of Ampère's circuital law from (4) by integrating over the surface S:

$$\int_s (\nabla \times \mathbf{H}) \cdot d\mathbf{S} = \int_s \mathbf{i} \cdot d\mathbf{S} + \int_s \frac{\partial \mathbf{D}}{\partial t} \cdot d\mathbf{S}$$

and applying Stokes' theorem:

$$\oint \mathbf{H} \cdot d\mathbf{L} = I + I_d = I + \int_s \frac{\partial \mathbf{D}}{\partial t} \cdot d\mathbf{S} \tag{6}$$

What is the nature of displacement current density? Let us study the simple circuit of Fig. 10.3, containing a filamentary loop and a parallel-plate capacitor. Within the loop a magnetic field varying sinusoidally with time is applied to produce an emf about the closed path (the filament plus the dashed portion between the capacitor plates) which we shall take as

$$\text{emf} = V_0 \cos \omega t$$

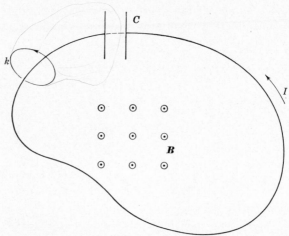

Fig. 10.3. A filamentary conductor forms a loop connecting the two plates of a parallel-plate capacitor. Within the closed path a time-varying magnetic field produces an emf of $V_0 \cos \omega t$.

Using elementary circuit theory, we may obtain the current in the loop as

$$I = -\omega C V_0 \sin \omega t$$

$$= -\omega \frac{\epsilon S}{d} V_0 \sin \omega t$$

where the quantities ϵ, S, and d pertain to the capacitor. Let us apply Ampère's circuital law about the smaller closed circular path k and neglect displacement current for the moment:

$$\oint_k \mathbf{H} \cdot d\mathbf{L} = I_k$$

The path and the value of $\mathbf{H}$ along the path are both definite quantities (although difficult to determine), and $\oint_k \mathbf{H} \cdot d\mathbf{L}$ is a definite quantity. The current I_k is that current through every surface whose perimeter is the path k. If we choose a simple surface punctured by the filament, such as the plane circular surface defined by the path k, the current is evidently the conduction current. Suppose now we consider the closed path k as the mouth of a paper bag whose bottom passes between the capacitor plates. The bag is not pierced by the filament, and the conduction current is zero. Now we need to consider displacement current, for within the capacitor

$$D = \frac{\epsilon V_0}{d} \cos \omega t$$

and therefore

$$I_d = -\omega \frac{\epsilon S}{d} V_0 \sin \omega t$$

This is the same value as that of the conduction current in the filamentary loop. Therefore the application of Ampère's circuital law including displacement current to the path k leads to a definite value for the line integral of **H**. This value must be equal to the total current crossing the chosen surface. For some surfaces the current is almost entirely conduction current, but for those surfaces passing between the capacitor plates the conduction current is zero and it is the displacement current which is now equal to the closed line integral of **H**.

Physically, we should note that a capacitor stores charge and that the electric field between the capacitor plates is much greater than the small leakage fields outside. We therefore introduce little error when we neglect displacement current on all those surfaces which do not pass between the plates.

Displacement current is associated with time-varying electric fields and therefore exists in all imperfect conductors carrying a conduction current. The drill problem below indicates the reason why this additional current was never discovered experimentally.

D10.3. Find the crest amplitude of the displacement current density associated with each of the following situations:

(a) A 1-Mc radio wave of 1 mv/m amplitude in air.

(b) A copper conductor ($\sigma = 5.8 \times 10^7$ mhos/m) carrying a conduction current density of 10^7 amp/m^2 at 1,000 cps (assume $\epsilon = \epsilon_0$ for copper).

(c) The air gap of a 60-cps induction motor in which the impractically small magnetic flux density may be expressed as $B_y = 10^{-7} \cos\left[377 \left(t - \frac{x}{3 \times 10^8} \right) \right]$.

$Ans.$ 0.1652×10^{-6} amp/m^2.

10.3. Maxwell's Equations in Point Form. We have already obtained two of Maxwell's equations for time-varying fields:

$$\mathbf{\nabla} \times \mathbf{E} = -\frac{\partial \mathbf{B}}{\partial t} \tag{1}$$

and

$$\mathbf{\nabla} \times \mathbf{H} = \mathbf{i} + \frac{\partial \mathbf{D}}{\partial t} \tag{2}$$

The remaining two equations are unchanged from their non-time-varying form:

$$\mathbf{\nabla} \cdot \mathbf{D} = \rho \tag{3}$$

$$\mathbf{\nabla} \cdot \mathbf{B} = 0 \tag{4}$$

Equation (3) essentially states that charge density is a source (or sink) of electric flux lines. Note that we can no longer say that all electric flux begins and terminates on charge because the point form of Faraday's law (1) shows that **E**, and hence **D**, may have circulation if a changing magnetic field is present. Thus the lines of electric flux may form closed loops. However, the converse is still true, and every coulomb of charge must have 1 coulomb of electric flux diverging from it.

Equation (4) again acknowledges the fact that "magnetic charges," or poles, are not known to exist. Magnetic flux is always found in closed loops and never diverges from a point source.

These four equations form the basis of all electromagnetic theory. They are partial differential equations and relate the electric and magnetic fields to each other and to their sources, charge and current density. The auxiliary equations relating **D** and **E**,

$$\mathbf{D} = \epsilon\mathbf{E} \tag{5}$$

B and **H**,

$$\mathbf{B} = \mu\mathbf{H} \tag{6}$$

defining conduction current density,

$$\mathbf{i} = \sigma\mathbf{E} \tag{7}$$

and convection current density,

$$\mathbf{i} = \rho\mathbf{U} \tag{8}$$

are also required to define and relate the quantities appearing in Maxwell's equations. We should add the force equation, written in point form as the force per unit volume:

$$\mathbf{f} = \rho(\mathbf{E} + \mathbf{U} \times \mathbf{B}) \tag{9}$$

The potentials V and **A** have not been included above because they are not strictly necessary although they are extremely useful. They will be discussed at the end of this chapter.

The following chapter is devoted to the application of Maxwell's equations to several simple problems.

10.4. Maxwell's Equations in Integral Form. The integral forms of Maxwell's equations are usually easier to recognize in terms of the experimental laws from which they have been obtained by a generalization process. Experiments must treat physical, macroscopic quantities, and their results therefore are expressed in terms of integral relationships. A differential equation always represents a theory.

Let us now collect the integral forms of Maxwell's equations of the previous section.

Integrating Sec. 10.3, Eq. (1), over a surface and applying Stokes' theorem, we obtain Faraday's law:

$$\oint \mathbf{E} \cdot d\mathbf{L} = - \int_s \frac{\partial \mathbf{B}}{\partial t} \cdot d\mathbf{S} \tag{1}$$

and the same process applied to Sec. 10.3, Eq. (2), yields Ampère's circuital law:

$$\oint \mathbf{H} \cdot d\mathbf{L} = I + \int_s \frac{\partial \mathbf{D}}{\partial t} \cdot d\mathbf{S} \tag{2}$$

Gauss's laws for the electric and magnetic fields are obtained by integrating Sec. 10.3, Eqs. (3) and (4), throughout a volume and using the divergence theorem:

$$\oint_s \mathbf{D} \cdot d\mathbf{S} = \int_{\text{vol}} \rho \, dv \tag{3}$$

$$\oint_s \mathbf{B} \cdot d\mathbf{S} = 0 \tag{4}$$

The integral equations (1) to (4) enable us to find the boundary conditions on $\mathbf{B}$, $\mathbf{D}$, $\mathbf{H}$, and $\mathbf{E}$ which are necessary to evaluate the constants obtained in solving Maxwell's equations in partial differential form. These boundary conditions are in general unchanged from their forms for static or steady fields, and the same methods may be used to obtain them. Between any two real physical media, from (1),

$$E_{\tan 1} = E_{\tan 2} \tag{5}$$

and from (2),

$$H_{\tan 1} = H_{\tan 2} \tag{6}$$

The surface integrals produce the boundary conditions on the normal components:

$$D_{n1} - D_{n2} = \rho_s \tag{7}$$

and

$$B_{n1} = B_{n2} \tag{8}$$

It is often desirable to idealize a physical problem by assuming a perfect conductor for which σ is infinite but $\mathbf{i}$ is finite. From Ohm's law, then, in a perfect conductor,

$$\mathbf{E} = 0$$

and it follows from the point form of Faraday's law that

$$\mathbf{H} = 0$$

for time-varying fields. The point form of Ampère's circuital law then shows that the finite value of i is

$$i = 0$$

and current must be carried on the conductor surface as a surface current. Thus, if region 2 is a perfect conductor, (5) to (8) become, respectively,

$$E_{\text{tan } 1} = 0 \tag{9}$$
$$H_{\text{tan } 1} = J_s \tag{10}$$
$$D_{n1} = \rho_s \tag{11}$$
$$B_{n1} = 0 \tag{12}$$

Note that surface charge density is considered a physical possibility for either dielectrics or imperfect conductors, but that surface *current* density is assumed only in conjunction with perfect conductors.

The boundary conditions stated above are a very necessary part of Maxwell's equations. All real physical problems have boundaries and require the solution of Maxwell's equations in two or more regions and the matching of these solutions at the boundaries. In the case of perfect conductors, the solution of the equations within the conductor is trivial (all time-varying fields are zero), but the application of the boundary conditions (9) to (12) may be very difficult.

Certain fundamental properties of wave propagation are evident when Maxwell's equations are solved for an *unbounded* region. This problem is briefly treated in the following chapter. It represents the simplest application of Maxwell's equations, because it is the only problem which does not require the application of any boundary conditions.

D10.4. Find the ratio of the magnitudes of the indicated vector fields in region 2 to those in region 1 if the vector field in region 1 makes an angle of 45° with the boundary surface.

(a) **E** field; region 1, air; region 2, dielectric, $\epsilon_{r2} = 2$, $\sigma_2 = 0$.

(b) **H** field; region 1, air; region 2, $\mu_{r2} = 2$, $\sigma_2 = 0$, $\epsilon_{r2} = 1$.

(c) **E** field; region 1, conductor, $\sigma_1 = 10^6$, $\epsilon_1 = \epsilon_0$, $\mu_1 = \mu_0$; region 2, conductor, $\sigma_2 = 2 \times 10^6$, $\epsilon_2 = \epsilon_0$, $\mu_2 = \mu_0$.

Ans. 2.37.

10.5. The Retarded Potentials. The time-varying potentials, usually called *retarded* potentials for a reason which we shall see shortly, find their greatest application in radiation problems in which the distribution of the source is known approximately. We should remember that the scalar electric potential V may be expressed in terms of a static charge distribution:

$$V = \int_{vol} \frac{\rho \, dv}{4\pi\epsilon R} \quad \text{(static)} \tag{1}$$

and the vector magnetic potential may be found from a current distribution which is constant with time:

$$\mathbf{A} = \int_{vol} \frac{\mu \mathbf{i} \, dv}{4\pi R} \quad \text{(d-c)} \tag{2}$$

The differential equations satisfied by V,

$$\nabla^2 V = -\frac{\rho}{\epsilon} \quad \text{(static)} \tag{3}$$

and $\mathbf{A}$,

$$\nabla^2 \mathbf{A} = -\mu \mathbf{i} \quad \text{(d-c)} \tag{4}$$

may be regarded as the point forms of the integral equations (1) and (2), respectively.

Having found V and $\mathbf{A}$, the fundamental fields are then simply obtained from

$$\mathbf{E} = -\nabla V \quad \text{(static)} \tag{5}$$

and

$$\mathbf{B} = \nabla \times \mathbf{A} \quad \text{(d-c)} \tag{6}$$

We now wish to define suitable time-varying potentials which are consistent with the above expressions when only static charges and direct currents are involved. Equation (6) apparently is still consistent with Maxwell's equations. These equations state that $\nabla \cdot \mathbf{B} = 0$ and the divergence of (6) leads to the divergence of the curl which is identically zero. Let us therefore tentatively accept (6) as satisfactory for time-varying fields and turn our attention to (5).

The inadequacy of (5) is obvious because application of the curl operation to each side and recognition of the curl of the gradient as being identically zero confront us with $\nabla \times \mathbf{E} = 0$. The point form of Faraday's law states that $\nabla \times \mathbf{E}$ is not generally zero. Let us try to effect an improvement by adding an unknown term to (5):

$$\mathbf{E} = -\nabla V + \mathbf{K}$$

taking the curl:

$$\nabla \times \mathbf{E} = 0 + \nabla \times \mathbf{K}$$

using the point form of Faraday's law:

$$\nabla \times \mathbf{K} = -\frac{\partial \mathbf{B}}{\partial t}$$

and (6), giving us

$$\nabla \times \mathbf{K} = -\frac{\partial}{\partial t} (\nabla \times \mathbf{A})$$

or

$$= -\nabla \times \frac{\partial \mathbf{A}}{\partial t}$$

The simplest solution of this equation is

$$\mathbf{K} = -\frac{\partial \mathbf{A}}{\partial t}$$

and therefore

$$\mathbf{E} = -\nabla V - \frac{\partial \mathbf{A}}{\partial t} \tag{7}$$

We still must check (6) and (7) by substituting them into the remaining two of Maxwell's equations:

$$\nabla \times \mathbf{H} = \mathbf{i} + \frac{\partial \mathbf{D}}{\partial t}$$

$$\nabla \cdot \mathbf{D} = \rho$$

Doing this, we obtain the more complicated expressions

$$\frac{1}{\mu} \nabla \times \nabla \times \mathbf{A} = \mathbf{i} + \epsilon \left(-\nabla \frac{\partial V}{\partial t} - \frac{\partial^2 \mathbf{A}}{\partial t^2} \right)$$

$$\epsilon \left(-\nabla \cdot \nabla V - \frac{\partial}{\partial t} \nabla \cdot \mathbf{A} \right) = \rho$$

or

$$\nabla(\nabla \cdot \mathbf{A}) - \nabla^2 \mathbf{A} = \mu \mathbf{i} - \mu\epsilon \left(\nabla \frac{\partial V}{\partial t} + \frac{\partial^2 \mathbf{A}}{\partial t^2} \right) \tag{8}$$

$$\nabla^2 V + \frac{\partial}{\partial t} (\nabla \cdot \mathbf{A}) = -\frac{\rho}{\epsilon} \tag{9}$$

There is no apparent inconsistency in (8) and (9). Under static or d-c conditions, $\nabla \cdot \mathbf{A} = 0$ and (8) and (9) reduce to (4) and (3), respectively. We shall therefore assume that the time-varying potentials may be defined in such a way that $\mathbf{B}$ and $\mathbf{E}$ may be obtained from them through (6) and (7). These latter two equations do not serve, however, to define *completely* $\mathbf{A}$ and V. They represent necessary, but not sufficient, conditions. Our initial assumption was merely that $\mathbf{B} = \nabla \times \mathbf{A}$, and a vector cannot be defined by giving its curl alone. Suppose, for example, that we have a very simple vector potential field in which A_y and A_z are zero. Expansion of (6) leads to

$$B_x = 0$$

$$B_y = \frac{\partial A_x}{\partial y}$$

$$B_z = \frac{\partial A_x}{\partial z}$$

from which we see that no information is available about the manner in which A_x varies with x. This information could be found if we also knew the value of the divergence of **A**, for in our example

$$\nabla \cdot \mathbf{A} = \frac{\partial A_x}{\partial x}$$

Finally, we should note that our information about **A** is given only as partial derivatives and that a space-constant term might be added. In all physical problems in which the region of the solution extends to infinity, this constant term must be zero, for there can be no fields at infinity.

Generalizing from this simple example, we may say that a vector field is defined completely when both its curl and divergence are given and when its value is known at any one point (including infinity). We are therefore at liberty to specify the divergence of **A**, and we do so with an eye on (8) and (9), seeking the simplest expressions. If we define

$$\nabla \cdot \mathbf{A} = -\mu\epsilon \frac{\partial V}{\partial t} \tag{10}$$

then (8) and (9) become

$$\nabla^2 \mathbf{A} = -\mu\mathbf{i} + \mu\epsilon \frac{\partial^2 \mathbf{A}}{\partial t^2} \tag{11}$$

$$\nabla^2 V = -\frac{\rho}{\epsilon} + \mu\epsilon \frac{\partial^2 V}{\partial t^2} \tag{12}$$

These equations are related to the wave equation, which will be discussed in the following chapter. They show considerable symmetry, and we should be highly pleased with our definitions of V and **A**:

$$\mathbf{B} = \nabla \times \mathbf{A} \tag{6}$$

$$\nabla \cdot \mathbf{A} = -\mu\epsilon \frac{\partial V}{\partial t} \tag{10}$$

$$\mathbf{E} = -\nabla V - \frac{\partial \mathbf{A}}{\partial t} \tag{7}$$

The integral equivalents of (1) and (2) for the time-varying potentials follow from the definitions (6), (7), and (10), but we shall merely present the final results and indicate their general nature. In the next chapter a study of the uniform plane wave will introduce the concept of *propagation*, in which any electromagnetic disturbance is found to travel at a velocity

$$U = \frac{1}{\sqrt{\mu\epsilon}}$$

through any homogeneous medium described by μ and ϵ. In the case of free space this velocity turns out to be the velocity of light, approximately 3×10^8 m/sec. It is logical, then, to suspect that the potential at any point is due not to the value of the charge density at some distant point at the same instant, but to its value at some previous time, since the effect propagates at a finite velocity. Thus (1) becomes

$$V = \int_{\text{vol}} \frac{[\rho]}{4\pi\epsilon R} \, dv \tag{13}$$

where $[\rho]$ indicates that every t appearing in the expression for ρ has been replaced by a *retarded* time:

$$t' = t - \frac{R}{U}$$

Thus, if the charge density throughout space were given by

$$\rho = e^{-r} \cos \omega t$$

then

$$[\rho] = e^{-r} \cos \left[\omega \left(t - \frac{R}{U} \right) \right]$$

where R = distance between differential element of charge being considered and point at which potential is to be determined.

The retarded vector magnetic potential is given by

$$\mathbf{A} = \int_{\text{vol}} \frac{\mu[\mathbf{i}]}{4\pi R} \, dv \tag{14}$$

The use of a retarded time has resulted in the time-varying potentials being given the name of retarded potentials. We shall apply (14) to the simple case of a differential current element in which I is a sinusoidal function of time in the following chapter. A simple application of (13) is considered in a problem at the end of this chapter.

We may summarize the use of the potentials by stating that a knowledge of the distribution of ρ and $\mathbf{i}$ throughout space theoretically enables us to determine V and $\mathbf{A}$ from (13) and (14). The electric and magnetic fields are then obtained by applying (6) and (7). If the charge and current distributions are unknown, or reasonable approximations cannot be made for them, the potentials usually offer no easier path toward the solution than does the direct application of Maxwell's equations.

SUGGESTED REFERENCES

1. Faraday, M.: "Experimental Researches in Electricity," B. Quaritch, London, 1839, 1855. Very interesting reading of early scientific research.

2. Stratton, J. A.: "Electromagnetic Theory," McGraw-Hill Book Company, Inc., New York, 1941. An advanced treatise. Maxwell's equations are introduced and discussed on page 1.

PROBLEMS

1. In the example described by Fig. 10.1, replace the constant magnetic flux density by the time-varying quantity $\mathbf{B} = B_0 \sin \omega t \, \mathbf{a}_z$. Assume that $\mathbf{U}$ is constant and the displacement y of the bar is zero at $t = 0$. Find the emf at any time t.

2. In the example described by Fig. 10.2, assume the voltmeter and its leads move to the right at velocity U_v, the source of the magnetic field moves to the right at velocity U_B, and the conducting sheet moves to the right at velocity U_c. Show that the magnitude of the voltmeter reading is BLU volts if (a) $U_v = U_B = 0$, $U_c = U$; (b) $U_v = U$, $U_B = U_c = 0$; (c) $U_v = 0$, $U_B = U_c = U$; (d) $U_v = U_B = U$, $U_c = 0$. Show that the emf is zero if (e) $U_v = U$, $U_B = 0$, $U_c = U$; (f) $U_v = 0$, $U_B = U$, $U_c = 0$; (g) $U_V = U_B = U_c = U$. Relative motion between which two objects is necessary for an emf to be developed?

3. A circular conducting disk of radius a lies in the $z = 0$ plane of a cylindrical coordinate system with center at the origin. It is rotated at a constant angular velocity of ω radians/sec in the $\mathbf{a}_\phi$ direction in the presence of a uniform magnetic field, $\mathbf{B} = B_0 \mathbf{a}_z$. Sliding contact is made at $r = 0$ and at $r = a$, $\phi = 0$, by two straight filaments extending L m in the $\mathbf{a}_z$ direction where they are connected through a high-resistance voltmeter. Find the magnitude of the voltmeter reading, and specify the direction of current flow in the filament lying on the z axis. This device is known as the *Faraday disk generator*.

4. A rectangular loop of wire containing a high-resistance voltmeter has corners at $(\frac{1}{2}a, \frac{1}{2}b, 0)$, $(-\frac{1}{2}a, \frac{1}{2}b, 0)$, $(-\frac{1}{2}a, -\frac{1}{2}b, 0)$, and $(\frac{1}{2}a, -\frac{1}{2}b, 0)$ and rotates about the x axis at a constant angular velocity ω, the first-named corner moving in the $\mathbf{a}_z$ direction at $t = 0$. Assume a uniform magnetic field $\mathbf{B} = B_0 \mathbf{a}_z$, and determine the emf induced in the rotating loop. Specify the direction of the small current flow.

5. Let the rectangular loop of Prob. 4 be stationary in its $t = 0$ position, and find the induced emf at that instant resulting from a magnetic field intensity in free space of $\mathbf{H} = 10^{-6} \sin (2\pi 10^8 t - 2\pi y/3) \mathbf{a}_z$. Take $a = 1$, $b = 2$.

6. Using the definition of mutual inductance in Chap. 9, show that the emf generated in a closed filamentary path which contains a high-resistance voltmeter is $-L_{21} (dI_2/dt)$, where the current I_2 flows in a second closed path and is the source of the time-varying flux producing the emf.

7. Remove the voltmeter from the first closed path of Prob. 6 so that the loop is perfectly conducting. A line integral $\oint \mathbf{E} \cdot d\mathbf{L}$ around the loop itself must then be zero since $E_{\tan} = 0$ along the perfect conductor. Show, therefore, that sufficient current I_1 must flow so that $-L_{21} (dI_2/dt) = L (dI_1/dt)$, where L is the self-inductance of the loop and I_1 is directed in the same sense as the closed line integral defining the emf in Prob. 6.

8. Filament A extends along the z axis and carries a direct current of 5 amp. Filament B forms a square with corners located at $(1,0,0)$, $(2,0,0)$, $(2,0,1)$, and $(1,0,1)$ at $t = 0$. A high-resistance voltmeter of negligible dimensions is included as a part of the square loop. The entire loop is moving with a velocity $\mathbf{U} = -10\mathbf{a}_x$. Find the voltage indicated by the voltmeter at $t = 0$.

9. Show that the ratio of the magnitudes of the conduction current density to displacement current density at any point in a conducting medium is $\sigma/\omega\epsilon$ if the applied electric field intensity varies sinusoidally with time at an angular frequency of ω radians/sec. Show also for a parallel-plate capacitor that this ratio is equal to the dissipation factor D, where $D = 1/Q = G/\omega C$ and G is the shunt conductance.

10. Show that the displacement current flowing between the two conducting cylinders of a coaxial capacitor is exactly the same as the conduction current flowing in the external circuit if the applied source is an emf of $V_0 \cos \omega t$ volts.

11. Find the magnitude of the displacement current flowing at $t = 0$ between the two plates of an air-filled parallel-plate capacitor, connected externally to a 100-volt battery, if the separation of the plates d is varied as $d = 2 \times 10^{-3}(1 + \frac{1}{2}\sin 100\pi t)$. The plate area is 0.9 m^2.

12. An air-filled parallel-plate capacitor consists of two circular plates of 10 cm radius and 1 mm separation. Assume a uniform surface charge density on each plate which varies with time, $\rho_s = \pm 10^{-9} \cos \omega t$ coulomb/m^2. If $\omega = 300$, calculate the electric field intensity and displacement current density in the region between the plates. Use Ampère's circuital law to obtain an expression for the magnetic field intensity at any point in the region between the plates. Show that the resultant fields do not satisfy the point form of Faraday's law. The explanation of this contradiction is suggested by Prob. 15.

13. Expand the divergence and curl operations in Maxwell's four equations, and separate the two vector equations into their three component equations in (a) cartesian coordinates; (b) cylindrical coordinates; (c) spherical coordinates. The eight equations obtained in each part represent Maxwell's equations for that coordinate system in the form in which they must be given if vector analysis is not used.

14. Use each one of Maxwell's four equations in point form to obtain as much information as possible about (a) **H**, if **E** = 0; (b) **E**, if **B** = 0.

15. In a-c-circuit problems involving transformers a magnetic flux density of the form $B = B_0 \cos \omega t$ is often used, where B_0 is a constant. Assume that the x axis coincides with the direction of **B** and that the given field refers to a point in air at which $\rho = 0$ and i = 0. (a) Show that such a field cannot satisfy Maxwell's equations. (b) Show that the field may satisfy Maxwell's equations if t is replaced by $t - y\sqrt{\mu\epsilon}$, and find the associated electric field intensity.

16. Assume free-space conditions ($\rho = 0$, i = 0) and express Maxwell's four equations in terms of **E** and **H** only. Take the curl of the point form of Ampère's circuital law, expand the double vector operation by using an identity on page 315, and substitute the point form of Faraday's law and Gauss's law for the magnetic field to obtain an equation in **H** alone, $\nabla^2\mathbf{H} = \mu\epsilon(\partial^2\mathbf{H}/\partial t^2)$. Obtain the analogous equation for **E** by first taking the curl of Faraday's law. These important equations are known as the *wave equations*.

17. Write Maxwell's equations in point form in terms of **E** and **H** as they apply to free space where i and ρ are zero. Show that the four equations which result when ϵ is replaced by μ, μ is replaced by ϵ, **H** is replaced by **E**, and **E** is replaced by $-\mathbf{H}$ are correct. This is a more general expression of the *duality principle* of circuit theory.

18. The region $x > 0$ is free space, and $x < 0$ is a perfect conductor. A certain solution of Maxwell's equations for $x > 0$ has led to the tentative expressions $E_x = A_1 \cos(\omega t - \beta z + \psi_1)$, $E_y = A_2 \cos(\omega t - \beta z + \psi_2)$, $E_z = A_3 \cos(\omega t - \beta z + \psi_3)$, where ω, β, A_1, A_2, A_3, ψ_1, ψ_2, ψ_3 are constants. (a) From a knowledge of the fields for $x < 0$ and of the boundary conditions at $x = 0$, determine which of the constants A_1, A_2, and A_3 are zero. (b) Apply Maxwell's equations to find H_y for $x > 0$ and $x < 0$, if only time-periodic solutions are desired. Two different solutions may be obtained for $x > 0$. (c) What must be the value of β if these two solutions are identical?

19. The region $x > 0$ is described by $\mu_1 = \mu_0$, $\epsilon_1 = 2\epsilon_0$, $\sigma_1 = 1$, and the region $x < 0$ by $\mu_2 = \mu_0$, $\epsilon_2 = 3\epsilon_0$, $\sigma_2 = 4$. The electric field intensity in the first region has the value at $x = 0$, $\mathbf{E}_1 = (1\mathbf{a}_x + 2\mathbf{a}_y + 3\mathbf{a}_z) \cos \omega t$. The boundary may carry surface charge density. (a) Find $\mathbf{E}_2$ at $x = 0$. (b) Find the surface charge density on the boundary surface, $x = 0$.

20. (a) Show that the tangential component of conduction current density is discontinuous at the boundary between two imperfect ($\sigma \neq 0$) dielectrics, and determine the ratio of the components on the two sides of the boundary. (b) Show that the tangential component of the displacement current density is also discontinuous at such a boundary, but not by the same factor.

21. A filamentary conductor, extending from $(0,0,-0.01)$ to $(0,0,0.01)$, carries a uniform current distribution which increases linearly with time, $\mathbf{I} = 10^6 t \mathbf{a}_z$, the expression being valid for all negative and positive time. The apparent discontinuity of the current at $z = \pm 0.01$ is remedied by other filaments not considered. Find the retarded vector magnetic potential on the z axis at $z = 0.02$, and compare this value with that which is obtained (incorrectly) if retardation is not considered. Why is the retarded potential not zero at $t = 0$ when the current is everywhere zero?

22. Two identical point charges whose values vary sinusoidally with time, $Q = 4 \times 10^{-6} \sin 2\pi 10^8 t$, are located in a spherical coordinate system at $r = 1$, $\theta = 0$, and $r = 1$, $\theta = \pi$. Find the retarded potential at a point $P(r = 1,000, \theta = 60°, \phi = 0)$ at $t = 0$. Compare this result with that which would have been obtained if retardation were neglected.

CHAPTER 11

SEVERAL APPLICATIONS OF MAXWELL'S EQUATIONS

In this chapter we intend to apply Maxwell's equations in an introductory and elementary way to the general topics of wave motion, skin effect, circuit theory, and radiation. The coverage of these subjects is intended to indicate the use and usefulness of the important equations presented in the preceding chapter and to introduce several important areas of interest in more advanced electromagnetic theory. Certainly we shall not be able to say that we are experts on any of these subjects after these few preliminary remarks.

11.1. Wave Motion. As we indicated in our discussion of boundary conditions in the previous chapter, the solution of Maxwell's equations without the application of any boundary conditions at all represents a unique problem. Usually it appears that a large number of different problems are being solved because different media are used. First solutions are obtained for free-space conditions, then for good conductors, good dielectrics, poor dielectrics, and poor conductors. These separate treatments are not necessary, however. It is possible (and not very difficult) to solve the general problem once and for all. Since our aims are moderate, we shall concern ourselves only with the two simplest special cases, the application to free space in this section and to a good conductor in the following section.

Let us rewrite Maxwell's equations for free space in terms of $\mathbf{E}$ and $\mathbf{H}$ only:

$$\nabla \times \mathbf{H} = \epsilon_0 \frac{\partial \mathbf{E}}{\partial t} \tag{1}$$

$$\nabla \times \mathbf{E} = -\mu_0 \frac{\partial \mathbf{H}}{\partial t} \tag{2}$$

$$\nabla \cdot \mathbf{E} = 0 \tag{3}$$

$$\nabla \cdot \mathbf{H} = 0 \tag{4}$$

and see whether wave motion can be inferred from these four equations without actually solving them. The first equation states that if $\mathbf{E}$ is changing with time at some point, then $\mathbf{H}$ has curl at that point and thus can be considered as forming a small closed loop linking the changing **E** field. Also, if **E** is changing with time, then **H** will in general also change with time, although not necessarily in the same way. Next we see from the second equation that this changing **H** produces an electric field which forms small closed loops about the **H** lines. We now have once more a changing electric field, our original hypothesis, but this field is present a small distance away from the point of the original disturbance. We might guess (correctly) that the velocity with which the effect moves away from the original point is the velocity of light, but this must be checked by a more quantitative examination of Maxwell's equations.

Let us first write Maxwell's four equations above for the special case of sinusoidal (more strictly, *cosinusoidal*) variation with time. This is accomplished by realizing that any component, such as E_x, may be written at a given point as

$$E_x = E_{xs} \cos \omega t$$

where E_{xs} is not a function of time (s for *static*).   Complex exponential notation is very helpful, and since

$$e^{j\omega t} = \cos \omega t + j \sin \omega t$$

we let

$$E_x = \text{real part of } E_{xs} e^{j\omega t}$$

and then usually let "real part of" be understood:

$$E_x = E_{xs} e^{j\omega t}$$

Taking a time derivative is therefore replaced by multiplication by $j\omega$:

$$\frac{\partial E_x}{\partial t} = E_{xs} j\omega e^{j\omega t} = j\omega E_x$$

and Maxwell's four equations in free space for sinusoidal time variation are then

$$\nabla \times \mathbf{H} = j\omega\epsilon_0 \mathbf{E} \tag{5}$$
$$\nabla \times \mathbf{E} = -j\omega\mu_0 \mathbf{H} \tag{6}$$
$$\nabla \cdot \mathbf{E} = 0 \tag{7}$$
$$\nabla \cdot \mathbf{H} = 0 \tag{8}$$

It should be noted that these four equations do not change in form if **E** and **H** are replaced by $\mathbf{E}_s$ and $\mathbf{H}_s$. For this reason we do not usually bother to indicate whether **E** includes or does not include the $e^{j\omega t}$ factor. We may add this factor whenever we wish to show the time variation explicitly. It is also evident that (7) and (8) are no longer independent relationships, for they can be obtained by taking the divergence of (5) and (6), respectively.

Our next step is to obtain the wave equation, a step we could omit because the simple problem we are going to solve yields easily to simultaneous solution of the four equations above. The wave equation is an important equation, however, and is a convenient starting point for many other investigations.

The method by which the wave equation is obtained is outlined in Prob. 16 of the previous chapter. The process can be accomplished in one line (using four equals signs) and yields for $\mathbf{E}$:

$$\nabla^2\mathbf{E} = -\omega^2\mu_0\epsilon_0\mathbf{E} \tag{9}$$

This concise vector equation is fairly formidable when expanded, even in cartesian coordinates, for three scalar equations result and each has four terms. The x component of (9) becomes, still using the del-operator notation,

$$\nabla^2 E_x = -\omega^2\mu_0\epsilon_0 E_x \tag{10}$$

and the expansion of the operator leads to the second-order partial differential equation

$$\frac{\partial^2 E_x}{\partial x^2} + \frac{\partial^2 E_x}{\partial y^2} + \frac{\partial^2 E_x}{\partial z^2} = -\omega^2\mu_0\epsilon_0 E_x \tag{11}$$

Let us attempt a solution of (11) by assuming a simple solution is possible in which E_x does not vary with x or y and the two corresponding derivatives are zero, leading to

$$\frac{\partial^2 E_x}{\partial z^2} = -\omega^2\mu_0\epsilon_0 E_x \tag{12}$$

By inspection, we may write down a particular solution of (12):

$$E_x = A e^{-j\omega\sqrt{\mu_0\epsilon_0}\,z} \tag{13}$$

reinsert the $e^{j\omega t}$ factor:

$$E_x = A e^{j\omega(t - z\sqrt{\mu_0\epsilon_0})} \tag{14}$$

and reduce to trigonometric form by taking the real part:

$$E_x = A \cos\left[\omega(t - z\sqrt{\mu_0\epsilon_0})\right]$$

where the arbitrary amplitude factor may be replaced by the value of E_x at $z = 0$, $t = 0$, E_{x0}:

indicates travel in +z direc.

$$E_x = E_{x0} \cos\left[\omega(t - z\sqrt{\mu_0\epsilon_0})\right] \tag{15}$$

Before we find any other field components we should understand the physical nature of the single component of the electric field we have obtained. We see that it is an x component, which we might describe as directed upward at the surface of a plane earth. The radical $\sqrt{\mu_0\epsilon_0}$

has the value $1/(3 \times 10^8)$ sec/m and is the reciprocal of a velocity U_0:

$$U_0 = \frac{1}{\sqrt{\mu_0\epsilon_0}} = 3 \times 10^8 \text{ m/sec}$$

Let us also allow the z axis to point east and take $z = 0$ in Chicago. In Chicago, then, the field is given by

$$E_x = E_{x0} \cos \omega t$$

which is a simple and familiar variation with time. A free charge (perhaps in a vertical receiving antenna) is accelerated up and down $\omega/2\pi$ times a second. In Cleveland, about 500 km east, we would find

$$E_x = E_{x0} \cos\left[\omega\left(t - \frac{5 \times 10^5}{3 \times 10^8}\right)\right] = E_{x0} \cos\left[\omega(t - 0.00167)\right]$$

indicating that the field strength in Cleveland is identical to that which existed in Chicago 0.00167 sec earlier. In general terms, we should then expect the field at any point z m east of Chicago to lag the reference field by $z \sqrt{\mu_0\epsilon_0}$ or $z/(3 \times 10^8)$ sec.

Let us change our viewpoint now and inspect the field everywhere at $t = 0$:

$$E_x = E_{x0} \cos\left(-\omega z \sqrt{\mu_0\epsilon_0}\right) = E_{x0} \cos \frac{\omega z}{U_0}$$

finding a periodic variation with distance. The period of this cosine wave as measured along the z axis is called the wavelength, λ:

$$\frac{\omega\lambda}{U_0} = 2\pi$$

$$\lambda = \frac{U_0}{f} = \frac{3 \times 10^8}{f}$$

At any point we find a sinusoidal variation with time of period $T = 1/f$ sec; at any time we find a sinusoidal variation with distance of period λ m; at every point and at every instant of time, E_x is directed vertically upward. Now let us consider the response as both time and location are varied. Certainly we may say that E_x is unchanged if $t - z \sqrt{\mu_0\epsilon_0}$ is unchanged, or

$$t - \frac{z}{U_0} = \text{constant}$$

and taking differentials, we have

$$dt - \frac{1}{U_0} dz = 0$$

$$\frac{dz}{dt} = U_0$$

The field is therefore moving in the z direction with a velocity U_0. Whatever the value of the field is instantaneously at $z = z_1$, $t = t_1$, it will have the identical value at z_2 at a time $(z_2 - z_1)/U_0$ sec later; it will also have the identical value at $t = t_2$, a distance $(t_2 - t_1)U_0$ m farther to the east. The electric field is in motion and is logically termed a *traveling wave*.

Let us now return to Maxwell's equations, (5) to (8), and determine the form of the **H** field. Given **E**, **H** is most easily obtained from (6):

$$\nabla \times \mathbf{E} = -j\omega\mu_0 \mathbf{H} \tag{6}$$

which is greatly simplified for a single E_x component varying only with z:

$$\frac{\partial E_x}{\partial z} = -j\omega\mu_0 H_y$$

Since we are using the complex exponential form of this equation, we must use the corresponding form for E_x, given by (13) or (14), and obtain H_y:

$$H_y = -\frac{1}{j\omega\mu_0} E_{x0}(-j\omega z \sqrt{\mu_0\epsilon_0}) \, e^{j\omega(t - z\sqrt{\mu_0\epsilon_0})}$$

$$= E_{x0} \sqrt{\frac{\epsilon_0}{\mu_0}} \, e^{j\omega(t - z\sqrt{\mu_0\epsilon_0})}$$

The trigonometric form is found by retaining only the real part:

$$H_y = E_{x0} \sqrt{\frac{\epsilon_0}{\mu_0}} \cos{[\omega(t - z \sqrt{\mu_0\epsilon_0})]} \tag{16}$$

We therefore find that this vertical **E** component traveling to the east is accompanied by a horizontal (north-south) magnetic field. Moreover, the ratio of electric to magnetic field intensities, given by the ratio of (15) to (16),

$$\frac{E_x}{H_y} = \sqrt{\frac{\mu_0}{\epsilon_0}} \tag{17}$$

is constant. Using the language of circuit theory, we would say that E_x and H_y are "in phase," but this in-phase relationship does not refer only to time but also to space. We are accustomed to taking this for granted in a circuit problem in which a current $I_m \cos \omega t$ is assumed to have its maximum amplitude I_m throughout the entire circuit at $t = 0$. Both (15) and (16) clearly show, however, that the maximum value of either E_x or H_y occurs when $t - z \sqrt{\mu_0\epsilon_0}$ is an integral multiple of 2π radians and neither field has the same phase relationship throughout all space. It is then remarkable that the ratio of these two components, both changing in space and time, should be everywhere a constant. For the free-space conditions assumed, the constant ratio of (17) may be evaluated numerically:

$$\frac{E_x}{H_y} = 377 \text{ ohms}$$

and the dimension of the ratio determined as ohms.

This wave is called a *uniform plane wave* because its value is uniform throughout any plane, z = constant. It represents an energy flow in the positive z direction. Both the electric and magnetic field are perpendicular to the direction of propagation and perpendicular to each other. This is typical of the flow of energy in space.

A uniform plane wave cannot exist physically for it extends to infinity in two dimensions at least and represents an infinite amount of energy. The distant field of a transmitting antenna, however, is essentially a uniform plane wave in some limited region. A wave reaching a receiving antenna in Cleveland from Chicago is analyzed as a uniform plane wave in the vicinity of the antenna; a radar signal impinging on a target is also closely a uniform plane wave.

Although we have considered only a wave varying sinusoidally in time and space, a suitable combination of solutions to the wave equation may be made to achieve a wave of any desired form. The summation of an infinite number of harmonics through the use of a Fourier series can produce a periodic wave of square or triangular shape in both space and time. Nonperiodic waves may be obtained from our basic solution by Fourier integral methods. Finally, waves in other directions may also be included, representing perhaps a wave propagating slightly south of east, or perhaps to represent a reflected wave propagating to the west after reflection from some obstacle. These topics are considered in the more advanced books on electromagnetic theory, and analogies are developed between wave propagation and reflection in free space and the propagation and reflection of voltage and current waves on transmission lines.

D11.1. The distant field of a certain antenna operating at 1 Mc is essentially a uniform plane wave. A coordinate system is selected at this distant point so that the electric field is directed in the x direction and propagates in the z direction. If the positive maximum is 1 mv/m and occurs at $z = 0$, $t = 0$, find the vector magnetic field intensity:

  (a) At $z = 0$, $t = 0$.
  (b) At $z = 60$, $t = 0$.
  (c) At $z = 100$, $t = 0.2$ μsec.

Ans. $\mathbf{H} = 5.25 a_y$ μa/m.

11.2. Skin Effect. The topics we are about to discuss now can be considered as an extension of the wave motion investigated above in free space, but with the difference that the medium, typically a metallic conductor, through which the wave is progressing has a high conductivity and large conduction currents. The energy represented by the wave therefore decreases as the wave propagates because ohmic losses are continuously present.

When displacement current was first introduced, we saw that the ratio of the conduction current density to the displacement current density in any conducting material is given by $\sigma/\omega\epsilon$. Choosing a poor metallic conductor and a very high frequency as a conservative example, this ratio for nichrome ($\sigma \doteq 10^6$) at 100 Mc is about 2×10^8. This extremely large number indicates that the study of fields in conductors may very well be undertaken by ignoring displacement currents at the outset. Let us write Maxwell's equations for a conducting material, again using periodic time variation as represented by $e^{j\omega t}$:

$$\nabla \times \mathbf{H} = \mathbf{i} = \sigma\mathbf{E} \tag{1}$$
$$\nabla \times \mathbf{E} = -j\omega\mu\mathbf{H} \tag{2}$$

It is unnecessary to write the two divergence expressions, for they may be obtained in one step from either (1) or (2).

Repeating the general procedure which led to the wave equation, we have

$$\nabla \times \nabla \times \mathbf{E} = -j\omega\mu\nabla \times \mathbf{H} = -j\omega\mu\sigma\mathbf{E}$$

and

$$\nabla^2\mathbf{E} = j\omega\mu\sigma\mathbf{E} \tag{3}$$

and, similarly,

$$\nabla^2\mathbf{H} = j\omega\mu\sigma\mathbf{H} \tag{4}$$
$$\nabla^2\mathbf{i} = j\omega\mu\sigma\mathbf{i} \tag{5}$$

Equation (5) follows immediately upon applying Ohm's law to (3).

Our object is a solution of (5) which will describe the distribution of current throughout a conductor to which an external field is applied. In order to avoid undue mathematical complexity, we shall assume that the half space $z > 0$ is a conducting medium in which displacement current may be neglected. The region $z < 0$ is free space in which conduction current is not present. It is through this latter region that energy is to be applied to the conducting material, and we may think of the source as producing a uniform plane wave, propagating in the z direction and having no variation in the x or y directions. We shall assume that a field,

$$\mathbf{E} = E_0 e^{j\omega t}\mathbf{a}_x \qquad \text{at } z = 0 \tag{6}$$

is produced at the conductor surface $z = 0$. Our problem thus is to solve (5), obtained directly from Maxwell's equations, in the conducting region described and subject to the boundary condition (6).

Since the applied field (6) is not a function of x or y, symmetry demands that $\mathbf{i}$ also not be a function of x or y and therefore

$$\frac{\partial^2 \mathbf{i}}{\partial z^2} = j\omega\mu\sigma\mathbf{i} \tag{7}$$

Furthermore, the electric field intensity is directed entirely in the x direction, and current flow at the surface must also be in the x direction. No forces are present which tend to move the conducting electrons in other directions, and we therefore choose i_y and i_z as zero and have

$$\frac{\partial^2 i_x}{\partial z^2} = j\omega\mu\sigma i_x \tag{8}$$

The solution of (8) is analogous to that of Sec. 11.1, Eq. (12), of the preceding section and may be written as

$$i_x = i_{x0}e^{-\sqrt{j\omega\mu\sigma}\,z}$$

or, with the reinsertion of $e^{j\omega t}$,

$$i_x = i_{x0}e^{-\sqrt{j\omega\mu\sigma}\,z}e^{j\omega t} \tag{9}$$

where i_{x0} = value of i_x at $z = 0$, $t = 0$. The trigonometric form of (9) is not obvious, but it is again obtained by taking the real part of the complex exponential expression. Let us first separate the exponent into real and imaginary parts by taking the square root of j:

$$\sqrt{j} = (\sqrt{1/90°} = 1/\underline{45°} =) \frac{1}{\sqrt{2}} + j\frac{1}{\sqrt{2}}$$

and writing (9) as

$$\begin{aligned}
i_x &= i_{x0}e^{-\frac{1}{2}(\sqrt{2}+j\sqrt{2})\sqrt{\omega\mu\sigma}\,z}e^{j\omega t} \\
&= i_{x0}e^{-\sqrt{\pi f\mu\sigma}\,z}e^{j(\omega t - \sqrt{\pi f\mu\sigma}\,z)} \\
&= i_{x0}e^{-\sqrt{\pi f\mu\sigma}\,z}\cos\left[\omega\left(t - \sqrt{\frac{\mu\sigma}{2\omega}}\,z\right)\right]
\end{aligned} \tag{9a}$$

Application of the remaining boundary condition (6) is accomplished by using the continuity of the tangential electric field intensity at $z = 0$:

$$i_{x0} = \sigma E_0$$

and therefore

$$i_x = \sigma E_0 e^{-\sqrt{\pi f\mu\sigma}\,z}\cos\left[\omega\left(t - \sqrt{\frac{\mu\sigma}{2\omega}}\,z\right)\right] \tag{10}$$

Equation (10) contains a wealth of information. Considering first the negative exponential term, we find an exponential decrease in the conduction current density with penetration into the conductor (away from the source). The "time constant" of this exponential decrease is measured in units of distance and is the distance at which the peak current density is e^{-1}, or 0.368 times its value at $z = 0$. This distance is denoted by δ and is termed the *depth of penetration*, or the *skin depth:*

$$\sqrt{\pi f \mu \sigma} \; \delta = 1$$

$$\delta = \frac{1}{\sqrt{\pi f \mu \sigma}} \qquad \text{meters} \tag{11}$$

Before considering the numerical values to be expected for the depth of penetration, let us consider the argument of the cosine term in (10). Evidently propagation in the z direction is again present, showing energy is being carried into the conductor away from the external source. The velocity of this traveling wave is found from (10) to be

$$U_c = \sqrt{\frac{2\omega}{\mu\sigma}} \qquad \text{m/sec} \tag{12}$$

and the wavelength λ_c is

$$\omega \sqrt{\frac{\mu\sigma}{2\omega}} \, \lambda_c = 2\pi$$

$$\lambda_c = \sqrt{\frac{2\omega}{\mu\sigma}} \frac{1}{f} = \frac{2\pi}{\sqrt{\pi f \mu \sigma}} = 2\pi\delta \tag{13}$$

At every point in the conductor, power is dissipated in ohmic losses, heating the conducting material. In a small volume of cross section $\Delta y \, \Delta z$ and length Δx, the total current in the cross section is

$$\Delta I = i_x \, \Delta y \, \Delta z$$

and the resistance is

$$\Delta R = \frac{1}{\sigma} \frac{\Delta x}{\Delta y \, \Delta z}$$

leading to an incremental power loss:

$$\Delta P = \frac{1}{2} |\Delta I|^2 \, \Delta R$$

$$= \frac{1}{2} |i_x|^2 \, (\Delta y)^2 \, (\Delta z)^2 \frac{1}{\sigma} \frac{\Delta x}{\Delta y \, \Delta z}$$

$$= \frac{1}{2} \frac{|i_x|^2}{\sigma} \, \Delta v$$

real part of the complex expression in order to obtain the correct instantaneous current.

We shall not attempt at this time to discover the "source of the source," but merely assume that it is constant.   The distribution of the current cannot be changed by any field which it produces.

The first step is the application of the retarded vector magnetic potential expression:

$$A = \int \frac{\mu[I]\,dL}{4\pi R}$$

which requires no integration for the very short filament assumed:

$$A = \frac{\mu[I]d}{4\pi R}\, a_z$$

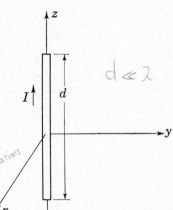

$d \ll \lambda$

Fig. 11.2. A differential current filament of length d carries a current $I = I_0 e^{j\omega t}$.

Only the z component of A is present, for current flow occurs only in the z direction.   At any point P, distant R m from the origin, the current is retarded by R/U sec and we have

$$A_z = \frac{\mu I_0 d}{4\pi R}\, e^{j\omega(t-R/U)}$$

Using a mixed coordinate system for the moment, let us replace R by the small r of the spherical coordinate system and then determine which spherical components are represented by A_z.   The small sketch of Fig. 11.3 helps to determine that

$$A_r = A_z \cos\theta$$
$$A_\theta = -A_z \sin\theta$$

and therefore

$$A_r = \frac{\mu I_0 d}{4\pi r}\,(\cos\theta)e^{j\omega(t-r/U)}$$

$$A_\theta = -\frac{\mu I_0 d}{4\pi r}\,(\sin\theta)e^{j\omega(t-r/U)}$$

From these two components of the vector magnetic potential at P we may find B or H from the definition of A:

$$B = \mu H = \nabla \times A$$

by merely taking the indicated partial derivatives. Thus

$$H_\phi = \frac{1}{\mu r} \frac{\partial}{\partial r} (r A_\theta) - \frac{1}{\mu r} \frac{\partial A_r}{\partial \theta}$$

$$H_r = H_\theta = 0$$

and
$$H_\phi = \frac{I_0 d}{4\pi} (\sin \theta) e^{j\omega(t-r/U)} \left[j \frac{\omega}{Ur} + \frac{1}{r^2} \right]$$

The components of the electric field which must be associated with this magnetic field are found from the point form of Ampère's circuital

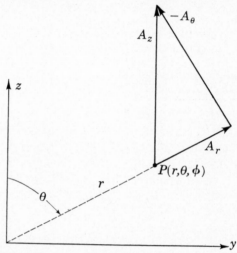

Fig. 11.3. The resolution of A_z at $P(r,\theta,\phi)$ into the two spherical components A_r and A_θ. The sketch is arbitrarily drawn in the $\phi = 90°$ plane.

law as it applies to a region in which conduction and convection current are absent:

$$\nabla \times \mathbf{H} = \frac{\partial \mathbf{D}}{\partial t}$$

or in complex notation,

$$\nabla \times \mathbf{H} = j\omega\epsilon\mathbf{E}$$

Expansion of the curl in spherical coordinates leads to

$$E_r = \frac{1}{j\omega\epsilon} \frac{1}{r \sin \theta} \frac{\partial}{\partial \theta} (H_\phi \sin \theta)$$

$$E_\theta = \frac{1}{j\omega\epsilon} \left[-\frac{1}{r} \right] \frac{\partial}{\partial r} (r H_\phi)$$

or
$$E_r = \frac{I_0 d}{2\pi} (\cos \theta) e^{j\omega(t-r/U)} \left[\frac{1}{\epsilon U r^2} + \frac{1}{j\omega\epsilon r^3} \right]$$

$$E_\theta = \frac{I_0 d}{4\pi} (\sin \theta) e^{j\omega(t-r/U)} \left[\frac{j\omega}{\epsilon U^2 r} + \frac{1}{\epsilon U r^2} + \frac{1}{j\omega\epsilon r^3} \right]$$

In order to simplify the interpretation of the bracketed terms in the expressions for H_ϕ, E_r, and E_θ, we shall make the substitutions $\omega = 2\pi f$, $f\lambda = U$, and $U = 1/\sqrt{\mu\epsilon}$, producing

$$H_\phi = \frac{I_0 d}{4\pi} (\sin \theta) e^{j(\omega t - 2\pi r/\lambda)} \left[j\frac{2\pi}{\lambda r} + \frac{1}{r^2} \right] \tag{1}$$

$$E_r = \frac{I_0 d}{2\pi} \sqrt{\frac{\mu}{\epsilon}} (\cos \theta) e^{j(\omega t - 2\pi r/\lambda)} \left[\frac{1}{r^2} + \frac{\lambda}{j2\pi r^3} \right] \tag{2}$$

$$E_\theta = \frac{I_0 d}{4\pi} \sqrt{\frac{\mu}{\epsilon}} (\sin \theta) e^{j(\omega t - 2\pi r/\lambda)} \left[j\frac{2\pi}{\lambda r} + \frac{1}{r^2} + \frac{\lambda}{j2\pi r^3} \right] \tag{3}$$

These three equations are indicative of the reason why so many of the problems involving antennas are solved by experimental rather than theoretical methods. They have resulted from three general steps: an integration (untypically trivial) and two differentiations. These steps are sufficient to cause the simple current element and its simple current expression to "blow up" into the complicated field described by (1) to (3). In spite of this complexity, several interesting observations are possible.

We might notice first the $e^{j(\omega t - 2\pi r/\lambda)}$ factor appearing with each component. This indicates propagation outward from the origin in the positive r direction with a wavelength λ and velocity $U = 1/\sqrt{\mu\epsilon}$. We use the term wavelength now in a somewhat broader sense than the original definition, which identified the wavelength of a uniform plane wave with the distance between two points, measured in the direction of propagation, at which the wave has identical instantaneous values. Here there are additional complications caused by the bracketed factor, which is a function of r. This variation must now be neglected in determining the wavelength. This is equivalent to a determination of the wavelength at a large distance from the origin, and we may demonstrate this by sketching the H_ϕ component as a function of r under the following conditions:

$$I_0 d = 4\pi \qquad \theta = 90° \qquad t = 0 \qquad f = 300 \text{ Mc}$$
$$U = 3 \times 10^8 \text{ m/sec (free space)} \qquad \lambda = 1 \text{ m}$$

Therefore

$$H_\phi = \left(\frac{1}{r^2} + j\frac{2\pi}{r} \right) (1/\underline{360°r})$$

The real part of H_ϕ is plotted against r in the range $1 \leq r \leq 2$ in Fig. 11.4a, and the curve is seen to be decidedly nonsinusoidal. Moreover, the instantaneous value is 1.00 at $r = 1$ and 0.25 at $r = 2$, one wavelength greater. If a similar sketch is made in the range $101 \leq$

$r \leq 102$, shown in Fig. 11.4b on a different amplitude scale, an essentially sinusoidal wave is obtained and the instantaneous values at $r = 101$ and $r = 102$ are 0.0000998 and 0.0000996. The maximum amplitudes of the positive and negative portions of the waveform differ by less than 1 per cent, and we may say that to all practical purposes the wave in this region is a uniform plane wave having a sinusoidal variation with distance (and time, of course) and a well-defined

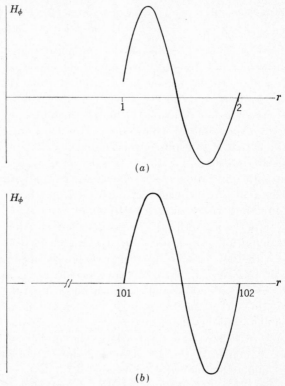

Fig. 11.4. The instantaneous amplitude of H_ϕ for the special case of a current element having $I_0 d = 4\pi$, $\lambda = 1$, is plotted at $\theta = 90°$ and $t = 0$ (a) in the region $1 \leq r \leq 2$ near the antenna, and (b) in the region $101 \leq r \leq 102$ distant from the antenna.

wavelength. This wave evidently carries energy away from the differential antenna, and we shall calculate this power shortly.

Continuing the investigation of (1) to (3), let us now take a more careful look at the square-bracketed expressions containing terms varying as $1/r^3$, $1/r^2$, and $1/r$. At points very close to the current element the $1/r^3$ term must be dominant. In the numerical example

propagating in polystyrene, which may here be considered a perfect dielectric for which $\epsilon_R = 2.53$. Compare these values with those which would apply in free space.

3. Show that if the y component of Sec. 11.1, Eq. (9), had been chosen, the resultant magnetic field would be $H_x = -\sqrt{\epsilon_0/\mu_0}\, E_y$ for propagation in the positive z direction.

4. Assume that the electrostatic expression for energy in the electric field applies also to time-varying fields, and use Sec. 11.1, Eq. (15), to calculate the instantaneous energy in the region bounded by the planes $x = 0$ and 1, $y = 0$ and 1, $z = 0$ and λ. Use similar methods to show that the instantaneous energy stored in the magnetic field is the same as that in the electric field. Use these results to show that the time-average power crossing the $z = 0$ surface of the region is $\frac{1}{2}\sqrt{\epsilon/\mu}\, E_{x0}^2$.

5. Determine the equation analogous to Sec. 11.1, Eq. (12), if the conductivity is not assumed to be zero.

6. Show that a second solution of Sec. 11.1, Eq. (12), is $E_x = Ae^{j\omega\sqrt{\mu_0\epsilon_0}\,z}$, and obtain and interpret the corresponding trigonometric expression.

7. Use Maxwell's equations to determine the **E** and **H** fields which are associated with **i** as expressed by Sec. 11.2, Eq. (10). Determine the ratio of tangential **E** to tangential **H** at the conductor surface as a complex number. This is termed the *surface impedance.*

8. Show that 86.5 per cent of the total power loss occurs in a region δ m thick at the conductor surface as stated in Sec. 11.2.

9. Show that the total conduction current crossing the $x = 0$ plane between $y = 0$ and 1 and $z = 0$ and ∞ is $\frac{1}{2}\sqrt{2}\,\delta i_{x0}\cos(\omega t - 45°)$. [HINT: Use Sec. 11.2, Eq. (9a), and consider phase relationships.]

10. Given the relative dielectric constant of sea water as 81, show that the assumption that displacement current is negligible is justified in Prob. D11.3c.

11. The inductance and capacitance per unit length of a coaxial transmission line of inner radius a and outer radius b have been found previously as $(\mu/2\pi)\ln (b/a)$ and $2\pi\epsilon/\ln (b/a)$, respectively. Assume an air-filled line, 1 m in length, $\ln (b/a) = 2$, terminated with an open circuit at one end and excited with an applied voltage at the other end at a frequency of 37.5 Mc. Assume also that the capacitance is concentrated at the open circuit and the inductance is concentrated in series with the input. Use circuit techniques to find the approximate input impedance, and then compare with the correct value from transmission-line theory, $Z_{in} = -j120$ ohms. Discuss the source of the error.

12. Given a perfectly conducting filament formed into a circular loop, consider case A, in which a physically small resistance of 10 ohms is inserted at one point in the loop, and case B, in which the same resistance and also a physically small 10-volt battery are inserted at different points in the loop. In case A a linearly increasing magnetic flux produces an emf of 10 volts around the loop. No flux is present in case B. Determine $\oint \mathbf{E} \cdot d\mathbf{L}$ about the filamentary path in both cases, and explain the difference.

13. Use the Poynting vector to show that the time-average power crossing each square meter on any plane normal to the direction of propagation of a uniform plane wave is $\frac{1}{2}\sqrt{\epsilon/\mu}E_{x0}^2$, as determined in a different way in Prob. 4.

14. Two differential current elements are described as follows: (1) at $P_1(0,-1,0)$; (2) at $P_2(0,1,0)$, $d_1 = d_2 = 0.2$, $\lambda = 8$, $\sqrt{\mu/\epsilon} = 120\pi$, $I_{01} = (5/\pi)\underline{/0°}$, $I_{02} = (5/\pi)\underline{/90°}$. (a) At $\phi = 90°$, $\theta = 90°$, $r = 800$, find $E_{\theta 1}$, $E_{\theta 2}$, and $E_\theta = E_{\theta 1} + E_{\theta 2}$.

(b) Find E_θ as a function of ϕ at $\theta = 90°$, $r = 800$.   (c) Plot the result of (b) on a polar plot showing $|E_\theta|$ versus ϕ.

15. An antenna is $\frac{1}{2}$ wavelength long end to end and has a sinusoidal current distribution along its length, $I = I_0 \cos (2\pi z/\lambda) \cos \omega t$. Break the antenna into six "differential" lengths, each $\frac{1}{12}$ wavelength long with a uniform current equal to the actual current at the mid-point of the small section, and find the total E_θ at the distant points (r, $\theta = 90°$, $\phi = 0°$) and (r, $\theta = 60°$, $\phi = 0°$). Compare with values from the exact expression for the distant field obtained by integration,

$$E_\theta = j \frac{60I_0}{r} \frac{\cos (90° \cos \theta)}{\sin \theta} e^{j(\omega t - 2\pi r/\lambda)}.$$

16. Briefly review the comments of the five men below in their books on electromagnetic theory regarding the interpretation of the Poynting vector as a true indication of the point-by-point value of the power density:

(a) J. A. Stratton.

(b) J. R. Smythe.

(c) H. H. Skilling.

(d) S. A. Schelkunoff.

(e) Ramo and Whinnery.

CHAPTER 12

CHARGED PARTICLES IN ELECTROMAGNETIC FIELDS

The useful output of most electromagnetic systems is closely associated with a mechanical force. This force may be applied to the voice coil of a loudspeaker, to the pointer of a meter, to the beam in a cathode-ray tube, to the shaft on a motor, and to other devices too numerous to mention. In the case of some devices used for illumination or heating purposes, forces must be applied to conduction electrons to increase their kinetic energy and thus make possible an energy transfer to the conducting material.

We have already discussed current flow and the electric field in conductors and need not discuss the forces on conduction electrons further. We have also discussed the cumulative force and torque on current-carrying conductors. We may therefore turn our attention now to the consequences of the application of forces to charged particles in a vacuum. The basic definitions of the electric field intensity **E** and magnetic flux density **B** are both given in terms of the force on a charged particle. We spent very little time, however, in determining the change in the position and velocity of the particle in response to these forces. At this time we shall apply the laws of classical dynamics to determine the trajectories of isolated particles in electric and magnetic fields, and then consider the movement of a space charge. This latter case differs from the case of the isolated particle in that the fields due to other moving particles are also important. Finally, we shall introduce relativistic effects and show that Newtonian or classical mechanics is insufficient at the higher particle velocities. The theory of relativity will also enable us to realize that what appears as an electric field to one observer is a magnetic field to a second observer who is in motion with respect to the first observer. Thus the description of a field as electric or magnetic depends upon the observer's frame of reference.

12.1. Motion in Electric Fields. The force on a particle of charge Q in an electric field **E** is given by

$$\mathbf{F} = Q\mathbf{E} \tag{1}$$

where the particle is considered to be a point charge. The electric field may vary both in space and with time, but we have found that time-varying fields in general imply an associated magnetic field and this magnetic field may also produce a force on a moving charge. This force we shall ignore for the present and consider only the effect of the electric field. The electric field is assumed to be independent of the motion of the charged particle.

We shall assume further that the particle is not restrained in any way and that there are no other forces applied to it. We thus do not consider the effect of any other charges which may move in response to the applied field, and we are effectively studying the motion of an isolated particle in a given field.

The force results in a time rate of change of momentum,

$$Q\mathbf{E} = \frac{d}{dt}(m\mathbf{U}) \tag{2}$$

which we shall temporarily simplify by assuming a maximum velocity which is a small fraction of the velocity of light and leads to a constant mass:

$$Q\mathbf{E} = m\frac{d\mathbf{U}}{dt} \tag{3}$$

Expanding (3) in cartesian coordinates, we have:

$$QE_x = m\frac{dU_x}{dt} \tag{4a}$$

$$QE_y = m\frac{dU_y}{dt} \tag{4b}$$

$$QE_z = m\frac{dU_z}{dt} \tag{4c}$$

and the components of the velocity may be replaced by the time derivatives of the coordinates:

$$QE_x = m\frac{d^2x}{dt^2} \tag{5a}$$

$$QE_y = m\frac{d^2y}{dt^2} \tag{5b}$$

$$QE_z = m\frac{d^2z}{dt^2} \tag{5c}$$

Our general problem, then, is to find the particle trajectory, given by expressing x, y, and z as functions of t, by the simultaneous solution of (5a–c) subject to given boundary conditions. Since we have second-order equations to solve, we require two boundary conditions for each

This equation could have been obtained much more easily if we had realized that only the radial component of the velocity would be present. It is (11) with the appropriate potential expression. The velocity after falling through a potential difference of V_0 volts between cathode and plate is the same in the cylindrical diode as in a parallel-plane diode.

The relationship between r and t cannot be expressed in terms of the elementary functions, and we shall not carry this example any further. It has served its purpose in showing the application in cylindrical coordinates of the basic component equations (20) to (22) of Newton's third law.

D12.1. Determine the magnitude of the velocity of an electron which leaves the cathode with zero velocity, at a point 1 cm from the cathode, if the anode-cathode potential difference is 200 volts and the diode is of the form:

(a) Parallel plane, anode-cathode separation of 2 cm.
(b) Cylindrical, $a = 0.5$ cm, $b = 2.5$ cm.
(c) Cylindrical, $a = 4$ cm, $b = 6$ cm.

Ans. 19.08×10^6 m/sec.

12.2. Motion in Magnetic Fields. The force on a moving particle in a magnetic field,

$$\mathbf{F} = Q\mathbf{U} \times \mathbf{B}$$

may be equated to the time rate of change of momentum:

$$Q\mathbf{U} \times \mathbf{B} = m\frac{d\mathbf{U}}{dt} \tag{1}$$

where we still shall consider the mass constant. In cartesian coordinates, (1) may be written in terms of the velocity components:

$$\frac{Q}{m}(U_y B_z - U_z B_y) = \frac{dU_x}{dt} \tag{2a}$$

$$\frac{Q}{m}(U_z B_x - U_x B_z) = \frac{dU_y}{dt} \tag{2b}$$

$$\frac{Q}{m}(U_x B_y - U_y B_x) = \frac{dU_z}{dt} \tag{2c}$$

or in terms of the cartesian variables directly,

$$\frac{d^2x}{dt^2} = \frac{Q}{m}\left(B_z\frac{dy}{dt} - B_y\frac{dz}{dt}\right) \tag{3a}$$

$$\frac{d^2y}{dt^2} = \frac{Q}{m}\left(B_x\frac{dz}{dt} - B_z\frac{dx}{dt}\right) \tag{3b}$$

$$\frac{d^2z}{dt^2} = \frac{Q}{m}\left(B_y\frac{dx}{dt} - B_x\frac{dy}{dt}\right) \tag{3c}$$

We find that we have simultaneous differential equations to solve even with a uniform magnetic field, and the solution is correspondingly more difficult than the electrostatic problem in this coordinate system.

Let us consider the fundamental example in which a uniform magnetic field $\mathbf{B} = B_0 \mathbf{a}_z$ is present and an electron enters the field at $(0,0,0)$ at $t = 0$ with an initial velocity $\mathbf{U} = U_{y0}\mathbf{a}_y$. Equation (3c) then indicates that $U_z = 0$ and $z = 0$ for all time, and (3a) and (3b) become

$$\frac{d^2x}{dt^2} = -\frac{e}{m} B_0 \frac{dy}{dt} \tag{4a}$$

$$\frac{d^2y}{dt^2} = \frac{e}{m} B_0 \frac{dx}{dt} \tag{4b}$$

Solving (4a) for dy/dt and substituting into (4b) allows us to eliminate y, and we have

$$-\frac{m}{eB_0} \frac{d^3x}{dt^3} = \frac{eB_0}{m} \frac{dx}{dt}$$

or

$$\frac{d^2U_x}{dt^2} = -\left(\frac{eB_0}{m}\right)^2 U_x$$

which is a form we have met several times before. The solution may be written:

$$U_x = A_1 \cos \omega_0 t + B_1 \sin \omega_0 t \tag{5}$$

where

$$\omega_0 = \frac{eB_0}{m}$$

From the initial velocity we must have $A_1 = 0$. If (4b) is solved for dx/dt and this expression is used in (4a), we obtain

$$\frac{d^2U_y}{dt^2} = -\omega_0{}^2 U_y$$

from which

$$U_y = A_2 \cos \omega_0 t + B_2 \sin \omega_0 t \tag{6}$$

where

$$A_2 = U_{y0}$$

The constants B_1 and B_2 should be known from the initial conditions, but it appears that they cannot be found. They have resulted from the method of solution, and not from the original problem itself, and we therefore apparently do not have enough initial conditions. They were introduced when the order of the equation was raised (note the d^3x/dt^3 term) during the simultaneous solution. We should therefore return to the basic equations (4a,b). Substituting (5) and (6) into (4a,b), we find

$$\frac{dU_x}{dt} = \omega_0 B_1 \cos \omega_0 t = -\omega_0(U_{y0} \cos \omega_0 t + B_2 \sin \omega_0 t)$$

The final velocity components are then

$$U_x = \frac{k}{\omega_0}\left(1 - \frac{\alpha\omega_0{}^2}{\omega^2 - \omega_0{}^2}\right)\sin \omega_0 t + \frac{\alpha k\omega}{\omega^2 - \omega_0{}^2}\sin \omega t \qquad (10)$$

$$U_y = \frac{k}{\omega_0}\left[1 - \left(1 - \frac{\alpha\omega_0{}^2}{\omega^2 - \omega_0{}^2}\right)\cos \omega_0 t\right] - \frac{\alpha k\omega_0}{\omega^2 - \omega_0{}^2}\cos \omega t \qquad (11)$$

and direct integration of these two equations and a simple application of the initial conditions yield the electron position as a function of time:

$$x = \frac{k}{\omega_0{}^2}\left[1 - \left(1 - \frac{\alpha\omega_0{}^2}{\omega^2 - \omega_0{}^2}\right)\cos \omega_0 t - \frac{\alpha\omega_0{}^2}{\omega^2 - \omega_0{}^2}\cos \omega t\right] \qquad (12)$$

$$y = \frac{k}{\omega_0{}^2}\left[\omega_0 t - \left(1 - \frac{\alpha\omega_0{}^2}{\omega^2 - \omega_0{}^2}\right)\sin \omega_0 t - \frac{\omega_0}{\omega}\frac{\alpha\omega_0{}^2}{\omega^2 - \omega_0{}^2}\sin \omega t\right] \qquad (13)$$

These equations are somewhat involved, and it is perhaps best to interpret them by first removing the alternating applied voltage. Setting $\alpha = V_1/V_0 = 0$, we have

$$x = \frac{k}{\omega_0{}^2}(1 - \cos \omega_0 t) \qquad (14)$$

$$y = \frac{k}{\omega_0{}^2}(\omega_0 t - \sin \omega_0 t) \qquad (15)$$

which are the parametric equations of a cycloid. This curve may be traced out by a point on the circumference of a rolling wheel, for the corresponding velocity components are

$$\left.\begin{array}{l} U_x = \dfrac{k}{\omega_0}\sin \omega_0 t \\[2mm] U_y = \dfrac{k}{\omega_0}(1 - \cos \omega_0 t) \end{array}\right\} \alpha = 0$$

showing an angular velocity of the wheel of ω_0 radians/sec and a translational, or forward, velocity of k/ω_0 m/sec. The radius of the wheel may be found from the linear velocity of a point on the circumference, ignoring the translation of k/ω_0 and producing a radius of $k/\omega_0{}^2$ m. This radius should also now be evident from (14) and (15). An electron therefore reaches a maximum distance from the cathode of $2k/\omega_0{}^2$ m in π/ω_0 sec, and if the plate-to-cathode separation d is less than this distance, the trajectory is ended as the electron strikes the plate. If d is sufficiently large, the electron returns to the cathode at a point $2\pi k/\omega_0{}^2$ m distant from the point at which it left. The maximum velocity occurs when the electron is nearest to the plate and is $2k/\omega_0$ m/sec, leading to a maximum kinetic energy of

$$KE_{max} = \frac{1}{2} m4 \frac{k^2}{\omega_0^2} = \frac{2mV_0^2}{d^2B_0^2}$$

This energy is completely returned to the electric field by the time the electron returns to the cathode.

If we now replace the a-c voltage and consider for simplicity only the very special case for which $\alpha\omega_0^2/(\omega^2 - \omega_0^2) = \frac{1}{2}$ and $\omega = 1.1\omega_0$, we have, from (12) and (13):

$$x = \frac{k}{\omega_0^2} (1 - \tfrac{1}{2} \cos \omega_0 t - \tfrac{1}{2} \cos 1.1\omega_0 t) \tag{16}$$

$$y = \frac{k}{\omega_0^2} \left(\omega_0 t - \frac{1}{2} \sin \omega_0 t - \frac{1}{1.1} \frac{1}{2} \sin 1.1\omega_0 t \right) \tag{17}$$

The two trigonometric expressions in (16) may be written in terms of sum and difference frequencies:

$$x = \frac{k}{\omega_0^2} (1 - \cos 0.05\omega_0 t \cos 1.05\omega_0 t)$$

which shows that the electron goes from the cathode a maximum distance of almost $2k/\omega_0^2$, returns almost to the cathode, turns around and goes a slightly smaller distance toward the plate, and continues oscillating back and forth with decreasing amplitude until it comes to rest at $x = k/\omega_0^2$ at $\omega_0 t = 10\pi$. The y component of the velocity is not zero, however.

The displacement in the y direction is again a linear translation superimposed on an oscillatory motion of decreasing amplitude. The combined motion is similar to that of a point on a rolling wheel where the point oscillates from the edge to the center at a relatively slow rate compared to the rotational velocity. At the instant the point is at the center, the velocity is only the constant translational component. This component is present when no a-c field is applied or when $V_1 = 0$. The kinetic energy of the electron at this point is therefore much less than it would be at this distance from the cathode if only the d-c field were present and the cycloidal path were being followed. This reduced energy therefore indicates that energy has been transferred from the d-c field to the electron, and thence to the a-c field. The device therefore will act as an oscillator and deliver energy to an external load at an angular frequency of ω.

If the electron is allowed to remain in the tube, the amplitude of its oscillations will again increase and it will remove energy from the a-c field. Means are therefore provided to remove the electron when it becomes of "unfavorable phase." In a corresponding way, an electron which begins its trajectory at a slightly earlier or later instant than $t = 0$ is also not as favorable as the particular electron we have followed. Means are also provided to speed up or slow down these electrons automatically until most electrons are grouped about the most favorable one. This is called *phase focusing*.

This example has served to indicate in a very general way how sinusoidal oscillations are made possible by the transfer of energy from a d-c source to an a-c source (or load). The general analysis is very difficult, and the effect of space charge produces further complications. This effect is discussed in the following section.

D12.3. Normalize the operating conditions of a parallel-plane magnetron by choosing $k = 1$, $\omega_0 = 1$. If $V_1 = 0$ and the particle enters the field at $(0,0,0)$ with $\mathbf{U}_0 = \mathbf{a}_x + \mathbf{a}_y$ at $t = 0$ and if the anode and cathode are both far distant from $(0,0,0)$, find the particle position at:

(a) $t = \dfrac{\pi}{2}$.

(b) $t = \pi$.

(c) $t = \dfrac{3\pi}{2}$.

Ans. ($x = 0$, $y = 13.42$, $z = 0$).

12.4. Space-charge Effects.

The general problem we are now going to set for ourselves is to follow the path of a single particle through a region in which many other particles are present and are in motion. The particular particle cannot be distinguished from its neighbors, and all will have the same characteristic motion in a small neighborhood. The presence of this large number of charges causes the fields to differ from those which would be present because of the applied (external) fields alone. The total field can be found only by using Maxwell's equations.

Thus, in addition to the basic (nonrelativistic) force equation on a particle of charge Q and mass m,

$$\mathbf{F} = m\,\frac{d\mathbf{U}}{dt} = Q(\mathbf{E} + \mathbf{U} \times \mathbf{B}) \tag{1}$$

we must apply Maxwell's four equations as they apply to an evacuated region ($\epsilon = \epsilon_0$, $\mu = \mu_0$, $\sigma = 0$). In terms of $\mathbf{E}$ and $\mathbf{H}$, we have

$$\nabla \cdot \mathbf{E} = \frac{\rho}{\epsilon_0} \tag{2}$$

$$\nabla \times \mathbf{H} = \mathbf{i} + \epsilon_0\,\frac{\partial \mathbf{E}}{\partial t} = \rho\mathbf{U} + \epsilon_0\,\frac{\partial \mathbf{E}}{\partial t} \tag{3}$$

$$\nabla \times \mathbf{E} = -\mu_0\,\frac{\partial \mathbf{H}}{\partial t} \tag{4}$$

$$\nabla \cdot \mathbf{H} = 0 \tag{5}$$

A solution of these equations must be obtained which satisfies the boundary conditions in space (tangential $\mathbf{E}$ and normal $\mathbf{H}$ vanish at conductor boundaries, for example) and also in time (initial position and velocity of the charged particle). This is a formidable problem, and we should feel satisfied in merely recognizing the conditions (1) to (5) which must be fulfilled and the type of boundary conditions which should be supplied and then met.

Let us gradually simplify the space-charge problem by making several assumptions. We first assume that no *applied* magnetic field is present. This, of course, immediately throws out an entire family of practical problems, but most of the problems remaining are still too difficult to solve exactly. This assumption does not allow us to set $\mathbf{H} = 0$ in Maxwell's equations, however, for the convection currents resulting from the motion of charge produce a magnetic field, and if we say that this field is also zero, we are in effect stating that there are no convection currents present. The magnetic fields produced by these convection currents are exceedingly small and have a negligible effect on the charges, however, and we may therefore set $\mathbf{B} = 0$ in (1):

$$\frac{d\mathbf{U}}{dt} = \frac{Q}{m}\mathbf{E} \tag{6}$$

Let us now eliminate $\mathbf{H}$ from (3) by taking the divergence of each side:

$$\boldsymbol{\nabla} \cdot \left(\rho\mathbf{U} + \epsilon_0 \frac{\partial \mathbf{E}}{\partial t}\right) = 0 \tag{7}$$

and rewriting (2) below:

$$\boldsymbol{\nabla} \cdot \mathbf{E} = \frac{\rho}{\epsilon_0} \tag{2}$$

to obtain three equations with the three dependent variables ρ, $\mathbf{E}$, and $\mathbf{U}$. The quantity within the parentheses in (7) is the total current density, convection plus displacement, and we shall represent it by $\mathbf{J}$:

$$\mathbf{J} = \rho\mathbf{U} + \epsilon_0 \frac{\partial \mathbf{E}}{\partial t} \tag{8}$$

$$\boldsymbol{\nabla} \cdot \mathbf{J} = 0 \tag{9}$$

We may eliminate ρ by substituting (2) into (7), obtaining

$$\mathbf{J} = \epsilon_0\mathbf{U}\boldsymbol{\nabla} \cdot \mathbf{E} + \epsilon_0 \frac{\partial \mathbf{E}}{\partial t} \tag{10}$$

Finally, $\mathbf{E}$ may be eliminated by using (6), leading to

$$\mathbf{J} = \frac{m\epsilon_0}{Q}\left[\mathbf{U}\boldsymbol{\nabla} \cdot \left(\frac{d\mathbf{U}}{dt}\right) + \frac{\partial}{\partial t}\left(\frac{d\mathbf{U}}{dt}\right)\right] \tag{11}$$

where U = constant, and then express (3) in terms of its scalar components:

$$E'_x = E_x \tag{4a}$$
$$E'_y = E_y - UB_z \tag{4b}$$
$$E'_z = E_z + UB_y \tag{4c}$$

Before we investigate the magnetic field seen by the moving charge, we may consider a few illustrations of the preceding equations. Equation (3) states that the electric field seen by the moving charge consists of the electric field recognized by the stationary observer and a term described in Chap. 10 as the *motional* electric field intensity. We found then that this leads to a *motional* emf which enables rapid solutions to be made in problems involving moving conductors. We should now realize that this method of attacking the moving-conductor problem is equivalent to solving the problem from the standpoint of the moving conductor or from a moving frame of reference.

As a specific example, consider a positive charge located at $(0,y,0)$ at $t = 0$ and having a velocity $\mathbf{U} = U\mathbf{a}_x$. A filamentary current of I amp flows along the x axis. In the fixed frame of reference, we see the charge moving in a magnetic field of

$$B_z = \frac{\mu I}{2\pi y}$$

but the charge sees an electric field, given by (4b), as

$$E'_y = -UB_z = -\frac{\mu U I}{2\pi y}$$

In either case the force on the charge is

$$F_y = F'_y = -\frac{Q\mu U I}{2\pi y}$$

Other fields may also be present in either frame of reference, but this cannot be determined until we specify the exact nature of the filamentary current. If it consists of the motion of positive charges in the $\mathbf{a}_x$ direction, then an electric field is also present in the fixed frame of reference, and (4b) shows that this field is unchanged in the moving frame. However, a magnetic field may also be seen in the world of the moving charge if the velocities of the single charge and of the line charge are unequal. This magnetic field we shall now investigate.

The magnetic fields experienced in the moving frame of reference are not as quickly found as were the electric fields given by (4). We cannot use the equality of forces in the two frames of reference, for the electron is stopped in its frame of reference, and consequently cannot determine a magnetic field by any measurement of force. We should seek an answer to the question, "What object, moving in combined electric and magnetic fields, experiences a force due to the electric field only when its velocity is *not* zero?" The answer is the purely hypothetical magnetic pole, sometimes referred to as the *magnetic charge*. The analogy to the electric charge is displayed by the following statement: A force is exerted on a stationary (electric, magnetic) charge only by the (electric, magnetic) field, but a moving (electric, magnetic) charge also experiences a force due to the (magnetic, electric) field. Without any discussion of the basic relationships involving magnetic charges,[1] we shall merely say that the force on a magnetic charge of M webers is

$$\mathbf{F} = M\mathbf{H} + M\mathbf{D} \times \mathbf{U} \tag{5}$$

and use (5) to find $\mathbf{H}'$ in terms of $\mathbf{H}$ and $\mathbf{E}$. We shall show that the result in one simple example agrees with the result we may obtain by a method not involving magnetic charges.

The force on the magnetic charge, as observed in the fixed frame of reference, must again be equal to the force observed by the magnetic charge in a frame of reference moving at a uniform velocity $\mathbf{U}$, where again $U \ll U_0$:

$$\mathbf{F} = \mathbf{F}' = M\mathbf{H} + M\mathbf{D} \times \mathbf{U} = M\mathbf{H}'$$

or
$$\mathbf{H}' = \mathbf{H} + \mathbf{D} \times \mathbf{U}$$

and
$$\mathbf{B}' = \mathbf{B} + \mu_0\epsilon_0\mathbf{E} \times \mathbf{U} \tag{6}$$

Therefore, for $\mathbf{U} = U\mathbf{a}_x$,

$$B'_x = B_x \tag{7a}$$

$$B'_y = B_y + \frac{U}{U_0{}^2} E_z \tag{7b}$$

$$B'_z = B_z - \frac{U}{U_0{}^2} E_y \tag{7c}$$

In obtaining these transformations we have assumed that M, μ_0, and ϵ_0 have the same value in both frames of reference. This is true for relatively small velocities.

Let us illustrate this transformation by again locating a charge Q at $(0,y,0)$ at $t = 0$. The charge has a velocity $\mathbf{U} = U\mathbf{a}_x$. An infinite line charge of ρ_L coulombs/m lies on the x axis. To a stationary

---

[1] A parallel discussion of electric and magnetic charges is given in the first chapter of "Hyper and Ultrahigh Frequency Engineering" by R. I. Sarbacher and W. A. Edson, John Wiley & Sons, Inc., New York, 1943.

9. Two line charges of equal and opposite charge density and equal and opposite velocity are coincident. Determine the fields in frames of reference which are (a) fixed, (b) moving at the velocity of the positive charges, (c) moving at the velocity of the negative charges.

10. A filamentary conductor carrying a direct current lies on the z axis, and a closed filamentary conductor forms a circle in the $\phi = 0$ plane. There is obviously no current induced in the closed loop. If the filamentary conductor is now given a uniform velocity in the z direction, is there any current in the closed loop?

11. Show that the mass of a charged particle which starts from rest and falls through a potential difference of V_0 volts is $m_0(1 + QV_0/m_0U_0^2)$ as observed from a fixed frame of reference.

12. Use the results of Prob. 11 to show that the velocity of the particle is

$$U = U_0 \sqrt{1 - \frac{1}{\left(1 + \dfrac{QV_0}{m_0U_0^2}\right)^2}}$$

13. The simple radial electric field about a point charge is present only when viewed from a frame of reference which is at rest with respect to the charge. (a) In such a frame of reference show that $E = 1$ volt/m at any point 1 m distant from a point charge of $4\pi\epsilon_0$ coulombs. (b) Consider now an observer having a uniform velocity in the x direction of $0.6U_0$. Show that a point which the moving observer sees as 1 m distant from the charge in the x direction is actually 1.25 m distant in the fixed frame of reference. (c) Show also that a point apparently 1 m distant in the y direction is actually 1 m distant. (d) Show that E at these two points, 1 m distant from the viewpoint of the moving observer, is 0.64 and 1.25 volts/m, respectively.

APPENDIX A

VECTOR ANALYSIS

A1. General Curvilinear Coordinates. Let us consider a general coordinate system in which a point is located by the intersection of three mutually perpendicular surfaces (of unspecified form or shape):

$$u = \text{constant}$$
$$v = \text{constant}$$
$$w = \text{constant}$$

where u, v, and w = variables of the coordinate system. If each variable is increased by a differential amount and three additional mutually perpendicular surfaces are drawn corresponding to these new values, a differential volume is enclosed within a rectangular parallelepiped. Since u, v, and w need not be measures of length, as, for example, the angle variables of the cylindrical and spherical coordinate systems, each must be multiplied by a general function of u, v, and w in order to obtain the differential sides of the parallelepiped. Thus we define h_1, h_2, and h_3 each as a function of u, v, and w and write the lengths of the sides of the differential volume as

$$dL_1 = h_1 \, du$$
$$dL_2 = h_2 \, dv$$
$$dL_3 = h_3 \, dw$$

In the three coordinate systems discussed in the first chapter, it is apparent that the variables and multiplying functions are

Cartesian:
$$u = x \qquad v = y \qquad w = z$$
$$h_1 = 1 \qquad h_2 = 1 \qquad h_3 = 1$$
Cylindrical:
$$u = r \qquad v = \phi \qquad w = z$$
$$h_1 = 1 \qquad h_2 = r \qquad h_3 = 1 \qquad\qquad (1)$$
Spherical:
$$u = r \qquad v = \theta \qquad w = \phi$$
$$h_1 = 1 \qquad h_2 = r \qquad h_3 = r \sin \theta$$

The choice of u, v, and w above has been made so that $\mathbf{a}_u \times \mathbf{a}_v = \mathbf{a}_w$ in all cases. More involved expressions for h_1, h_2, and h_3 are to be expected in other less familiar coordinate systems.

A2. Divergence, Gradient, and Curl in General Curvilinear Coordinates. If the general development of the divergence in Secs. 3.6 and 3.7 is applied to the general curvilinear coordinate system, the flux of the vector $\mathbf{D}$ passing through the surface of the parallelepiped whose unit normal is $\mathbf{a}_u$ is

$$D_{u0} \, dL_2 \, dL_3 + \frac{1}{2} \frac{\partial}{\partial u} \left(D_u \, dL_2 \, dL_3 \right) du$$

313

or
$$D_{u0}h_2h_3\,dv\,dw + \frac{1}{2}\frac{\partial}{\partial u}\,(D_uh_2h_3\,dv\,dw)\,du$$

and for the opposite face is

$$-D_{u0}h_2h_3\,dv\,dw + \frac{1}{2}\frac{\partial}{\partial u}\,(D_uh_2h_3\,dv\,dw)\,du$$

giving a total for these two faces of

$$\frac{\partial}{\partial u}\,(D_uh_2h_3\,dv\,dw)\,du$$

Since u, v, and w are independent variables, this last expression may be written as

$$\frac{\partial}{\partial u}\,(h_2h_3D_u)\,du\,dv\,dw$$

and the other two corresponding expressions obtained by a simple permutation of the subscripts and of u, v, and w. Thus the total flux leaving the differential volume is

$$\left[\frac{\partial}{\partial u}\,(h_2h_3D_u) + \frac{\partial}{\partial v}\,(h_3h_1D_v) + \frac{\partial}{\partial w}\,(h_1h_2D_w)\right]du\,dv\,dw$$

and the divergence of $\mathbf{D}$ is found by dividing by the differential volume:

$$\nabla\cdot\mathbf{D} = \frac{1}{h_1h_2h_3}\left[\frac{\partial}{\partial u}\,(h_2h_3D_u) + \frac{\partial}{\partial v}\,(h_3h_1D_v) + \frac{\partial}{\partial w}\,(h_1h_2D_w)\right] \tag{2}$$

The components of the gradient of a scalar V may be obtained (following the methods of Sec. 4.6) by expressing $d\mathbf{L}$ in general curvilinear coordinates:

$$d\mathbf{L} = h_1\,du\,\mathbf{a}_u + h_2\,dv\,\mathbf{a}_v + h_3\,dw\,\mathbf{a}_w$$

dotting ∇V with $d\mathbf{L}$ to obtain the differential increase in V:

$$dV = (\nabla V)_uh_1\,du + (\nabla V)_vh_2\,dv + (\nabla V)_wh_3\,dw$$

keeping v and w constant:
$$dv = dw = 0$$

and obtaining

$$(\nabla V)_u = \frac{dV}{h_1\,du}\bigg|_{v,w\text{ const}} = \frac{\partial V}{h_1\,\partial u}$$

The remaining components are found in a similar manner, and the gradient is then

$$\nabla V = \frac{\partial V}{h_1\,\partial u}\,\mathbf{a}_u + \frac{\partial V}{h_2\,\partial v}\,\mathbf{a}_v + \frac{\partial V}{h_3\,\partial w}\,\mathbf{a}_w \tag{3}$$

The components of the curl of a vector $\mathbf{H}$ are obtained by considering a differential path first in a $u = $ constant surface and finding the circulation of $\mathbf{H}$ about that path, as discussed for cartesian coordinates in Sec. 8.3. The contribution along the segment in the $\mathbf{a}_v$ direction is

$$H_{v0}h_2\,dv - \frac{1}{2}\frac{\partial}{\partial w}\,(H_vh_2\,dv)\,dw$$

and that from the oppositely directed segment is

$$-H_{v0}h_2\,dv - \frac{1}{2}\frac{\partial}{\partial w}\,(H_vh_2\,dv)\,dw$$

The sum of these two parts is

$$- \frac{\partial}{\partial w} (H_v h_2 \, dv) \, dw$$

or

$$- \frac{\partial}{\partial w} (h_2 H_v) \, dv \, dw$$

and the sum of the contributions from the other two portions of the path is

$$\frac{\partial}{\partial v} (H_w h_3 \, dw) \, dv$$

or

$$\frac{\partial}{\partial v} (h_3 H_w) \, dv \, dw$$

The $\mathbf{a}_u$ component of curl $\mathbf{H}$ is therefore

$$(\boldsymbol{\nabla} \times \mathbf{H})_u = \frac{1}{h_2 h_3} \left[\frac{\partial}{\partial v} (h_3 H_w) - \frac{\partial}{\partial w} (h_2 H_v) \right]$$

and the other two components may be obtained by cyclic permutation. The result is expressible as a determinant:

$$\boldsymbol{\nabla} \times \mathbf{H} = \begin{vmatrix} \dfrac{\mathbf{a}_u}{h_2 h_3} & \dfrac{\mathbf{a}_v}{h_3 h_1} & \dfrac{\mathbf{a}_w}{h_1 h_2} \\[2mm] \dfrac{\partial}{\partial u} & \dfrac{\partial}{\partial v} & \dfrac{\partial}{\partial w} \\[2mm] h_1 H_u & h_2 H_v & h_3 H_w \end{vmatrix} \tag{4}$$

The Laplacian of a scalar is found by using (2) and (3):

$$\nabla^2 V = \boldsymbol{\nabla} \cdot \boldsymbol{\nabla} V = \frac{1}{h_1 h_2 h_3} \left[\frac{\partial}{\partial u} \left(\frac{h_2 h_3}{h_1} \frac{\partial V}{\partial u} \right) + \frac{\partial}{\partial v} \left(\frac{h_3 h_1}{h_2} \frac{\partial V}{\partial v} \right) + \frac{\partial}{\partial w} \left(\frac{h_1 h_2}{h_3} \frac{\partial V}{\partial w} \right) \right] \tag{5}$$

Equations (2) to (5) may be used to find the divergence, gradient, curl, and Laplacian in any orthogonal coordinate system for which h_1, h_2, and h_3 are known.

A3. Vector Identities. The vector identities listed below may be proved by expansion in cartesian (or general curvilinear) coordinates. The first three identities are concerned with operations on sums, the next three apply to operations when the argument is multiplied by a scalar function, the three following apply to operations on scalar or vector products, and the last four concern the second-order operations.

$$\boldsymbol{\nabla} \cdot (\mathbf{A} + \mathbf{B}) \equiv \boldsymbol{\nabla} \cdot \mathbf{A} + \boldsymbol{\nabla} \cdot \mathbf{B} \tag{6}$$

$$\boldsymbol{\nabla}(V + W) \equiv \boldsymbol{\nabla} V + \boldsymbol{\nabla} W \tag{7}$$

$$\boldsymbol{\nabla} \times (\mathbf{A} + \mathbf{B}) \equiv \boldsymbol{\nabla} \times \mathbf{A} + \boldsymbol{\nabla} \times \mathbf{B} \tag{8}$$

$$\boldsymbol{\nabla} \cdot (V\mathbf{A}) \equiv \mathbf{A} \cdot \boldsymbol{\nabla} V + V \boldsymbol{\nabla} \cdot \mathbf{A} \tag{9}$$

$$\boldsymbol{\nabla}(VW) \equiv V \boldsymbol{\nabla} W + W \boldsymbol{\nabla} V \tag{10}$$

$$\boldsymbol{\nabla} \times (V\mathbf{A}) \equiv \boldsymbol{\nabla} V \times \mathbf{A} + V \boldsymbol{\nabla} \times \mathbf{A} \tag{11}$$

$$\boldsymbol{\nabla} \cdot (\mathbf{A} \times \mathbf{B}) \equiv \mathbf{B} \cdot \boldsymbol{\nabla} \times \mathbf{A} - \mathbf{A} \cdot \boldsymbol{\nabla} \times \mathbf{B} \tag{12}$$

$$\boldsymbol{\nabla}(\mathbf{A} \cdot \mathbf{B}) \equiv (\mathbf{A} \cdot \boldsymbol{\nabla})\mathbf{B} + (\mathbf{B} \cdot \boldsymbol{\nabla})\mathbf{A} + \mathbf{A} \times (\boldsymbol{\nabla} \times \mathbf{B}) + \mathbf{B} \times (\boldsymbol{\nabla} \times \mathbf{A}) \tag{13}$$

$$\boldsymbol{\nabla} \times (\mathbf{A} \times \mathbf{B}) \equiv \mathbf{A} \boldsymbol{\nabla} \cdot \mathbf{B} - \mathbf{B} \boldsymbol{\nabla} \cdot \mathbf{A} + (\mathbf{B} \cdot \boldsymbol{\nabla})\mathbf{A} - (\mathbf{A} \cdot \boldsymbol{\nabla})\mathbf{B} \tag{14}$$

$$\boldsymbol{\nabla} \cdot \boldsymbol{\nabla} V \equiv \nabla^2 V \tag{15}$$

$$\boldsymbol{\nabla} \cdot \boldsymbol{\nabla} \times \mathbf{A} \equiv 0 \tag{16}$$

$$\boldsymbol{\nabla} \times \boldsymbol{\nabla} V \equiv 0 \tag{17}$$

$$\boldsymbol{\nabla} \times \boldsymbol{\nabla} \times \mathbf{A} \equiv \boldsymbol{\nabla}(\boldsymbol{\nabla} \cdot \mathbf{A}) - \nabla^2 \mathbf{A} \tag{18}$$

DIMENSIONS AND UNITS

The three fundamental dimensional units of classical mechanics are mass, length, and time, symbolized by the dimensional symbols $[M]$, $[L]$, and $[T]$. It is then possible to determine the dimensions of the remaining mechanical quantities in terms of these fundamental dimensions, and we find that velocity has the dimensional symbol $[LT^{-1}]$, force has the symbol $[MLT^{-2}]$, and so forth. When the theory of heat is considered, a fourth fundamental dimensional unit for temperature $[\theta]$ is customarily introduced, and the fifth fundamental dimensional unit is associated with electromagnetic phenomena and is usually taken as charge $[Q]$.

It is not necessary that five fundamental dimensional units be chosen;[1] either more or less may be used, and we shall later consider briefly one system in which no fundamental electromagnetic dimensional unit is used. However, the five selected above are conventional and familiar.

The dimensional symbols of the other electrical quantities may be found by using the dimensional equation for Coulomb's law:

$$[\epsilon_0] = \left[\frac{Q^2}{FR^2} \right] = [M^{-1}L^{-3}T^2Q^2]$$

the definition of E:

$$[E] = \left[\frac{F}{Q} \right] = [MLT^{-2}Q^{-1}]$$

and so forth. The dimensional symbols of the magnetic terms begin with I:

$$[I] = \left[\frac{Q}{t} \right] = [QT^{-1}]$$

and the process continues with the force between current elements to determine $[\mu_0]$:

$$[\mu_0] = \left[\frac{FR^2}{I^2L^2} \right] = [MLQ^{-2}]$$

the magnetic field intensity:

$$[H] = \left[\frac{I}{L} \right] = [L^{-1}T^{-1}Q]$$

and so on. The dimensional symbols of the electromagnetic quantities appearing throughout this book are given in Table B-1 below, in the order in which they are introduced.

[1] See H. L. Langhaar, "Dimensional Analysis and Theory of Models," p. 5, John Wiley & Sons, Inc., New York, 1951, or W. K. H. Panofsky and M. Phillips, "Classical Electricity and Magnetism," p. 375, Addison-Wesley Publishing Company, Reading, Mass., 1955.

The information in this table may be used to check the dimensions of derived equations and, in this way, to show algebraic mistakes. For instance, the total power radiated by a differential current element as found in Sec. 11.4 is shown to be dimensionally correct as follows:

$$P_{av} = \frac{\pi}{3} \sqrt{\frac{\mu_0}{\epsilon_0}} \left(\frac{I_0 d}{\lambda}\right)^2$$

$$P = \left[\left(\frac{MIQ^{-2}}{M^{-1}L^{-3}T^2Q^2}\right)^{1/2} \left(\frac{T^{-1}QL}{L}\right)^2 \right] = [ML^2T^{-3}]$$

Dimensional analysis cannot provide any information about numerical factors, nor can it differentiate between such expressions as $\nabla \cdot \mathbf{D}$, $\nabla \times \mathbf{D}$, $d\mathbf{D}/dx$, and $\partial \mathbf{D}/\partial x$ (all are $[L^{-3}Q]$). It is evident that the dimensions of a single new quantity appearing in an equation can be found rapidly by writing the corresponding dimensional equation. As a simple example,

$$\mathbf{E} = \nabla \times \nabla \times \mathbf{\Pi}$$

shows that the dimensions of $\mathbf{\Pi}$ (called the *Hertz vector*) are $[ML^3T^{-2}Q^{-1}]$.

A system of units must next be defined. We shall first describe the rationalized mks (or Giorgi) system, which is used in this book and is now standard in electrical engineering and much of physics. The fundamental unit of length is the meter, defined simply as the distance between two marks on a platinum-iridium bar preserved at the International Bureau of Weights and Measures at Sèvres, France. The second is the fundamental unit of time and is defined as 1/86,400 part of the mean solar day. The standard mass of one kilogram again is defined as the mass of an international standard in the form of a platinum-iridium cylinder at Sèvres. The unit of temperature is the absolute degree, defined by Lord Kelvin on the basis of the second law of thermodynamics. This unit does not concern us in the study of electromagnetic fields.

The fifth unit is that of charge and is chosen as the coulomb. Before explicitly defining the coulomb, we first define the newton, the mks unit of force, from Newton's third law as the force required to produce an acceleration of one meter per second per second on a one-kilogram mass. The coulomb is then defined through Coulomb's law by stating that two point charges of one coulomb each, separated one meter in a vacuum, repel each other with a force of $10^{-7}U_0{}^2$ newtons, where U_0 is the velocity of light in meters per second and U_0 is a fundamental natural constant.

The reason for this involved definition becomes clearer if several additional steps are taken. We see that ϵ_0 is numerically equal to $1/4\pi$ times the reciprocal of the magnitude of the force between these two unit charges of one-meter separation, or

$$\epsilon_0 = \frac{1}{4\pi \times 10^{-7}U_0{}^2} \qquad [M^{-1}L^{-3}T^2Q^2]$$

However, the subsequent definition of μ_0 and a study of wave phenomena show that

$$U_0{}^2 = \frac{1}{\mu_0\epsilon_0} \qquad [L^2T^{-2}]$$

and therefore

$$\mu_0 = 4\pi \times 10^{-7} \qquad [MLQ^{-2}]$$

TABLE B-1. DIMENSIONS AND UNITS OF THE ELECTRIC AND
MAGNETIC QUANTITIES IN THE GIORGI SYSTEM

Symbol	Name	Dimensions	Unit
F	Force	MLT^{-2}	Newton
Q	Charge	Q	Coulomb
r	Distance	L	M
ϵ_0	Permittivity	$M^{-1}L^{-3}T^2Q^2$	Farad/m
E	Electric field intensity	$MLT^{-2}Q^{-1}$	Volt/m
ρ	Volume charge density	$L^{-3}Q$	Coulomb/m^3
v	Volume	L^3	M^3
ρ_L	Linear charge density	$L^{-1}Q$	Coulomb/m
ρ_s	Surface charge density	$L^{-2}Q$	Coulomb/m^2
Ψ	Electric flux	Q	Coulomb
D	Electric flux density	$L^{-2}Q$	Coulomb/m^2
S	Area	L^2	M^2
W	Work, energy	ML^2T^{-2}	Joule
V	Potential	$ML^2T^{-2}Q^{-1}$	Volt
I	Current	$T^{-1}Q$	Amp
i	Current density	$L^{-2}T^{-1}Q$	Amp/m^2
R	Resistance	$ML^2T^{-1}Q^{-2}$	Ohm
G	Conductance	$M^{-1}L^{-2}TQ^2$	Mho
σ	Conductivity	$M^{-1}L^{-3}TQ^2$	Mho/m
C	Capacitance	$M^{-1}L^{-2}T^2Q^2$	Farad
P	Polarization	$L^{-2}Q$	Coulomb/m^2
H	Magnetic field intensity	$L^{-1}T^{-1}Q$	Amp/m
J_s	Surface current density	$L^{-1}T^{-1}Q$	Amp/m
B	Magnetic flux density	$MT^{-1}Q^{-1}$	Weber/m^2
μ_0	Permeability	MLQ^{-2}	Henry/m
Φ	Magnetic flux	$ML^2T^{-1}Q^{-1}$	Weber
V_m	Magnetic scalar potential	$T^{-1}Q$	Amp
A	Vector magnetic potential	$MLT^{-1}Q^{-1}$	Weber/m
U	Velocity	LT^{-1}	M/sec
T	Torque	ML^2T^{-2}	Newton-m
M	Magnetic moment	$L^2T^{-1}Q$	Amp-m^2
L	Inductance	ML^2Q^{-2}	Henry
ω	Angular velocity	T^{-1}	Radian/sec
λ	Wavelength	L	M
δ	Skin depth	L	M
P	Power	ML^2T^{-3}	Watt
p	Power loss per unit volume	$ML^{-1}T^{-3}$	Watt/m^3
$\mathcal{P}$	Poynting vector	MT^{-3}	Watt/m^2

It is evident, therefore, that although Q is the fundamental dimensional unit, the
simplest numerical value has been assigned to μ_0. Thus, in retrospect, we have
essentially defined the permeability of free space as $4\pi \times 10^{-7}$ henry/m, recognized
the validity of the relationship $U_0{}^2 = 1/\mu_0\epsilon_0$, expressed the permittivity of free
space in terms of the factor $4\pi \times 10^{-7}$, and the square of the velocity of light in

free space as $\epsilon_0 = 1/(4\pi \times 10^{-7}U_0{}^2)$, and thereby found the correct numerical value of the force to be used in the definition of the coulomb.

This is much the same as if we had defined a standard mass and length as before, chosen time as the next fundamental dimensional unit, and then defined the fundamental unit of time as the "jiffy," the time required to travel one meter at the velocity of light in free space. The velocity of light would then have the simple value of one meter per jiffy, but the value of the standard jiffy would depend upon a measurement analogous to our measurement of the velocity of light in the mks system. Scientists would devise elaborate experiments not to determine the velocity of light (one meter per jiffy as every schoolboy knows) but to ascertain the number of jiffies in a mean solar day.[1]

The units in which the other electric and magnetic quantities are measured are given in the body of the text at the time the quantity is defined, and all can be related to the basic units already defined. The units are also given in Table B-1 for easy reference.

Finally, other systems of fundamental dimensional units have been used in electricity and magnetism. In the electrostatic system of units (esu), Coulomb's law is written for free space:

$$F = \frac{Q_1 Q_2}{R^2} \qquad \text{esu}$$

and the dimensional symbol for charge is expressible in terms of the mechanical units as $[M^{1/2}L^{3/2}T^{-1}]$. Thus the number of fundamental units is reduced by one. One of the undesirable consequences of this reduction is that less dimensional information is available for the electrostatic quantities. For example, D and E both have the esu dimensional symbol of $[M^{1/2}L^{-1/2}T^{-1}]$, and the possibility of their confusion is present. It is also evident that fractional exponents are necessary. The gram and centimeter are the fundamental units of mass and distance, and the esu system is therefore a cgs system.

In a similar manner the electromagnetic system of units (emu) is based on Coulomb's law for magnetic poles, and the dimensional symbol of the magnetic pole may be written as a function of only $[M]$, $[L]$, and $[T]$. When electric quantities are expressed in esu units, magnetic quantities in emu units, and both appear in the same equation (such as Maxwell's curl equations), the velocity of light appears explicitly. This follows from noting that in esu, $\epsilon_0 = 1$, but $\mu_0\epsilon_0 = 1/U_0{}^2$, and therefore $\mu_0 = 1/U_0{}^2$ and in emu, $\mu_0 = 1$, and hence $\epsilon_0 = 1/U_0{}^2$. Thus, in this intermixed system known as the Gaussian system of units,

$$\nabla \times \mathbf{H} = 4\pi\mathbf{i} + \frac{1}{U_0}\frac{\partial\mathbf{D}}{\partial t} \qquad \text{(Gaussian)}$$

Other systems include the factor 4π explicitly in Coulomb's law, and it then does not appear in Maxwell's equations. When this is done the system is said to be rationalized. Hence the Gaussian system is an unrationalized cgs system (when rationalized it is known as the Heaviside-Lorentz system), and the Giorgi system we have used throughout this book is a rationalized mks system.

Table B-2 gives the conversion factors between the more important units of the rationalized mks system and the Gaussian system. The conversion factor X is used by setting one mks unit equal to X Gaussian units. For example, 1 coulomb = 3×10^9 statcoulombs. The velocity of light is to be used in cgs units; that is, $U_0 = 2.99793 \times 10^{10}$ cm/sec $\doteq 3 \times 10^{10}$ cm/sec.

[1] Given in the latest Jiffyland scientific journals as $(2{,}590{,}211 \pm 7)10^7$ jiffies.

TABLE B-2. CONVERSION OF MKS UNITS TO GAUSSIAN UNITS

Quantity	mks unit	X	Gaussian unit	
Q	Coulomb	$10^{-1}U_0$	Statcoulomb	(esu)
E	Volt/m	$10^6/U_0$	Statvolt/cm	(esu)
D	Coulomb/m^2	$4\pi \times 10^{-5}U_0$	Lines/cm^2	(esu)
ρ	Coulomb/m^3	$10^{-7}U_0$	Statcoulomb/cm^3	(esu)
V	Volt	$10^8/U_0$	Statvolt	(esu)
I	Amp	10^{-1}	Abamp	(emu)
H	Amp/m	$4\pi \times 10^{-3}$	Oersted	(emu)
B	Weber/m^2	10^4	Gauss	(emu)
L	Henry	10^9	Abhenry	(emu)
C	Farad	$10^{-9}U_0{}^2$	Statfarad	(esu)
R	Ohm	10^9	Abohm	(emu)
ϵ	Farad/m	$4\pi \times 10^{-11}U_0{}^2$	....	(esu)
μ	Henry/m	$10^7/4\pi$	....	(emu)
σ	Mho/m	10^{-11}	Abmho/cm	(emu)

MATERIAL CONSTANTS

Table C-1 lists typical values of the relative dielectric constant ϵ_R for several common insulating or dielectric materials. The values should only be considered representative for each material, and they apply to normal temperature and humidity conditions and to very low audio frequencies.

TABLE C-1. RELATIVE DIELECTRIC CONSTANT

Material	ϵ_R
Air	1.0006
Bakelite	4.9
Glass (Pyrex)	5
Neoprene	6.7
Nylon	3.7
Plexiglas	3.4
Polyethylene	2.26
Polystyrene	2.53
Porcelain	6
Quartz (fused)	3.8
Soil (sandy)	3
Teflon	2.1
Water (distilled)	80

Table C-2 gives the conductivity σ for several good conductors, good insulators, and for a few intermediate materials which cannot generally be classed as either. The values apply at zero frequency.

TABLE C-2. CONDUCTOR AND INSULATOR CONDUCTIVITY

Material	σ, mhos/m
Silver	6.17×10^7
Copper	5.80×10^7
Aluminum	3.72×10^7
Brass	1.5×10^7
Nichrome	0.089×10^7
Water (sea)	4
Water (distilled)	2×10^{-4}
Soil (sandy)	10^{-5}
Bakelite	10^{-9}
Porcelain	2×10^{-13}
Quartz (fused)	10^{-17}

INDEX

323